D1541087

1nsepara6le

Faith – Family – Fatherhood

Affirmations:

"I believe without doubt, that if 1nsepara6le is taken through the mind into the heart, it will change lives and challenge people, particularly fathers, to never quit in doing good for in due season we shall certainly reap if we do not lose heart." – *Former Congressman Jay Dickey, Jr. – Arkansas*

"1nsepara6le is an honest, open heart dissection of a condition affecting far too many children of a spiritually divided home. This biography has the potential to heal and restore lives crippled by the chains of generational bondage." – *Brenda Teele Jackson, TV Personality – Dallas, Texas*

"This is a captivating biography that proves what the unconditional love of a father can accomplish despite being faced with an unlimited amount of insurmountable challenges just to be a dad. This is a must read and must see movie." – *Lissa Druss Christman, CCO, Culloton Strategies – Chicago*

"a riveting story, which I found to be both heartbreaking and spiritually uplifting. It will inspire you and challenge you to re-evaluate your personal commitments to faith, family and parenthood. This narrative is simply life changing." – *Byron K. Reed, Senior VP, Community Development Wells Fargo & Company – Los Angeles*

"I believe this story is God-ordained.... and I look forward with anticipation to the impact this book will have on people from all walks of life, which will potentially touch the lives of all who read this book. The relationship this Dad fosters with his son should not be the exception, but the rule." – *David Hornsby, DFW International Airport, Department of Public Safety – Dallas/Fort Worth*

"1nsepara6le is a powerful testimonial and narrative that unveils the power of what faith in God can do through a focused father who was determined to be accountable for his actions, which established a hope that not only delivered his son, but also the mother of his son from bondage, who had spent 20 years keeping the two of them separated." – *JC Watts, Jr. Former Congressman – Oklahoma*

1nsepara6le

Faith – Family – Fatherhood

Mark Bradley
With "Pops"

SGP
Sports Group Publishing
Dallas - Fort Worth

FIRST EDITION:

Published by Sports Group Publishing (SGP)

Converted in the United States

ISBN 978-0-9831398-1-2 (Hardcover)

ISBN 978-0-9831398-3-6 (e-Español)

ISBN 978-0-9831398-0-5 (Mobi)

Information about special discounts for bulk purchases, visit www.inseparable16.com

---

Cover Design: Shayne Bingham

The Author's Note

Inseparable is a true story, but it is not a work of "Journalism" in the highest form of its definition by any means.

Once I got permission from my beloved parents to write this book, I went into it with an understanding that many of the events, circumstances, and situations, as I lived them, would require a lot of research and interviews with the people associated with our story. And because this was an impromptu decision, I didn't have tangible notes or recorded conversations with the characters involved in this story in hand. Therefore, this work reflects our present-day recollection of our experiences over a period of twenty-five plus years.

The names and various identifying characteristics of specific people in this book have been changed for their protection. Conversations between characters have been reconstructed from memory given by those who are *the* actual people of the story, or, in some cases, we had to imagine the occurrences based on our best understanding and recollection of these events.

Certain events have been condensed and some individuals are composites. There are a few scenes within this story that are recreations of events of which my father and I had no personal *firsthand* experience. In those cases, the scenes are anticipatively predicted based on the best information we could collect.

With that understanding, the goal of this manuscript is to tell my story as accurately as possible in an effort to, in some way, positively impact the lives of others.

The Contents

Introduction

You see them during nearly every sporting event in the country. They call them cutaways.

Usually, it's a camera shot of the mother of an athlete, accompanied by comments from the game day announcer noting that the mom is the *sole* reason the athlete is where he or she is today. Of course, there are exceptions to the rule: the dad who has raised two Super Bowl winning quarterbacks. Or the father who was fortunate to have coached his son through Pop Warner, high school, and college; and even the dad who didn't have a household of athletes, but rather future doctors and lawyers and investment bankers, for which he had to nurture and guide them to their call in life.

But the story you're about to read is so abnormally unique it just might help make the exception…the new rule!

For some, it may seem too good to be true. In a society that has often cast dads as the deadbeats and moms as the heartbeats of the family, this story is about a man who was determined not to conform to that stereotypical template, and a mystified little boy who, because of his father's inspired determination, beat the odds, and not only lived to receive the blessing, but inspired him to tell the tale.

It's a story that couldn't be timelier. Despite the efforts of many conscientious moms, the headlines, including that of USA Today, a couple of years ago, reflect the lives gone wrong of numerous young athletes, all of whom have one thing in common: nearly all of them grew up without a conscientious father.

Consequently, they too, led lives that lack the qualities of good character, while having children who had nothing more than their poor example to follow, as the generational curse continued.

But imagine a young man, raised within one of the worst dysfunctional family environments you can think of, with all the ingredients for failure, who by God's grace through faith, manages to escape these deadly circumstances. Then, after finding a wife, and beginning to live the blessed life, he's suddenly slammed with a revelation that would turn his entire world upside down!

This revelation you, as the reader, will discover is all too common. However, this father's response to such a shocking revelation is anything but—common.

This is a narrative about an already successful young man whose spiritual convictions are tested to the max, and the life of a scared, confused, and misguided little boy whose life is changed forever. It show's what *faith, family* and *fatherhood* are all about, and proves, undeniably, that *with God, all things become possible to them that believe.*

1

Reflections

The downtown Chicago Hilton was one of the finest hotels in the city. It had great views of Lake Michigan and Grant Park, richly appointed room furnishings, 32-inch televisions, and great room service. In fact, it was darn near as comfortable as my new contemporary town house, which explains why a National Football League franchise would choose a hotel with such elegance as its team hotel for home games.

While a lot of my teammates came from the same small town America I grew up in, it didn't take long before we were trading our Timex for a Rolex, that Hooptie for a Bentley, and our hip-hop clothier for a high-level fashion consultant. So a night-before-the-game stay at the downtown Hilton was merely keeping these young millionaires in the style to which we had so quickly become accustomed. Yeah right! I may be a rookie, but it didn't take long for me to learn that the Chicago Bears wanted their players well fed and well rested. Of course, if Tom Bodett had one of his roadside inns this close to Soldier Field, they'd be tempted to tell ole Tom to "leave the light on for us." The Bears were known league wide for being what my agent called, "fiscally" responsible.

I took one more look in the full-length mirror before leaving the room. Despite the frigid Chicago winters, I figured one of my heavy-duty zip front sweaters with a light under layer would be more than enough to ward off the Chi-town chill. Believe me, I'm the last person who would have thought anything less than goose-down drawers would have been enough to fight the "Chicago Hawk." But months of practice and play in the Illinois elements made a 29°-degree day downright balmy. Ginger Zee, the weatherwoman on Channel 5, said today's forecast called for partly sunny skies, highs in the lower 30s, lows in the mid-teens.

And as usual, she makes her pitch with class and style, but she's not nearly as exciting and alluring as Lauren Jiggetts. She was the best reason to watch NBC5. Anyway, mid-teens, huh, ok, cool—maybe we'll break out the Kenneth Cole twill, just in case. I have no idea who Kenneth Cole is, but he does make a nice Hawk— resistant coat.

After patting my pockets to make sure I had my wallet and checking my wrist to secure the clasp of my watch, it was now time to go to work. I took one last look around the room, making sure I'd left nothing behind. On second thought, the room may have been comfortable, but it was way too traditional for the kid. Certain I had everything, I crossed the ten steps from my room to the elevators. An ordinary hotel stay and I would have requested a room far from the noise of an active elevator. But thanks to the Bears, and perhaps a few NFL rules, to keep us secure, players and team personnel were the only ones allowed on our floors. After tapping the down button, I took my cell phone off my hip and hit the touch screen.

"I'm ready—I'll meet you at the valet stand."

Another touch ended the call.

Surprisingly, no one is on the elevator when the doors open, and I get to ride the fifteen floors to the lobby solo. But even before the doors open, I can hear the sound of Bear fans calling the names of my teammates. As I make my way through the lobby, past the Pavilion dining room and towards the main entrance, the enthusiasts begin to shout, "Mark.... Mark Bradley.... sign this for me Mark—Mark.... we love you, Mark."

It didn't take that long into my NFL life before I learned to smile, sign, and walk. Some fans could be a bit pushy, others were downright rude, but there was the alternative—no one asking for an autograph at all if there was no career to warrant it. So as soon as I had signed what seemed like a couple dozen, I was at the valet area and some of Chicago's finest are there too, helping hold back the Bear faithful as parking attendants reunite players with their Rovers, Lamborghinis, and in my case, a Mercedes Benz SL55 AMG. I can see my roommate, Robbie Gould, stepping into his SUV, and as I turned to tip the valet another of the faithful yells, "Awesome car, Mr. Bradley".

And suddenly I hear this familiar voice say, "Mr. Bradley, huh" as I hear the trunk of the car open and close. Looking clean and debonair, and often mistaken as one of the players—it's my Dad. And make no mistake about it—Pops is cold! Always well groomed, well dressed, articulate, and politically correct. He is what my generation would call—silk smooth...

As I eased into the driver's seat, my Dad's cell rings. He's wearing his Bluetooth, so he's able to talk hands free, allowing him to get in and strap in. Making our way to Soldier Field, I can't help but think about, well, everything. In the driver's seat of this new vehicle is a southern boy from Pine Bluff, Arkansas, chosen 39th overall in the 2005 National Football League (NFL) Selection Draft from the University of Oklahoma.

I am living the dream. But the hell I went through to get here makes me appreciate every day I get the opportunity to stay here. There are several great stories to be told throughout the NFL locker rooms; players who come from families which exemplify love, faith, and structure—pressed by hard work, integrity, and discipline. But there are also far too many players in this league like me, who weren't raised in an environment in which good character is produced.

Not that my family needed to be perfect by any means, no one family is, but such a severe level of dysfunction induced a multitude of bad decisions; those made for me, and those made, without proper guidance, by me. But each of those decisions, through a distant and unwelcome admirer, was used to teach me some valuable lessons, which prepared me for this incredible opportunity I get to live everyday, and established an inroad into an even better life to come.

Along the way, I learned to have a healthy respect for firearms; and that *bad company corrupts good character;* and if we're smart we will only seek advice from those who are truly qualified to give it; *and that in all thy getting, get understanding, for wisdom is the principal thing;* and without love you can't really truly—live.

Seeing Soldier Field looming in the distance often reminded me of God's goodness, mercy, and grace. And that favor doesn't always seem fair. As a consequence, I get the distinct privilege to create opportunities for a few others who are less fortunate in life, and at one point, my hands bore the scars of a decision that left me wondering how I even had an opportunity at life.

Traffic was moving better than usual, so we made it to the stadium security entrance in record time. While some of the yellow-jacketed personnel waved their mirrored wands under the car, another led a Doberman around the perimeter. For a moment, I said to myself, *its true, dogs can take on the personality of their masters.*

My thoughts were interrupted by the Doberman's master, who ask, "How we feelin' about it today, Mark?"

"Feelin' good—gotta get it done," I replied.

As I eased into a parking space a few yards from the Bears locker room, I could hear my father wrapping up his phone call. But to do justice to this story, it would be fair to inform you at this juncture, that my Dad is also my agent, marketing consultant, spiritual advisor, and *my best friend*, by choice, I might add—*we are one*. A love relationship that is often unheard of and uncommon throughout many of our communities, especially the African American community. And as a major credit to him, this man never sacrificed his position as my father to befriend me despite having to wrestle, fight, and war with an entire family just to have access to me. As you may have figured, my parents were not married and probably under the circumstances, it may have been best that they weren't. I'll explain my position on this later but I was born out of wedlock during a time when abortion had begun to rear its ugly head in the black community.

However, I'm grateful that my mother didn't choose to abort, as so many teenage pregnancies unfortunately resulted in. But there is no doubt as to where I might be if my

Dad hadn't made some extreme sacrifices in an effort to protect me from a multitude of internal family conflicts that so many young men succumb too. Contrary to my story, most of my fellow NFL locker room colleagues would champion their mothers as being the vessel that made the sole difference in their lives, but for me, it was my father who had to re-establish my foundation, which eventually gave me 'a real' chance to succeed in this precious thing called—life.

From the NFL locker room to the NFL boardroom, he's pretty much participated in some way in it all. In fact, as of the 2005 draft, we became the first father/son/player/agent combination in the history of the NFL, who both just happen to have played this great game of football at the *same high school*; *same university*; *same jersey number*; *drafted into the same league; played the same position*; *and coached by some of the same people.*

As I turned the key to its off position, I glanced over at him, as accustomed, and as a part of our pre-game ritual, he stuck his left hand out, palm up, for me to join hands in touching, while he led us in a short prayer to the throne of grace.

In those moments, I'd often thank God for blessing me with such a loving father who single handily fought an unbelievable fight to give me a chance at the abundant life. But amazingly, for the first eight years of my life—I really didn't even know the man!

2

Duplicity

From the onset, as a toddler, I lived with my mother, Denise Davis, and her parents, Leola and Odell Davis, in Southeast Arkansas in a little town known as Pine Bluff, population about 60,000. One of my uncles was still in grade school so he was stationary, but throughout the course of my tender years, there were several relatives that lived with us on various occasions, while their rarely seen parents lived in different states.

At times there were as many as seven to eight of us living in this small three-bedroom home. And as far back as I can recall, I don't remember any of them being attentive to me, other than my grandfather Odell, or any displaying much respect for one another. But this was a reasonably educated house where church on Sundays was an absolute first and getting a college degree was often pushed as the absolute second.

As for my Mom, I thought what most kids think of their mothers: she was really pretty and dependable. But being pretty was relative, especially growing up in the sea of testosterone in which my mom lived. However, to validate my opinion, her hard earned status of becoming a cheerleader at a predominately white high school meant she was indeed regarded as one of the attractive girls on campus, but her yearbook pictures might throw you off a bit. This popular teenager, who wore her hair like her brothers, in sort of an Afro-shag, rarely put on any makeup, which reinforced her tomboyish reputation. Still, being a cheerleader in a school that nearly graduated six hundred plus students in her class wasn't too shabby.

Nevertheless, in her senior year, my Mom started to shed this cute "diamond-in-the-rough-tomboy" status. Someone apparently encouraged her to do something with her hair and to use a little make-up to accent her already flawless complexion. Soon my mother went from a girl "with potential" to a highly "sought after" prospect. Along with her newfound appearance came some confidence, and even a little ego. For someone soon to be regarded as one of the finest girls in Southern Arkansas, only the cream of the male crop would do. At the time, it was the local star—Danny Bradley.

Danny was an all-around athlete, excelling at track, football, and baseball. He soon emerged as an outstanding high school quarterback for the Pine Bluff Zebras and was about to seriously offend the entire state by deciding to play for an Arkansas native at the University of Oklahoma, Barry Switzer. But before he left, my Mom and Danny became "phone friends," which stemmed from a class they had together. They often had marathon conversations about a lot of things, including his first flight, the intricacy of recruiting, and why he really chose Oklahoma over the University of Arkansas.

She became a great sounding board for him, and he had obviously become, as expected, an even more fascinating prospect to her. My Mom was well aware of the fact that he was involved with another classmate but never allowed this reality to get in the way of her weekly chats or her desire to go beyond the "friendship zone."

Another of the guys on her radar was an athlete from nearby Jefferson Prep named Reginald Mayberry who attended our church. They would talk from time to time and even went out on a few dates, but to no avail. She liked him nearly as much as she was digging the other, but Mayberry was never the "big-time" national sports prospect as local VIP—Danny Bradley.

So, when the summer of 1981 rolled around and my Mom announced she was pregnant, she informed her parents, Odell and Leola Davis, that her baby's daddy—was Mayberry. And for the first 17 years of my life, I was known as Mark Anthony Mayberry, born January 29, 1982. My birth certificate and all legal records documented this fact and my nickname among my peers was M&M.

Mayberry didn't live with us; I don't think they were ever really that serious. But he was a decent man and spent a lot of time with me at the Davis's, where Saturdays always meant watching college football.

"Mark, sit your butt down, boy…. Mayberry get your son, please," my Mom would often holler many a Saturday afternoons. From the time I was two years old, the entire family of seven, Mayberry, and a family friend or two, would be glued to the TV. And ninety-nine percent of the time, they'd be watching the local hometown idol, Danny Bradley and the OU Sooners, or channel surfing to capture all his halftime and post-game highlights of the day; and many they were.

In 1983-84, Danny was one of only a few *black* quarterbacks at a major college program. Turner Gill at Nebraska, Randall Cunningham at UNLV, and Walter Lewis, the first black quarterback at Alabama, were all getting major national TV exposure. But in Pine Bluff, and perhaps in the entire state of Arkansas, it was all about the homegrown talent—the one that got away. His exploits were watched with a mixture of both envy and admiration but no household expressed more resentment and negativity toward Danny Bradley than the members of my family.

As beer and soda can tops were poppin', so were the remarks about Danny's play. On this day, it was the Oklahoma Sooners vs. O-State Cowboys. The winner would go to the Orange Bowl and a shot at the National Championship. Like OU, O-State was loaded with talent, with Hall of Famer Thurman Thomas, was all any team could handle. But at no particular point in the game and for no particular reason, my *uncles* would just "express themselves."

"When the last time you saw this dude in Pine Bluff?"

Without waiting for an answer, a friend hollers, "Look at him, Bradley got skills!"

Then, as if remembering the first question, *another uncle* is heard from. "You know how these guys get when they make it, they forget where they come from."

"These guys don't go back into the communities that raised them," Odell replied.

"Why should he, Odell—ain't nothing in this town for these young men," Leola said.

The family friend then blurts out, "My question is why didn't he go to Arkansas?"

"Why," an uncle answered, "becuz he think he too big for Arkansas."

"No—that's not true," Denise replied. "He strongly considered Arkansas and he really liked Lou Holtz a lot, but he wanted to play quarterback—and OU recruited him to play that position—Arkansas didn't," she concluded.

It was as if E. F. Hutton had spoken. All heads turned simultaneously and looked at her, as Denise paused, smiled, and shrugged her shoulders and said, "What—it was in the sports section of the newspaper."

Another uncle mockingly said, "When you start reading the sports section, Dee?"

"Yeah, I don't recall seeing that info in the paper," another says.

And Odell sputtered out, "Maybe he wasn't good enough to play QB up on the hill. Arkansas got a pretty good quarterback in Brad Taylor."

About this time, like clockwork, OU makes a big play and all the attention returns to the game. And you guessed it, Bradley, the Big-Eight's Offensive Player of the Year hits another Arkansas product, Little Rock Parkview's tight-end Keith Jackson for a touchdown to put this game out of reach for OSU—the house goes silent.

As the old saying goes, you could hear a pin drop, and the celebration was on in Norman, Oklahoma and the Sooners fans must have sensed their envy, because they flooded Owens Field with barrels of Oranges signifying the bowl game their team often hosted, The FedEx-Orange Bowl in Miami, Florida on New Years night.

As the officiating crew cleared the field, the ABC camera crew captures great shots of OSU Head Coach Pat Jones, OU's Barry Switzer, and Pine Bluffs—Danny Bradley. As the clock winds down, Danny takes the last snap, takes a knee, and suddenly rushes over to the OSU sideline to congratulate Coach Jones, Thurman Thomas, and yet another Arkansas product, offensive assistant Houston Dale Nutt, as Spencer Tillman breaks out with a historical move, the Billy Sims wiggle; while the Sooners fans again inundate Owens Field with Oranges.

Suddenly, the family friend chimes in again, “Hey man, how did Switzer come in here and snatch Danny Bradley and Keith Jackson from the Hogs?”

No response from any of the hosts of this get-together.

“OU bout to play in the National Title Game, dude, with two of our state’s best players,” the friend goes on to say.

Still no response, so, at this point, he had the floor.

“And isn’t Switzer, Houston Nutt, and Pat Jones former Razorbacks too? And didn’t this guy #90 for O-State, the All-American, Leslie O’Neal, play ball at Little Rock Hall.

“Yeah, he did,” one relative replied.

“So, this is the Razors vs. the Backs,” the friend shouted!

“Nah, this is the Sooners vs. the Cowboys,” Mayberry sarcastically reconfirms as he re-entered the room with me from my potty break. “OU do the Orange Bowl almost every year—don’t forget, the Sooners are a *elite* program.”

Most of the time my Mom would listen silently at these kinds of game-day get-togethers and reflections, as if lost in deep thought. It was the only time she seemed to just watch, look, and listen, while Mayberry, when present, would play it off with a shrug. It’s my understanding that he never really participated in the slanderous attacks, during these gatherings, but he really didn’t oppose them, either.

Weekdays meant work for my mother, and she had a few minimum-wage jobs over the course of my first couple of years. But for some strange reason, my mother had become more and more frustrated as wave after wave after wave of articles, TV reports, and area gossip rolled in about this guy—Danny Bradley. And that frustration reached a boiling point in late April 1984 while she was at her favorite beauty shop. As my Mom is having her hair shampooed, a local TV reporter is talking about their hometown personality, and all the ladies in the shop start talking about him too.

The beautician working on my Mom says, “Didn’t you have a thing with Danny Bradley when y’all was at Pine Bluff High?”

Before my Mom could get a word in, another hairdresser says, “Girl, I just read an article about him, he’s about to make a lil money, huh.”

“Yeah, I heard,” my Mom utters.

Another customer who has been listening, decides to chime in on the subject. Leaning forward in her chair, she says with emphasis, “Lord, some folks are just *blessed coming in and blessed going out.”*

With my Mom head still being palmed like a basketball, warm jets of water alternately rinsing, working up a rich soapy lather; the part of the salon experience she enjoyed most, but on this day she almost feels like running, with soapy hair and all, as far away from this conversation as she can. In her mind, just like the soap on her scalp, which comes to a-lather, she has a secret, and all this talk about Danny Bradley is beginning to get her—lathered up.

Thankfully, soap, water and her hairdresser's fingers combined, help to make hearing every syllable of the gossiping comments impossible. Yet her shampoo is complete, just in time to hear another patron turn and say as she is heading out the door, "Girlfriend, that coulda' been you about to get paid."

It took every muscle in my mother's body not to say what she felt and thought: *I may not have him, but trust me, I do—have him.*

The salon experience not only documented her frustrations, but it was now starting to make her feel very uncomfortable about her detachment from this guy. She began to reflect on a moment the previous year when she saw him at a local sporting event, during his spring break in '83. It presented her with the first chance to inform him that her baby boy that accompanied her in the stroller that day—was his baby boy.

As he plays Mr. Big-shot, signing a few autographs and shaking a few hands she approaches him nervously but cool, calm, and collected. He quickly begins to devote his attention toward her. They greet each other with pleasantries as she comments about his new level of celebrity status.

"What's up, Mister Bradley?" She says.

"Hey, what's up? Look at you...you look great," he replied.

"Thank you—so do you," she said with sensuality.

"This is your kid?" Danny asked, as he stooped down to say hi but noticed that this handsome lil boy's face was half-covered by a cotton blanket and asleep.

"Yeah, this is my lil man," she replied.

Unfortunately, the chat lasted all of fifteen seconds as Danny suddenly felt a little lightheaded as he stood up.

She asked, "You aright?"

"Yeah, I'm cool—just got a lil dizzy."

Nevertheless, he quickly regrouped as my mother begins to fill his space with eyes of interest and admiration. He likewise responded.

"I'll be in town a few days, give me a call at my parents, let's get together and have lunch or dinner and get caught up," he said.

"Same number?" She asked.

"Same number," he replied.

"Expect my call for sure," she said with a flirtatious smile as Danny began to respond to another one of their classmates from high school vying for his attention.

My mother fades back into reality, regretting this missed opportunity to have a much more serious conversation about her secret as the beautician continues prepping her hair. But she's immediately lured back into deep thought for which this reflection, not only validates both of their weaknesses with promiscuity, but it also establishes "the motive" for which my Mom was now operating from within.

As you may have figured, she took him up on his invitation. She recalls their conversations by phone, and gets him caught up on the gossip around town. She updates him as to how life has treated her regarding love and relationship. She makes known through small talk that her love affair with her baby's daddy, Mayberry, wasn't quite working out, but otherwise all was well with her and the family. And the night before he was to head back to OU, she hook's up with him. But unfortunately, instead of her sharing with him that her fourteen-month-old kid is his kid, she lays it down with him again—and conceives another one.

She snaps out of this deep trance, she begins to think, *I deserve better than what I'm getting out of this deal. But if I tell him the truth, what will he do? Will he turn toward me or against me? Well, whatever he choose to do—if I can't have him, he for damn sure, need to take care of me and my son.*

Danny's popularity was off the charts. Add to the mix his reasonably good character, marketability, and personality; no matter where you might have grown up, you had to admire a guy like my father. This guy had class, style, and a ton of talent. And more importantly, despite this *promiscuity* issue he was obviously struggling with, he was indeed a *born again believer* who had expressed his love for God, even in his youth, by often walking to church on many Sunday mornings, alone, between the tender ages of seven and thirteen while his mother worked two jobs in the absence of his own father.

Now, I'm not, under any circumstances, giving him a pass, but this small town kid from rural Arkansas, with not much to talk about, brag about, or even smile about—somehow kept the faith. They said he wasn't big enough, smart enough, or good enough, and even white enough. But with the support of a devoted mother, despite having to deal with a domestically violent father, Danny, by the grace of God, had managed to put himself in a position to make it, despite having failed many times along the way.

And to his credit, this same man taught me over the course of my youth, that even though I was conceived out of an act of sin, I was not, by any means, sin itself, or what many would call a bastard child. He preached that I had been fearfully and wonderfully made from above, convinced that God knew me before He formed me in my mothers womb; teaching that Christ sacrificed everything, giving His life that I may experience this life, more abundantly; having died once for all sins, forever; proving God's grace for mankind; documenting His faithfulness and willingness to forgive and cleanse us from all unrighteousness, if we would confess our own personal sins, since all of us have failed and come short of His glory.

As you could imagine, as a teenager, these were difficult concepts for me to grasp, but as I got older and came into adulthood, these revelational truths brought clarity to the kind of relationship I should be experiencing with the Lord, which caused me to view God and my brothers and sisters in Christ entirely different, including my parents shortcomings. Not that they didn't need to try living a life of holiness anymore—*for* holiness is necessary to walk in righteousness; but holiness, he taught, comes by way of a by-product of God's grace, not a way to God's grace; and that knowing God and understanding His grace will cause a man to live more holier than he ever could on purpose in his own strength, he would often say; that the born-again experience was designed to change a man on the inside first, as he renewed his mind in the things of God, before we could expect to see that change on the outside in his actions, later.

Nevertheless, after about two-and-a-half years of feeling disconnected and a bit left out, my Mom decided to establish herself in the equation by making her secret known, especially after having heard rumors that he had proposed to his college sweet heart.

But to back track, it was now about 11 a.m. on a Saturday in early-August of 1984. While Danny was getting prepared to lead his Sooners Team into the Orange Bowl at a shot at the National Championship—my Mom had me on her hip, browsing the isles at Wal-Mart, when she saw a familiar face, Danny's cousin, Bo Harris.

Now is the perfect time, she thought!

As they get closer to one another, Bo hollers over the ambient noise in the crowded store, "Denise, what's up, girl?! Is that your lil cub?!"

"Yeah, this is my lil boy, Mark," she replied, as she approaches Bo.

Bo smiles and says, "I heard you had a baby but I've never seen you with him.

"Tell your girl we've got to get Mark and TJ together to play sometime. I think they're about the same age," she says. "Mark is three, how old is TJ?"

Bo pauses and says, with some hesitation, "TJ just turned four—maybe five."

Denise shook her head and said, "Bo, you don't know how old your own son is?"

"Well, hey, it's a guy thing," Bo replied.

"Yeah, okay," she said back.

"I bet Mark's Pops doesn't know exactly how old he is either."

"Well, I must admit, you got a great point," she says with a smile.

"See—there it is, I'm not the only clueless father," Bo replied with a giggle.

"Hush—you need to quit!" She responded.

"Speaking of Mark's dad," Bo continued. "Who is this baby's daddy?"

Denise thought, *he just walked right into this trap,* "Who does he look like?"

Bo takes a step back and takes a long look and says, "Don't know, can't make it out."

"You sure—you can't tell?" She asked.

Bo stared again before saying, "I don't know, I can't see a resemblance of anybody?"

"Bo!" She says with a warm smile.

He shrugs his shoulders as Mark blurts out, "Mayberry my daddy, mama."

Bo immediately jumps on that and says, "Mayberry his daddy," as he laughs but suddenly stopped and asked, "Who is Mayberry?!"

"My daddy," Mark replied.

Denise, content that she had baited the hook juuust right, thought it was time to reel it in, but not here, not now. So she smiles and winks at Bo and said, "Can you come by the house later this afternoon—round about three-four o'clock? I'm staying with my parents right now—you know where they live, right?"

"I think so," he replied, while he thought about it.

"Cool.... I'll see ya between three and four," she responded.

It is almost 3:15 p.m. when Bo's 1980 Red Chevrolet four-door pulls up to the Davis residence. Mark was playing in the front yard under the watchful eye of his grandfather, Odell. After a quick, "Hi ya doin' sir, what's up Mark," Bo knocks on the side door.

Seconds later, Denise steps out and tells her father to go inside, she'll watch Mark.

Odell gets up from his chair wearing what appeared to be a ring on every finger with five matching gold chain necklaces. And Bo waits till he hears the side door by the carport shut before he says, "Yo dad look like a full-blooded Indian, girl!"

Keeping her eye on Mark, she says, "Yeah, he's half Indian."

"Half! Girl, that man is every bit of Cherokee, Choctaw, and Apache!" He replied.

Denise busts out with a laugh, "You oughta quit!" She screams.

Bo began to laugh a bit and said, "I thought I was at the wrong house till I saw Mark."

Denise just shakes her head as they both share a giggle.

“So, what’s up, its 3 p.m.— who’s the lucky guy?”

“Come on now, Bo, who does he look like?” Denise asked again.

“Yeah,” Bo said as he took another hard look at Mark playing in the yard, who is oblivious to the life changing drama unfolding right under his runny little two-year old nose, “I been thinking about it but I can’t figure it out. But I did do a lil investigation work, and my sources tell me that this dude Mayberry, from out there in Jefferson Prep is indeed your baby’s daddy.”

“Look at you,” she said. “You have done a lil homework, huh?”

Bo shakes his head with a bit of confidence, and said, “I got a lil Kojack in me. It tends to surface every now and then when I need to prove a lil somthin somthin.”

“Okay, Kojack, I hate to burst your bubble, but Mayberry ***is not*** the father,” she said.

“Really,” he responded, now confused as to what’s really going on here, especially since she’s gone this far to enlighten him. He’s now saying to himself, *The kid says Mayberry is his father; people in the streets say Mayberry is his father; I’m pretty sure Mayberry thinks he’s the father, but she saying Mayberry IS NOT the father.*

Bo turns and looks at Denise and asks, “So, who’s the father—do I know him?”

“Oh yeah, you know him very well.”

“Did he go to school with us?”

“Yep, he graduated in my class of ‘81 not your class of ’82,” she added.

“Sounds more like a statement than a question,” Bo said, “Give me a hint?”

“He played sports,” she answered.

“Sports,” he repeated.

“Yep—big-time sports,” she replied as Bo went into deeper thought.

“Come on Bo, you gotta know who I’m talking about.”

Suddenly, he drops his head in shock and said, “No freaking way!”

Denise smiles and patiently waits for his answer.

“Danny Bradley?!”

Dee’s smile gets brighter with an obvious sense of relief attached.

“Yep—that’s Danny’s boy,” she replied.

“Come on man—Danny ain’t told anybody in the family about havin a son.”

But no matter how many times she played it out in her head, there was no way she could make her next words sound any less incriminating.

“Well—unfortunately—**he doesn’t know.**”

Bo, staring at Mark, snaps his head back around as if on a swivel, and asks, “What do you mean he doesn’t know?”

Denise, now staring at the pavement, felt Bo's eyes glued on her and said, "I don't know.... I guess I got scared and panicked."

"Denise—Danny is a good dude, girl, you gotta tell him," he replied.

"I know, everything was going so well for him—I just didn't want to get in the way."

"Come on Dee, you gotta tell him," Bo expressed.

"I agree but I just didn't know how to break the news to him."

Bo leaned back against the family car parked in the driveway, his mind racing through a bunch of scenarios: *First of all, she wanted me to be the bearer of this unfortunate news. Second, why this girl wait so long before she try to tell somebody?*

At that moment, Bo believed he knew the answer to that question, *cuz is bout to blow up perhaps NFL Big and now he just happens to have a two-three year old son.*

"Looka here," Bo said, "I'll take Mark over and introduce him to my aunt Shelly and uncle Duke, and help you break the ice a bit—Mark will be fine. His parents are cool people—but you gotta be the one to tell Danny about this, Dee."

"Alright, Bo, protect my baby," Denise said as if this wasn't her plan all along.

Bo's thoughts were, *girl please—you got yourself in a twist and now you want somebody to bail you out!*

But Bo kept his cool, thinking more about Mark, Mayberry, and now his cousin Danny as to why he must keep a level head here. "Denise Davis," he says, "I got this. These are my kinfolk, girl! And yours too, at this point—don't ya think?"

"Yeah, I guess so," as she shakes her head in agreement.

Bo's face said it all; he was willing to help her, but he knew he couldn't trust her.

"Come here Mark," she flagged. "You remember Bo from Wal-Mart today?"

Mark shakes his head, yes.

"He's gonna take you to get some of your favorite candy, okay?" Denise said.

"Candy!" Mark replied.

I had absolutely no idea how much life-changing chatter had been going on about me, but I did understand the word "candy." At that age, my grandpa Odell said when it came to candy, I would drop my toys faster than Mike Tyson dropped Mike Spinks!

And with a complete stranger holding my hand, I got into his car with joy, excited about my candy. But little did I know, instead of stopping by a candy store, we stopped by some other folks door—Duke and Shelly Bradley, my newly alleged grandparents. And from this point forward, life as I knew it would never be the same.

3

The Allegation

As we entered the house, the way Ms. Shelly Bradley tells the story; she came to the door and saw Bo holding this cute little boy in his arms and said, "Hey Bo, hey TJ!"

Then she quickly took a retake, "That's not TJ, who lil boy is that?"

"It's not mine and its not TJ," Bo replied.

"Hey lil cutie," Shelly said. "You got another baby, Bo?"

"No I don't," as he smiles. "Why—does he look like me?"

Shelly looks again as she closes the door. "Kinda sorta," she replied.

"Take a good look—who do you think he looks like," he asked?

She looks closely but can't paint the picture. By now they have made their way to the master bedroom, where her husband Duke is sitting and relaxing. Having heard Bo and his wife's conversation as they made their way down the hallway, he's looking curiously at the little boy, too, as Bo placed him into his lap.

Shelly says, "He does look a little like you."

Duke chimes in.

"You have another baby, Bo?"

Before Bo answers, Shelly stoops down to eye level: "What's your name little cutie?"

"Mark," the little boy softly says.

"How old are you, Mark?" She asked.

"Three," as his whispers get even softer while holding up *four* fingers.

"Who's your daddy?"

Bo, looking on, gets a little nervous by her questions but Mark bails him out by fading into an even softer, "Can't hear ya" whisper with only his lips moving.

Shelly turned and said, "Bo, come on now; who's this child's daddy?"

Duke chimes in again and said, "Who is his mother?"

Bo smiles and pauses for a second and says, "I took an oath, I can't tell you who his mama is but I can tell you who the daddy is, I think—it's a lil complicated."

"Complicated—boy, who is this baby daddy," Shelly asked?!

Bo pauses for a moment as if he didn't really want to do this. And with all eyes now glued on him, he was trapped and had to deliver. He thought to himself, *I hope y'all ready for this*. He then takes a deep breath and said, **"It's Danny's lil boy."**

I think the expression Shelly would use when she tells the story is, *you could've blown her and Duke over with a feather.*

"Danny!" She shouted with a look of shock. "Bo, come on now, don't play with me boy, hell, oops, excuse me, I almost cussed," and then covered her mouth.

Duke abruptly looks up at Bo and then back at Mark who is still sitting in his lap, and says, "What cho say! Danny doesn't have any kids, Bo!"

"It appears that perhaps he does now," Bo replied.

"Who is this boy's Mama, now, stop playing with me!" She continued.

"Well, I'll be. He does kind of look a lil like Danny at this age, Shelly." Duke said.

"Oh, hell, Duke—don't you start that—you know darn well Danny don't have any kids. Now who's this child's mama, Bo?!" Shelly asked.

Bo laughs to keep the mood light for Mark's sake and now his.

"I'm sure after today, she'll be in touch with you. If she doesn't I'll personally run her out this town myself….I told her I'll help her break the ice, but she gotta clean it up."

By now with no candy, no familiar faces, and in a strange location, Mark did what any two-three year-old would do under the circumstances—cry!

"Ok, lil fella, it's time to get you back to your mama," Bo said.

Duke kindly places him in a standing position; Bo grabs his hand as they begin to walk toward the front door.

Still stunned by the revelation, Duke says again, "He really does kind of look a lot like Danny at that age."

"Duke, stop! Bo, who is this child's mother?" Shelly asked as she began to get serious.

After no response, except a smile, Shelly shot back, "Okay, I'll just call Mr. Danny, and see what he got to say about this," as they made their way to the door.

Bo suddenly stops before exiting the house, and tells Mark to go stand by the car and turns and says, "Aunt Shelly, don't call Danny about this just yet. If he doesn't know, let her be the one to tell him. If she doesn't—we will. But for now, if this is true, and unfortunately, I kinda believe it could be, let's make her fess up."

"But Bo, come on now, Danny needs to know about this craziness," she replied.

"I understand that, that's why I'm here," he said as he keeps an eye on Mark. "I saw this kid and his Mom at Wal-Mart today. She shared this information with me in an obvious attempt to get this message to Danny, without havin' to deliver it herself. So I decided to bring Mark over because this man need to know, if this truly is his son. But if we bail her totally out, she will forever attempt to use us to get information to him. And that craziness can get way out of hand," Bo said.

"Absolutely, if it's true," Duke said. "We don't want Danny to think we're involved in any of this mess. We need to know more before we implant ourselves into this deal, especially since he just got engaged—so we must be careful with this information."

"Please," Shelly said. "This is not the first women claiming to have a baby by somebody that didn't want them."

"I understand," Bo said. "I've had a few claims against me that were false, but unfortunately, Danny's promising career and the fact that he's about to get married may be her motivation for coming out with this. So, the sooner he knows the better. But she needs to be the one to fess up—not us," Bo said. "And my sources tell me that this particular girl has been fascinated with him for a long time."

"Well, it appears that he's been pretty fascinated with her, too, if this child is indeed his," Duke added with concern.

"Obviously, uncle Duke, but he's not denying her the opportunity to be this kids mother, but she is denying him the right to be his father, if this is true," Bo said.

"But why she wait until now—did she tell ya that?" Shelly asked.

"I asked her that question. She said she got scared and didn't know how to tell him, and didn't want to get in the way of his career," Bo replied.

"What damn career, Bo?! The boy didn't have a career when this child was conceived! Or born! He was simply trying to survive at Pine Bluff High, okay, with two broke parents trying to figure out why they so freakin broke! And if I got my facts straight.... he stood on the sideline *as a spectator* his first couple of years at OU—so what career?!"

"Well, when you put it like that, it definitely sounds premeditated," Bo answered.

"Y'all know this some BS," Shelly said.

Duke jumps in again, "Let's at least give the young lady the benefit of the doubt, honey, before we rush to judgment."

"Benefit of the doubt—Duke please, that sound like some mess you said back when some of these women were claiming you as the father of a kid or two or three. So don't get me started," she replied.

"Shelly, all I'm saying is let's give this young lady the benefit of the doubt—we don't know the truth about this just yet," Duke replied with concern.

"I agree," Bo immediately said. "But at the end of the day, if true, Mark is your grandson Aunt Shelly, and right now—we don't even know this kid. And he lives right down the street from here."

Bo's comment set the stage for this concert to finally begin as Mark begins to get a bit impatient. So, Bo says his goodbyes and exits as Shelly and Duke watch them drive away—partially confused and stunned.

A few months go by, and Danny is now in the middle of the season, getting prepared to take on the Longhorns in the Cotton Bowl. Texas was the nations top ranked team that week and OU was ranked #2 by the Associated Press; the first time ever these two historical dominate programs entered the Red River Shootout as the top two teams in the country, believe or not. But in the interim, there were still no phone calls, notes, letters or conversations initiated by Denise with Danny or the Bradleys, which meant she hadn't intended going directly to him or them.

He was still unaware, and his parents did what any parent would do, or should do—pray, protect, and investigate. And in a small town where people talk and gossip all the time, knowing the right people and certainly the right questions to ask, people in New York City will sing and reveal the most intimate details.

But the smaller the landscape, the further one might be from the truth and the smaller the town, the bigger the lies and the more diverted they seem to get. But when you do a lil hairstyling from home, as Shelly did for many of the members of her church, oh yeah, you can be sure that there will be some dialogue going on about this matter. But fortunately, it wasn't her church clients from the sanctuary who provided the wave of evidence; it was her future hope-to-be daughter-in-law, Rhonda, her oldest son's girlfriend, that presented the mother of this kid named Mark.

You see Denise, who was now on a mission, befriended one of Rhonda's relatives, who had recently shared the loaded information with her. So while dining at a local ice cream shop, "Baskin-Robbins," Rhonda sees Denise and Mark walk in and at such point she chose to tell what she knew.

"Shelly, take a close-close look at that lil boy right there."

"Where—with the Davis girl?" Shelly asked.

Rhonda, not knowing that Shelly's nephew, Bo, had already brought that same little boy by the house not too long ago, asked, "Who does he look like to you?"

And Shelly, taken aback, while putting the two together, and knowing where Rhonda is going with this, says, "I'm not sure" as she looks at Mark and back at Denise.

And Denise, who now notices Shelly and Rhonda, suddenly steps over and behind Mark in an effort to hide him from their view.

"She's been telling people that's Danny's baby," Rhonda said. "One of my relatives said that Denise told her that Mark was really Danny's son—not this other dude, and I don't believe it, Shelly—that boy just don't look like Danny to me—does he to you?"

Meanwhile, Shelly is thinking, *Well, I'll be.... Denise Davis is this boy's mother.*

"Who is that child's father?" Shelly asked.

"This guy name Mayberry from out in Jefferson Prep," Rhonda replied. My family have known Mayberry for years, and we see him with that lil boy all the time."

So Shelly, now convinced that Denise is shielding her son from them, gets up and walks over and says, "Denise, how you doing?"

"Fine and you?" Denise responds, jittery.

"I've been better," Shelly frankly replied.

Rhonda, in a bit of shock, makes her way over too. "Hey Denise—hey Mark. I see you around town on occasion with this handsome lil boy, who is his daddy?" She asked as she bends over to get eye to eye with him.

"Mayberry," Mark shyly answers, which immediately makes Denise even more uncomfortable knowing that Shelly had already been told, by Bo, that Danny was Mark's father, not Mayberry. The cashier calls Denise's number just in the nick of time. So, she grabs her son's ice cream cone, waves, and exits.

Shelly rushes home to tell Duke what she'd discovered, but he isn't there. However, her oldest son, JB, was waiting to pick up Rhonda, and gets an ear full from them about Mark, Denise, and Mayberry. And JB, who often played the role of protector in the absence of their father, didn't take kindly to the rumor or accusation.

"Look, Rhonda, don't be spreading this mess about Danny regarding this girl's BS. And Mama, let Denise step up and deal with this on her own. If she's been saying for the past two or three years that this dude Mayberry is the father, then, hell, Mayberry is the boy's father," JB said.

"Well, I don't believe it's true anyway," Rhonda responded. "And Denise's timing clearly tells me what this nonsense might be about."

"But if this is true, somebody is going to have to tell Danny," Shelly says.

"Mama, I'm telling you, we don't need to get involved in this mess with this girl. Let her step up and tell him! All she's attempting to do is communicate with Danny through you, me, and anybody else she can get to talk about it. So make her do it—not you. Cause, if he knew, he wouldn't be sending any messages back to anybody—he's going straight to her upfront! I'm through with it!" JB says as he abruptly exits the house, as Rhonda follows.

However, Shelly was aware of another situation involving Denise, which she had not told anyone: *an encounter she also claimed led to a pregnancy—an incident that took place, in her house, during spring break of 1983. And with this new information, apparently this was at least the second time they got together, and perhaps the last.*

So, prior to this particular one-night rendezvous, they had no contact with one another, except that other 'one-night rendezvous' that produced Mark. And without much of Danny's input, Denise, with her mothers support, decided she didn't want child number two and chose to abort. And maybe she couldn't imagine giving birth to his second child if she was *unwilling* to hip him to the first.

Since she had not been as open and forthright as hoped for, Danny found himself between a rock and a hard place. Consequently, not knowing if her claim was totally true, out of frustration, he granted her request and helped pay for the abortion, an unfortunate incident that took place before he even met his wife, Pam.

Now this was the saddest moment of the story for me as the writer. During a time when abortion was being politically and socially encouraged throughout the black community, with *abortion clinics* strategically placed within the walls of our community, my mother, Denise, accompanied by her mother, Leola, shows up at the Bradley's to pick up the cash needed from his mother Shelly, to fund her decision to abort and my alleged father paid for it. It's not easy processing this reality even as we speak.

But despite their faith in God, neither of them, then, understood the social-economic and spiritual implications of an abortion. Having now matured as people, parents, and as believers in the gospel of Christ, an abortion, today, would not remotely be a possible option for my mother; nor would this man of character I know today, would ever consider funding such an irresponsible decision. Therefore, I thank God, that in the wake of over 50 plus million babies having been aborted since its legalization in 1973, its gratifying to know that my mom would not, under any circumstances, encourage any young lady to abort unless perhaps the life of that mother was in eminent danger.

Nevertheless, the Bradleys were starting to get a bit concerned. Shelly, unbeknownst to Duke, began to calculate the past events that involved Denise Davis. And as she adds up the years from which Denise claims to have had the abortion, she realizes that unless her first grade mathematics score was off, "Mark would currently be about 18 months—not nearly three."

By mid-December of '84, Danny was getting dressed after their last practice session before finally heading off to Miami to host the Washington Huskies in that Orange Bowl contest I mentioned earlier.

Coach Switzer had given the team a few days off to complete their final semester exams and go home for Christmas a couple of days, if one so wished. However, as Danny was looking through his messages left in his locker, he notices one from Denise Davis. Nothing out of the ordinary, but just a message. It wasn't abnormal for a guy with his status to receive messages, out of the blue, from people he either didn't know or had previously known or shared space with.

And as usual, very few received a call back. And given his past history with Denise, he decided "not" to return that call either; making the majority of these bundle of messages, trash. But by the time he was ready to call it a night, after hours of studying for his exams, he sat admiring the engagement ring he had purchased for his fiance' Pam, when his apartment phone rings. Its his mother, informing him, too, that Denise Davis has been trying to reach him.

"Yeah, I got a message through the football office today, what's up with her? I haven't talked to Denise since about early '83."

"About the time she had the abortion?" Shelly asked.

"As a matter of fact, it was," he replied. "She didn't seem to want to talk much then so what's up with her now—did she say?"

"No, she just asked if I would have you call her, so call her and see what's up?"

"Tonight?" Danny asked, as he looks at his watch. "It's 1 a.m., mother!"

"Baby, shc said anytimc tonight."

"At 1 a.m.?"

"Apparently so, son. She said it was kind of urgent—give her a call and see what going on with her," Shelly replied.

"And she didn't say what was so urgent?" He asked.

"No—not really. She just asked if I could get you to call her—tonight."

Unfortunately, Shelly knew exactly what her call was all about, but had become convinced that this time she was going to let this issue play itself out on Denise's clock—not hers. So she stayed cool, calm and collected under the circumstances.

"What's the number?" Danny asked, as he reaches for a pen.

After jotting down the number, he says, "Aright, I'll give her a call."

He hangs up and then dials her number. And on the second ring, as if she was waiting for this call, he hears a familiar voice.

"Denise Davis—Danny, what's up—how are you?"

"Hey, what's up with you? Long time no talk too," she said.

"Yeah—it's been a minute, but things are well—just trying to find my way."

"Find your way? I'd say you've found your way, Mister Bradley," she said. "You got people is this town that either despise you or wanna be you."

"Well—hey, it's a tough place on a young fella trying to make it out."

"Who you tellin—I still remember those fools from across town who walked up on you with guns, at the car wash, a couple of summers ago—showing out—and this town was like a national tabloid after that incident," she said.

Danny, is thinking, *this conversation reminds me of our old chats from our high school days which makes me even more curious as to what could she possibly want to discuss with someone that she hasn't had much contact with in three years.*

"Yes, an unfortunate situation—could've lost my life. But God is good," he replied.

"Did the knuckle head ever apologize, I heard he did?" She asked.

"He actually did—said his homeboys had put him up to it behind an incident that happened at some party with a relative of mine," Danny shares.

"Wow, I heard it was behind this infatuation his girlfriend had with you," she said.

"Well, I wouldn't know anything about that, he said involved an incident dealing with my cousin, Bo, and some of his buddy's, but enough about me—what's up with you? How's your family?" Danny asked.

"Everybody is good.... I'm just working, staying busy. It keep me out of trouble."

"And your boy from Jefferson Prep—are things any better?" He asked.

"Nah—it's not working out," she replied.

"Sorry to hear that. You obviously have a lot invested, and I'm sure your son is probably pretty attached to his Dad by now."

"Somewhat, but my Dad spends the most time with him though," she replied.

"Oh—Okay. How old is he now?" He asked.

"He'll be three in a few weeks and thinks he's twenty-three," Denise said jokingly.

"I understand," Danny replied likewise, with a slight giggle. "So what's up—my Mom said you needed me to reach out to you—urgently?"

"Well—I wanted to say congratulations to you on all your success at OU, you've made out well for yourself, and I heard through the grapevine that you're getting married soon," she stated.

"And where did you here that?" Danny asked.

"Come on now, you know people in this town are all over your business like 24/7."

"Well, unlike most rumors floating around that town, that one happened to be true," he pleasantly replied. "We plan on court-housing it in a few months and have the wedding the following year in perhaps April-May of 86."

"And why are you guys choosing to do it that way?" She asked curiously.

"Well, with both of us pushing to graduate by the fall of '85, we figure this would be the best way to move forward under the circumstances."

"Well—congratulations, again, I'm sure she's a great girl."

"She aright," he said, as Denise, with sort of a distant gesture, giggles at his comment and says, "I'm sure she's more than just aright—you marrying her aren't you?."

"Point well taken," he replied, as he now leans toward a close in an effort to get some sleep. He had given Denise about fifteen minutes of his unavailable time and served his fiduciary duty—but for now he's got some personal and professional business to handle in the classroom and in Miami at the FedEx Orange Bowl.

"It was great chatting, Dee, but I gotta get going. Stay in touch and out of trouble."

"I will...thanks for calling at such short notice and so late, but there is one other thing I wanted to discuss with you," she said.

"Okay—go ahead, what's up?" He replied, while looking at his watch.

Then there was a long, what seemed like a thirty-second, pause from Denise.

"I'm sorry—I've been having a tough time with this," she said as her voice cracked.

"Dee—go ahead—what's up—it's me."

"I know it but it's not as easy to talk to you like I did back in school."

"I understand it's been a minute but it's cool—talk to me," he replied. "What's up?"

Denise takes a deep sigh and Danny, who is now past his allotted time, starts to become a bit concerned as to what his old acquaintance is struggling to say. After all she initiated this call—not him. So, he decides to help her by using a little reverse psychology, and said, "I can always give you a shout tomorrow after my exams."

"No—No—No I'd rather talk now," she replied with hesitation.

Now Danny slips in a light sigh and stands up, especially with the history he's had with Denise. And right when he was about to try to encourage her to get to the point—she abruptly got it out.

"You have a son, Danny."

"I have a what?"

"You have a son," she repeated.

Danny pulls the phone away from his ear, looks at the receiver as if a ghost had spoken. He then places it back to his ear and asked, "What do you mean I have a son, Denise?!"

She paused again and then said, "In January 1982, I gave birth to a seven pound boy from an encounter we had back in May of '81 right before you left for college. I apologize for not telling you then but I didn't want to get in the way of your career. So I decided that now was probably the best time to come clean about it—**my son, Mark, is your son, Danny."**

Danny drops the phone, frozen in place as he stands in front of his apartment desk, in a state of shock. He momentarily loses track of time and space, finally falling back into the chair. Although, truth be told, if there had not been a chair, he wouldn't have even felt the fall. He leans back in shock as he could hear Denise's voice coming from the receiver on the floor, *"Hello.... Hello.... Hello."*

With his eyes closed he suddenly sees an Ford LTD, windows fogged, and now he sees *his* face, deep in the throes of ecstasy, Denise's body beneath him. The operators recorded voice and the sound breaks his thoughts, as he reaches over to hang it up.

Needless to say, he didn't get any sleep that night and struggled to make good on his final exams. And to regroup and think this thing out, Danny begins canceling every speaking engagement that he had already committed to doing, in an effort to wrap his mind around this huge life-changing allegation, including one at his church in Pine Bluff. He had suddenly become too embarrassed to take the stage given the circumstances of Denise's alleged claim. And one could only imagine what might be going on in the mind of a young man with such a promising future.

Nevertheless, he was determined to stay focused on finishing what he started at the University of Oklahoma, with a degree still left to obtain, and a shot of taking home the National Championship trophy at the Orange Bowl. But would he have enough strength and courage to carry this added weight of potentially having a three-year-old son that he didn't even know existed; knowing he was just months away from marrying his college sweetheart? Or would he simply do what most men or athletes have been known to do, after being accused of being the *newly alleged* father of somebody else's son, ignore it?

The Complication

4

By the close of New Years night of 1985, Danny had officially proposed to his sweet-mate, her birthday, but unfortunately, the Sooners lost their opportunity at making history. The Huskies won the FedEx Orange Bowl on a night filled with unexpected uncertainties, including the Sooner Schooner invasion onto the field, prematurely, after a Sooners score, which severely cost OU in a game with so much at stake. And in turn awarded Brigham Young college football's grandest prize—the National Championship.

Danny had a sub-par night, failing to live up to his MVP performance he had unanimously earned throughout the '84 season. But still, he had a lot to be thankful for. He had accomplished just about everything you can accomplish after having to overcome such a tough upbringing. And he probably played about as well as one could expect given these new life-changing circumstances. But the good news is, this man cared enough to care about being a father despite having to take on this enormous responsibility to perform his best on the biggest stage in College Football.

Nevertheless, the pressure didn't get any lighter, after his failure to capture the championship, he was off to Tokyo, Japan to participate in, then, one of the most prestigious College All-Star games of the American game, known as the Japan Bowl, which invited the top players from across the U.S. to showcase their talent for pro scouts. That years bunch included Heisman winner Doug Flutie, Boston College; Mike Tomczac, Ohio State; Al Toon, Wisconsin; Randal Cunningham, UNLV; Mike Stoops, Iowa., etc. Coaches Jimmy Johnson of Miami and Haden Fry of Iowa were selected as the East / West skippers. In this game, Danny would showcase his ability to play wide-receiver, not quarterback.

Even though he managed to have a good time while there the two weeks, he had a heavy heart. Denise's announcement was gnawing at him daily as he looked for ways to approach this ridiculous situation with his soon to be wife, who had just accepted his proposal in marriage, delightfully.

Upon his return from Japan, he had found enough courage to share this bombshell with his fiance, in hopes of keeping this up-front and open communication line between them, positive. But not before he called a few friends back home in Pine Bluff to do a little PI'ing regarding Denise's allegation.

And as expected, Denise was still publicly promoting and tagging Mayberry as the father of her son, Mark, despite her claim that such was not the case. And since nothing seemed to have changed between Mark and his current father, reliable sources documented that Mayberry and Denise appeared to be a happy couple with child; a proud papa who was often around town bragging about his son, Mark Mayberry.

But as Danny intently shares Denise's allegation with Pam, just weeks before their court-house ceremony in Norman, Pam was understanding and civil, but had one question: "Could this kid still possibly be yours?"

Danny assures her that anything was indeed possible, but that he didn't believe her story to be remotely true, given all the factors involved. And if so, by any stretch of the imagination, Denise would have a lot of explaining to do to a lot of people, including the kids current father.

At that, Pam chalked it up as some ploy to get paid somehow or Denise's effort to come between their relationship in someway. Not at all that uncommon given this crazy world we live in today.

Consequently, by the end of April 1985, Danny and Pam had married and the Los Angeles Rams selected him in the collegiate draft as a wide-receiver. This couple was headed for Hollywood, and life was now even better for the Bradleys'.

In the meantime, Shelly was still a little concerned with all the rumors that continued to slowly make their way to her doorstep, tagging Danny as the kid's father. But he assured his mother that he didn't believe, at all, that Denise's son was indeed his son, and gave all of his reasons as to why he was so certain. And though it all seemed to make sense, Shelly decided to leave well enough alone, at least, for now. But the slight resemblance of the two of them still bothered her a bit.

By the *4th of July* weekend of '86, about a year-and-a-half removed from my "meet the Bradley's" event, the Davis house is filled with family and friends, eating, drinking, playing cards and dominoes with loud music banging in the background. And like most four-five-year-olds, I'm constantly getting in the way, or *interrupting grownups' conversations*.

My granddad Odell, at this point, was still the closest thing to a day-to-day father I'd had. So I tended to follow him around and paid attention to nearly everything he did. This time it was watching him partake in a common *4th of July* custom in the south—pointing a pistol in the air and firing off a few rounds!

I was really fascinated with my granddad's .22 caliber pistol. I watched as he fired it into the Pine Bluff sky, high-fived a few of his house guests, and then made his way back into his bedroom, where he placed the gun between the mattress and box spring of the bed. With his hand palming the top of my head, Odell leads me back to the living room, where he sits down at a card table, propping me on his lap as he prepares to slam some dominoes. I start disrupting their game a bit too much so my granddad puts me down and tells me to go watch TV.

During these days, they didn't have the Cartoon Network or Nickelodeon, so before long I was bored with television. I did remember where Odell had put his gun, though. No one noticed as I made my way to the master bedroom, and, as if I placed it there myself, I went straight to the spot where he had hidden the pistol.

At this time, shows like Magnum P.I., Hill Street Blues and Miami Vice, none of which I understood, other than the fact that they all had cool guns like the one I now held in my hand.

After a few minutes of imaginary cops and robbers, I decided to examine my new toy more closely. I didn't understand why the trigger on my granddad's gun was harder to pull than the one on my "Mattel." So I gripped the pistol with both hands, one on the barrel and the other on the trigger. I must have looked like I was trying to open a bag of potato chips. And it worked, the gun goes off—BANG!

The shot rang out through the house and seemingly the whole neighborhood to me. And suddenly I noticed myself sitting on the floor with blood all over my hands and shirt. And then I screamed!

The loud bang rushes Odell and others into the bedroom, where they find me, in a state of shock, with blood all over my shirt. My grandfather scoops me up and carries me through the house, which is now in chaos, hollering at the top of his voice for people to get out of the way, open the door, and grab my keys!

To this day I don't know what other relatives got in the car with us. And understandably, my grandfather didn't totally recall either. But shortly after, I lose consciousness as Grandma Leola frantically calls the hospital to tell them her grandson is being brought in with a gunshot wound. Odell is running red lights, flashers on, everyone in the car in a state of panic.

My mother was working that July 4th, so when she got to the hospital after receiving word I'd been shot, she was still wearing her waitress outfit and my daddy Mayberry arrived at almost the same time, I was told. All I remembered were the ceiling lights as they wheeled my gurney down the corridor.

And left standing in the Emergency Room (ER) waiting area were my mom, and granddad, who were pacing and crying, while being comforted by Mayberry and other relatives, who were also—terrified!

A few hours later, a doctor enters the waiting area and approaches Denise, who's crying and rocking back and forth, her arms folded across her chest. The physician on call tells her, "Mark's going to be alright, but it appears that he's lost a little blood. Right now it doesn't look like he'll need a blood donor, but it wouldn't ever hurt to always know who a match might be."

My parents, certain that one of them would be a match, said, "Okay, we understand—he's our son, when can we see him?" Denise asked.

With a stern look on his face, the physician addresses everyone, who by now has gathered around him, anxious to know my condition. "Soon, but first a police report must be filed by the hospital. This is a four-year old child with a gunshot wound. I'm sure someone from the police department and social services will be with you shortly," he said as he walked away.

Until that moment, my Mom had been in a state of shock. The talk of police and social services broke her out of it.

"Social services, they are not going to take my baby from me!"She shouted. Mayberry attempts to console her, but Denise is still too agitated, sitting back down in the waiting area, rocking back and forth, looking at no one in particular, not willing to hear anything her dad or any other family member had to say.

Odell is reminded he has to move his car, which is illegally parked, so Mayberry heads out of the Emergency Room entrance to reposition it, leaving Odell to sit across from his daughter, wondering how he could have let this happen to his grandson, and what must his only daughter be thinking!

Truth is, only a select few have any idea what Denise's thoughts might be, and none of them are in that ER.

"Donors.... police.... social services? Lord, how did I get myself into this craziness!"

She places her hands over her face and thinks back to a night over four years ago. This time as she begins to reflect, she remembers *that same* parked car, a Ford LTD to be exact. It's as if she's having an out-of-body experience. The windows are fogged but she suddenly makes out two figures of a man and woman. The woman's face is visible, it's her own, obviously in the throes of ecstasy and passion, her arms wrapped around the back of a well-built man.

Unexpectedly, a loud voice on the hospital PA system snaps her back into the present, at which point, under her breath she says to herself, *"Damn it, Danny Bradley."*

Back In Los Angeles

Over a couple of thousand miles away, Danny didn't have a clue about the newest events going on back in Pine Bluff. He was in L.A., Hollywood swinging with his newly wedded wife, Pam Beasley-Bradley. He was entering his second year with the Rams, as a mid-round draft pick out of Oklahoma. And despite having lost to the Chicago Bears in the 1986 NFC Championship Game, this Rams team was in position for greatness.

Ironically, as the drama was unfolding back in Pine Bluff, Danny was closing out a full day mixed with both relaxation and business. The Rams were in the early stages of camp and were given a couple days off. And since their training camp facilities were local, held at Cal-State Fullerton University, players would often drive across town to spend time with their family. And Danny likewise did the same. Since his Anaheim condo was only 10 miles from the Rams camp-grounds, he too went home to have a lil R&R with his wife, Pam. But beforehand he had lunched it with teammate and mentor Ron Brown (RB), who was a successful entrepreneur beyond the field of play.

During these days, Player Development programs and internship opportunities, within the walls of the NFL didn't exist. Like many players, Danny and RB had to create their own *life-after-football plans*. RB, who had started his own exotic car dealership to complement his custom wheel and accessory business, was now grooming Danny on how the entrepreneurial game is played. And Danny, too, being sharp beyond his years, aspired to also use the NFL stage to connect with the right folks in areas of interest and launch his own venture. In this case, the *health and fitness business* was the business of choice, and he decided to celebrate with a night out on the town with his wife, Pam.

They arrived at this exclusive restaurant on Sunset Boulevard in what would become Danny's car of choice, a two door drop–top *convertible conversion* with the exotic wheel and tire package, compliments of *Ron Brown's Auto Wheel and Accessories*, who was known for hooking up all the player's rides in Southern California.

Pam was stopping both men and women in their tracks, wearing a Halston original that was tasteful, showing off her best assets, as Danny sported a custom clothier, too.

It was a highlight night for this honeymoon couple—a night of a little dining, dancing, and dating. They talked *faith, family* and *finances,* and documented this night as one to remember. By the time they arrived at their contemporary condo in Anaheim, Pam and Danny were both hotter than the month itself. Entering the home through the carport garage, she immediately heads for the stairs, which leads to the bedroom. She seductively turns to Danny, who is headed for his unfinished office.

"Don't take too long. It's time you come handle your business."

"Babe, I'm on it, let me turn these lights off and I'll be right up."

Looking towards his office he sees the message light blinking on the office phone and he decides to check it. It's his mom, whose voice has a tone of concern, so he immediately picks up the receiver and dials her number.

After making several attempts, Shelly finally answers and says, "Son, I thought you might want to know that Denise's little boy, Mark, had a gunshot incident a few weeks ago and I believe Social Services and the Police Dept. might be investigating the cause. I'm not sure about what happened and who might be involved, but the word is that this was a self-inflicted gun-shot wound, however, others are saying that kid's father may have been involved. Regardless, it sounds like this kid is in real danger, are you sure this child is not your son?"

Danny pauses and drops his head, not wanting to even think about the possibility of this allegation again, much less what might be really going on behind it, says, "Yes, I'm sure," he calmly replied with concern.

"Well, I think you should call her and see what's going on?" Shelly said as she gently hangs up as Danny slightly slams his receiver down on his desk after hearing a dial tone.

"Damn it!" He shouted.

Apparently having heard the sound, Pam comes halfway down the stairs, wearing a sheer two-piece short negligee.

"What's up? What are you doing? And why is the phone off the hook?"

In as calm a voice as he can muster, he sobers up with the quick and says, "Sorry babe, I'm on my way up. My mother called and I was just hanging up with her."

"What could yo mother want this time of night? It's after 2 a.m. in Pine Bluff."

"I was just returning her call from a message left earlier. All is well," as he places the receiver back on the hook.

There was a slight pause, then Pam said, "You trippin—yo mother gon get you fired—that's what's gon happen," as she makes her way back up the stairs talking to herself underneath her breath.

Pam wasn't buying his story and definitely didn't want to hear any story involving his mother. And he knew exactly how his wife felt about his Mom, so he didn't press.

At this point, Danny was simply trying to digest this enormous bit of information, for which he couldn't fathom the idea of it really being true, though he knew such was a possibility. As he tries to regroup, he looked to the positives and recalls his rookie orientation class and the voice of a Rams team representative: *"There will be women approaching you from all walks of life, and some from your past, attempting to take advantage of you financially—claiming you as the father of their three-four-five-year old child—get these things thoroughly checked out before you make any decisions. Our records show that far-to-many of these accusations turn out to be false and untrue."*

Talking to himself, he tries to calm his anger, *This can't be.... I just didn't think she was that kind of girl.... Denise trippin..... I'm going to bed.*

Reaching for the office light switch, something on the inside held him. And with one hand on the switch, the other rubbing his eyes, he stops, thinks, and reconsiders. *How can this be.... This kid legally carries the name of another man.... It can't be!*

Once again, Danny hears that Rams rep's voice, *"Get these things thoroughly checked out before you make any decisions—and if true—handle your business like a responsible father and a professional."*

He suddenly reaches for the phone book and finds the airline flight reservations number and calls to schedule an early morning trip to Little Rock, Arkansas.

5

The Predicament

The next morning Danny was booked on the first available flight to Little Rock, but forgot that Pam was leaving the same morning to Dallas/Fort Worth to visit her parents. So, he changed his flight until late morning, knowing that his flight would also connect through D/FW.

The reschedule allowed him to postpone having to deal with that conversation before he knew for certain the outcome of this allegation. Nevertheless, as soon as he arrived at the Long Beach Airport, 11 a.m. Pacific Time, 1 p.m. Central, he stopped at a pay phone and called his receivers coach to make known his family emergency, for he still had a day and a half before he was to report back to camp. He then called Dallas to likewise inform his wife, through his mother-in-law, that he was headed home to deal with a family emergency and he'd contact her later to explain.

The gate attendant was announcing final boarding for the flight to Little Rock seconds after he'd hung up the phone. Since he was only a few feet from the gate, there was no need to rush. Once on board, Danny stowed his duffle bag, strapped himself in, and tried to relax as the flight attendant began welcoming passengers on the PA system.

Meanwhile, in Pine Bluff, grandma Shelly is at home washing dishes and chatting with Jo, her sister, Bo's mother, about the gunshot incident and Denise's allegation, which is now all over the streets of PB.

"I don't really know much about Denise Davis," Shelly said.

"Well I do," Jo replied. "When that boy was at OU, every time I saw her, she's always asking about Danny.... '*how's he doing.... who's he dating.... take me the next time you guys go see him.'"* I wanted to say, girl, don't you have a man and a family; the last place you should be is somewhere chasing behind somebody else's man. She is Danny crazy—do you hear me!"

"You never told me that she was hounding you like that," Shelly said?

"What's it to tell—it's not just Dee—okay! There are grown woman in this town with full-fledge families chasing that boy," Jo said.

"Well—I'm kind of hoping that this is not true, Jo. Danny just doesn't need this right now," Shelly replied with a disappointed undertone.

"Not with that unpredictable woman he married too—Pam will go the hell off on you, her, and definitely him when she finds out about this craziness!" Jo says with another giggle. Shelly stops washing dishes again for a split second to respond to Jo's ridiculous comment.

"Jo—this incident happened before Danny even met Pam, why would she be that unreasonable," Shelly said, as she turns the water off to wipe down the area. "Now—I admit, I didn't think she was right for him, but I don't think Pam would be that irrational, Jo.... Pam ignant—but she's not stupid."

"Shelly, please, you know Pam is half-crazy," as she continues to giggle. "That's why you didn't want him to marry her, cuz she crazy—and gon' get stupid on somebody if she find out Danny has a four-five year old child she doesn't know about," Jo said as she enjoys this gossip session.

"Maybe so—but I doubt Pam will clown like that with sooo much to lose, Jo."

"And I'm telling you," Jo said. "That's exactly why Pam Beasley-Bradley will clown—she got way too much to lose and will not, under no circumstances, tolerate another woman that she knows is, at least, after one thing—money.... Couple that with Dee being an attractive woman too—oh yeah, there will be some furniture moving around in somebody's house, sista girl!"

"Well, I don't know how she would justify that kind of response if she really loves him as much as she claims she does—she did marry him," Shelly says.

"Well—I don't know, either, but what I do know is this: Pam is a lot like me—she gon' clown!" Jo replied with certainty.

Suddenly, this concerned mother of three concludes her domestic chores, looks Jo right square in the eye and makes one of the best quotes heard in recent years.

"Jo, I've told all three of these boys, Danny, JB, and Craig to keep their damn zippers up and waistbands snapped! And stop acting just like their once upon a time hustling daddy—trying to be the *sugar dick daddy with the candy nuts."*

Jo screams, "Now that's some good stuff, girl! Where in the world did you get that?! *Sugar dick daddy with the candy nuts!* I got to use that one! I like that!"

"Hell, I'm serious," Shelly said.

"I know it—but that's a good line, girl."

Then Jo begins to calm down and get a little more serious about the matter.

"But you know, Danny, like a lot of young men, and way too many old men, put themselves in this kind of unnecessary situation. And many of these trifling young women are claiming to be on birth control—and carrying around condoms in their purses, punched holes in them—in an attempt to trap these naïve young men.... coming up pregnant and charging one man for another man's crime.... And again it ain't just Denise, there's a lot of young men that have been falsely charged with a baby that is not theirs—you tell me, what young man would want to be Mayberry, or Danny for that matter?" Jo asked. "Who might not have ever known, if he hadn't been so accomplished."

"Perhaps, but one thing I do believe, if this is his child—he will handle his responsibility," Shelly said. "I can't say that right now about my other two, but Danny will not disown this child despite what Denise's motives might be. But I do have a feeling that this situation is likely to turn his life completely upside down."

"It's Pam that's gon' to turn this situation upside down," Jo said.

"Well, I called Denise last night to try to find out more about this gunshot wound, but she couldn't talk and said she would call me back."

"Well, I gotta go, keep me informed about that conversation. At the rate Denise is going somebody might get seriously hurt."

It's now about 7:45 a.m., Jo gets up to head for an appointment. As she exits, Shelly decides to call Danny again before his workouts to get a feel of where his head might be about this latest bit of news. And just as his phone was beginning to ring, simultaneously, her doorbell rings. So she hung up and looks out her kitchen window. Guess who—it's Denise. *Maybe I can get to the bottom of this rumor, straight from the horses mouth,* Shelly says to herself, as she rushes to the door.

"Denise—what's going on?" Shelly said surprisingly.

"I hope it's okay to stop by without calling, first. I wasn't in a position to talk last night, so I thought I'd drop in for a chat."

"Sure, come in. How's Mark? Shelly asked, as they made their way to the kitchen.

"He's fine...still wearing a small bandage on his hand he injured. But he's making his way back physically and more important, emotionally.

"What happened, Denise? There's a lot of rumors floating around out here about this incident?" Shelly asked with concern.

"Well, Mark happened to go back to the location he saw my father hide his hand gun the night of the 4th, and began playing with it and managed to pull the trigger and shot himself in the hand.... After hearing the shot ring out, Daddy and a few other family members rushed in and saw him sitting on the floor in shock with blood all over him. They picked him up and rushed him out the door to the ER to discover it was only a injury to the hand. I was at work when it happened, but once I arrived at the hospital, I was a wreck, they were a wreck, and Mark was, obviously, a wreck.

"Well, as you well know, guns and kids is not a good mix, Dee."

"Yeah, I'm looking to move out of my parents house as soon as I can save enough to make it happen," Denise soberly replied.

"How is Mayberry dealing with all of this?" Shelly asked.

"Up and down," Denise replied. "He thinks I should let Mark live with him."

"I can understand that, Denise," Shelly said. "He's just trying to protect his son."

"I'm sure but he now knows that Mark is not his son. I informed him the week after the gunshot incident that he *was not* Mark's biological father. I didn't know what to expect but I wasn't quite ready for him to be unwilling to accept the truth," Dee stressfully replied. "Nor did I expect Danny to respond the way he did."

"What was his response? Shelly asked.

"He didn't tell you?" Dee asked surprisingly.

"He shared his feelings regarding your claim, but didn't share the details."

"Well," she said, after pausing. "I told him *my son is his son,* and I tried to explain what happened, when it happened, and where it happened—but then, the phone suddenly went silent. I don't think he hung up but he didn't say anything. I said 'hello' about three or four times, but got no response. So I decided to hang up."

"Well Dee, as you might imagine, that kind of unexpected information could send a person into a light shock. With all Danny has going on, it could be tough to process that kind of information, instantly on the spot, especially knowing how you've set this thing up. He's aware that Mark is legally named after another man, who still believes that Mark is his son.... Plus, he's got a new wife, a new team, living in a new city, battling a few new injuries—that's a lot for a young man to deal with, baby, regardless of who you are and where you might have come from."

"I recognize that Ms. Bradley, but I'm not trying to make life any more difficult for Danny. He is Mark's biological father. I didn't expect him to jump for joy but I didn't expect this reaction either," Dee said with humility. "But I'm just glad it's out—he now knows—I've done my part."

"Well, Dee, if true, I don't blame you. This is not the kind of life changing information any young mother would ever want to keep secret. He may have some reservations as to whether he believes you or not without proof, Denise, but keep in mind, we don't have to lie to look like we're lying. You did name this kid after another man," Shelly said.

That remark pushes a button, turning the docile Denise, into one with a attitude.

"Understood," Dee replied. "But I'm not lying about this, Ms. Bradley. He is his father, independent of a paternity test.... You've seen Mark around town, what do you think?" Denise asked sarcastically.

"I see the similarities, Dee, but I assure you this is not about what I think, this is now about what Danny thinks. And he's probably wondering what you might have been thinking over the past few years.. And if I know him, he will not leave any stone un-turned to get to the truth. He's gonna want to talk to you, Mark, Mayberry, and anybody else he may think might be involved."

"I don't have a problem with that," Denise frankly replied.

"And your parents, what do they think about all this?" Shelly asked.

"They're fine about it."

"So you don't have any problems with him talking to them about any of this?"

Dee's attitude shifted back to docile, "Well, yes and no. I don't want this to get out of hand, Ms. Bradley. All I'm trying to do is make this right, as Dee went on.

Shelly paused and thought to herself, *Dee, anytime a woman denies a man his lawful right to father his child, especially a decent one, it's already out of hand."*

"Denise," Shelly said, as she jumps back in at the first opportunity. "I can assure you that if Mark is indeed his son, he will not reject or neglect his duties as his father. The other two boys of mine would go completely off or tell you where to get off, but Danny will not neglect this child. I raised him as best I could without his father being around much and that same kid helped lead his Dad back to the Lord. So, he will not become what he despises."

And as Shelly was about to make another point, the phone interrupted her. She answers it, it's Danny. Not wanting to let on whom she was talking to, she said, "Hey, how are you," in so animated of a tone that Danny suddenly asks her if she was okay. She assures him that all was well. And sensing that she couldn't talk freely, he decided to get to the point as Denise listens cluelessly.

"I'll be there this evening, can I trust you not to tell anyone, including Denise?"

"Of course," she replied.

Knowing he had said all he needed to say, he hung up. Shelly continued, pretending to be still talking to someone. "Aright, great, but I'll call you back, bye-bye," she said into a dead receiver—then returned the phone to its cradle.

Denise started to get up from the table, not really wanting to leave just yet, but the message from Shelly's phone call was clear, she had things to do.

"Ms. Bradley, I need to get going."

Shelly could tell that Denise was in between humility and reality. She wants to confess but she also now seemed unsure if she really wanted to deal with the consequences of her decisions.

"Baby, I'm gonna talk to Danny and I'll let you know what comes of it but you might hear from him before I do," Shelly said as they make their way to the door. They hugged and she watched for a few seconds as Denise made her way to her car.

Shutting the door behind her, despite her son's request, Shelly knew she had to gather the troops and circle the wagons. The first call she made was to her husband, Duke, who was at work, followed by one to her oldest boy, JB. She told them both that this was somewhat of a family emergency, and to make their way to the house by 5:30 p.m. promptly. Once she hung up the phone she said to herself, *Lord, I hope this thing doesn't get out of control.*

By 6:15 p.m. Danny is sitting in the back of a Yellow Cab as it makes its way from Little Rock Airport to Pine Bluff. The cab driver appeared to be in his early fifties, with an outfit straight out of the sixties. Khaki waist jacket over a less than white t-shirt, well worn Levi's rolled at the cuff two times, and topped off by a weathered Arkansas Razorback ball cap.

He was a spry old dude, Danny thought, judging by the way he bounced off the hood of his cab, as he noticed a fare approaching. About 25-30 miles into the drive, his head was now pounding, a sign that he was beginning to feel the stress. He notices the ***Pine Bluff next exit signs,*** when he began looking up for the next rest area or gas station, anyplace with a phone. He didn't want to make this all important call from home. And he needed something to cure an Excedrin Headache.... But thought to himself, *not even Excedrin has a pill for this unbelievable nonsense.... Focus DB, focus.... For the good Lord promises to never leave me or forsake me.*

"Sir," Danny said. "Could we pull into the next gas station please? It's really important that I get to a pay phone."

"Sho nuff son. There's one comin up just over that rise. Whole bunch of phones fo ya. Yes sa, whole bunch a phones."

Danny thought the cabbie reminded him of Grady from ***"Sanford and Son"***, although younger than the character himself looked or was played on TV. While reaching in a side pocket of his duffle for his calling card to make this call, the gas station his driver spoke of appeared, and oh yeah, it had a row of phones!

He stepped out and placed his call to his wife in Texas through a long distance operator. In the middle of his call, Danny sees his driver attempting to eavesdrop on his call, but ignored his efforts.

"Sweetie.... I left you a message with your mom.... I understand but I don't need this right now.... That's not what I said to her.... I don't have any info yet sweetie.... come on honey, yes, yes, this is an important situation.... I'll stop through Dallas on my way back to LA and explain.... Babe, I got to get back for workouts and practice.... The Rams is not my life, it's my job.... Did you forget we have a couple of days off.... Babe.... come on Pam—don't do this.... I love you.... Hello.... Hello.... Pam!" he said.

He gets back into the taxi knowing the cabbie had heard his agitated remarks. But Danny knew he had much bigger problems than a nosy cab driver. Namely, and in no particular order, *an agitated wife who wanted answers he couldn't give, and some baby-mama-drama which could not have come at a worse time!*

And as expected, he was lost in these thoughts when his driver finally lured him into a chat after racking his brain along the way trying to figure out who this well dressed young man might be.

"Couldn't help but hear your conversation. You play for the Rams?

Danny soberly nods, "Yep," as he stared out the backseat passenger window.

"What's your name young fella?"

Looking at the driver's rear view mirror allowed the two to make eye contact.

"Bradley," Danny replied and quickly looked away to discourage the conversation.

"Bradley—Bradley.... Oklahoma, Danny Bradley?" the cabbie asked.

Danny politely nodded again as he continued to stare out the window in obvious deep thought. Slapping his palms on the steering wheel with emphasis, the cabbie said, "Boy, I thought I recognized you. I remember when you quarterbacked them Sooners. I saw you in the Orange Bowl Game. Ha, Ha, boy, you sure could get it done—yes sa! You could get it done, young fella!"

Danny nods again as he forces out a grim smile then fades again into deep thought as he toiled with a more pressing situation. To not be disrespectful, he pretended to be listening as the cabbie reminisced about his days at OU. Having been an MVP quarterback at a *dominant* major college program, he had become humbly accustomed to dealing with both the criticism and the praise. He clearly understood it came along with the business. But he knew, of all times, this wasn't the time to tangle with either. He was now hit with a defensive alignment that he didn't quite know how to read or the right play to call.

While evaluating all the possibilities, suddenly he notices the cabbie had taken off his baseball cap and extended it to him, and said, "You got to sign my cap!"

"Sure," Danny said with a pleasant face as he reached for the cab driver's cap.

The driver then also tossed him a pen and said, "Yes sa, yes sa. I got some braggin' rights in this town now!"

As Danny positions himself to write, the cab was turning onto his parent's street, where he noticed three cars in the driveway, instead of the one vehicle he expected.

He then thought, *despite my request for anonymity, my mom called a town hall meeting with the whole family.*

As they pulled up in front of the Bradley home, he finished signing the lid of the cab driver's baseball cap and reached inside his coat pocket and asked, "How much for the ride?"

"No sa! No sa! This trip is on me. Seeing a hometown boy get a good education and make it big, that's enough payment for me!"

"You sure?" Danny asked, while glancing at the meter that read $55 dollars.

"Absolutely, young fella—I got ya covered!"

"You sure!"

"Yes sa!" The cabbie emphatically replied.

"Thank you, sir," Danny said graciously.

But, before exiting, Danny places a $100 dollar bill inside the inseam of the signed baseball cap and handed it back to the cabbie.

"Good to meet ya son, keep up the good work," the cab driver said, as he looked admiringly at the new signature gracing his old Razorback cap.

As the cabbie pulled away, he probably watched as his long distance fare got smaller and smaller in his rear view mirror, and more than likely realized he simply got caught up into the moment. And by the time he approached the first stop sign, he paused, and must have begun feeling the pain of what it may have cost him for not collecting that much-needed fare.

Nevertheless, as he was just about to perhaps call himself a few choice names, he had to notice the crisp $100.00 bill inside the hat, which had to have left this kind and honorable taxi driver speechless with no other thought except to say, thank you Lord!

6

The Element of Surprise

It's now about 6:55 p.m., and Danny pauses to assess how he might best handle this sensitive subject matter with his unexpected family members. As he approaches the front door, he takes a deep breath and then reached for the family key. He could hear them talking as he searched for the spot where it's usually stashed, but couldn't find it. But as he reaches for the doorbell, his mother opens the door and immediately reached out to hug him, while Duke, his father, and JB, stood behind her waiting to greet him.

"Hey son, its good to see you."

"Likewise," Danny replied.

"What's up? What the hell you doing in town?" JB asked.

"JB, watch your mouth," Duke shot back, giving his son an exasperated look as Danny slightly smiled. "Just here to handle some personal business."

Meanwhile, ignoring his father's advice, JB said, "Well, if I don't get some tickets to the 49er's game this year, I'm gon cut your.... Shelly cuts him off and yelled, "JB!"

Danny thought, *I love em, but some things never change.*

"Consider it done."

But Danny didn't waste any time. "Mom, dad, let me talk to you guys for a minute."

As the three of them make their way on to the back of the house, JB knew something serious was going down, but couldn't quite figure it out. However, unbeknownst to Danny, he had at least an idea why his brother suddenly rushed to town.

Once in the master bedroom, Duke relaxed next to the dresser, Shelly sat on the edge of the bed, and Danny sat in his dad's recliner and turned toward Shelly.

"What can you tell me about this situation with Denise," Danny asked, frankly.

"What do you mean?" She asked in return.

"Other than what we've already discussed, is there more that you're not telling me?"

"No, son, there isn't. Why, what's going on?" She asked.

"I feel like there's pieces of this puzzle that you seem reluctant to share with me."

"No.... I'm careful, but not reluctant, son," Shelly replied. "This is a very sensitive and serious issue that seems to have your name thrown right dab in the middle, And doesn't seem like its going to go away, sweetie."

"Okay," he responded out of frustration. "Can you ensure that I get a paternity test done at Jefferson Regional Clinic (JRC) first thing in the morning?" Danny asked.

"Yes, I think I can make that happen?"

Danny then took a step his mother was unprepared for. “You have Denise’s number, right, let’s call her?”

Shelly reaches over and grabs her phone book out of her purse as Duke looks on patiently. She dials the number and hands Danny the receiver.

And on about the fifth ring, Odell, Denise’s father answers — “Hello.”

“Denise, please, sir,” Danny says.

Odell pauses, unsure if this was a call she would want to take, covers the receiver and muffled something to Denise, who asks, “who is it?”

Odell responded quietly. “I don’t know, it sounds like a bill collector.”

Denise takes the phone, “Hello.”

“Denise—Danny.”

“Oh, hey—what’s up?”

“I’m in town for a day and I’ve arranged for a paternity test to be done in the morning, can you and your son be at my mother’s house by 8:00 a.m.?”

“Sure,” she replies, after a pause.

“Do you have a problem with that?” He asked.

Denise, who was taken aback a bit, had never heard this tone in Danny’s voice before—so direct and straight to the point.

“No, I don’t have a problem with that. It just would have been nice for you to have let me know you were coming,” she said.

“The feelings are mutual.” Danny sarcastically replied, with calmness though.

Not waiting to give her a chance to say anything but what he needed to know, he quickly asked to be sure, “What’s Mark’s last name?”

“Mayberry,” she replied.

“I take it that this is the same guy you’ve told he’s the father, correct?”

“It is,” she replied.

“What’s his first name again? Danny asked.

“Reginald. Why?” She now sarcastically asked.

“Does Mayberry know you are alleging that his son is now somebody else’s son?

“Yes—he knows.”

“When did you tell him?”

“A while back—what’s up?” She asked, again.

He had told himself that he would remain cool, but the more she spoke, the more upset he became, but still managed to keep his cool. “A while back like when, Denise? Yesterday, last week, last month, last year—what’s a while back?” He asked.

"About a couple of months ago, Danny," she replied.

"What did you tell him?"

Denise paused again before saying with a slight attitude, "I told him the truth."

"Denise, I have a wife, and a life, can you possibly share with me what you told him?"

"As I told your mother last night I informed Mayberry right after the gunshot incident, which I'm sure you've heard rumors about, that Mark was not his biological son—but yours," Denise slightly shot back.

Danny looks over at his mom and said, "And his response was?

"He was upset but he's been cool about it," Dee said as a matter of fact.

"Okay—are we on for 8 a.m.?" he asked.

"I'll be there at 8 a.m.," Denise confidently replied.

As Danny handed the phone back to his mother, Duke, not having been in the know of all the rumors, realized during Danny's conversation that this is the mother of the lil boy Bo brought by the house over a year-or-so ago."

"Bo—how did he get involved in all this?" Danny asked.

"Back in the summer of '84, Bo brought that child by after Denise approached him at Wal-Mart," Shelly said. "Apparently, unwilling to do it herself, she found someone to do it for her."

"Why didn't somebody call me?" Danny asks, while throwing his arms in the air with a look of disgust on his face.

"I started to call you son," Shelly replied, "but JB and your father didn't think we had enough information to make that call, back then. And Bo said he would make sure this child's mother would contact us directly with an explanation. She finally called several months later, trying to explain, asking if I would get you to call her. I did, apparently you guys talked, and that's all I really know about it."

The three of them sit in silence for a moment, as Danny struggles with believing how so many people knew about this kid without informing him. Shelly senses that her greatest concern, *of this thing getting way out of hand,* is about to come true.

Duke, breaks his silence, "Well, a paternity test is a smart move, son. But why didn't you wait till the season was over to deal with this?"

Danny takes a deep breath, pauses, and said, "I don't know. I was restless last night and this whole gunshot thing just bothered me a bit."

"Gunshot—what gunshot?!" Duke asked.

Danny paused, again, as Shelly jumps in to help explain: "Mark allegedly found a hand gun in the house and accidentally shot himself in the hand 4th of July weekend after seeing his grandfather fire off a few rounds."

"Really," Duke replied with concern, as he began to keenly process the situation.

"And I guess I didn't want to wait another five minutes not knowing the truth much less another five months, especially if this kid is indeed my son and perhaps in danger with access to firearms," Danny wearily concluded.

"Unfortunately, we're not sure what's going on with Dee and that child," Shelly adds.

"Well, given the fact that these allegations may not even be true," Duke says, "this could have waited, son.... This gunshot incident concerns me a bit.... If you recall, you could've lost your life once before behind the lies of some young lady, that we later discovered, you really didn't even know.... So, let's be very careful with this situation, son, until you learn more about what's really going on between Dee, this kid, and this child's current father—somebody can get seriously hurt, son, regardless of the truth."

Danny, out of anguish and despair says, "Maybe I could've come up with a better plan, *mother,* if I had known these things as they happened. I am potentially risking my job making this trip on such short notice."

Now it was Shelly who gets a lil snappy.

"First of all, I didn't lay down with Denise—you did. And I didn't start this lie—she did. Now if the kid is yours, playing with guns, I, too, understand why you were encouraged to come check this matter out, but please make no mistake about it, this is your issue with Denise—not mine."

Danny rose from the chair as a distant clap of thunder causes him to look out his parent's bedroom window. But still, he needed some air.

"I'm headed for a walk," he disappointedly said.

There was another clap of thunder. Duke then says, "It's raining, son."

"Tell me about it," he replied, as he exits the room.

Upon leaving, Danny see's JB leaning up against the wall with his head down, eavesdropping on their conversation. JB looks up as Danny walks right past him with a straight face, and said, "Get the 411 on Mayberry?"

Shortly, Duke exits the room to go reason with his overly concerned son, who was now out walking in the rain. He knew from experience that this was a life-changing situation, which couldn't have come at a more inopportune time. He, too, realized that he could have a grandson living just blocks away that he didn't even know.

This father of three, who was once a thug, a street fighter, and a womanizer, had a couple of adult daughters living in town that he really didn't know either. He knew of them but he never got to really spend any time with them. The woman he married, whom he abused for years, had taken some time before accepting them. Children that his three boys also never knew despite this small-populated town they all resided.

Therefore, he knew all to well what his son was facing, especially with his level of achievement and extended opportunities. He had a new target on his back which would not go unnoticed in small town America. Couple this new life with also having a feisty wife, oh yeah, if true, he could potentially lose it all if he made any commitments to be a part of this kid's life. So, this was to be Danny's biggest challenge yet, and Duke was curious as to how this young man, whom he made so many parental mistakes with, would respond to it all. So, at the very least, Duke thought, *let me make sure he gets the kind of spiritual advice I may not be qualified to give.*

By 7:45 p.m. Duke and Danny had made it back to the house. Danny needed a change of his now damp clothes, and Duke focused on ensuring he received some much needed counseling. As they were re-exiting, Danny's Aunt Jo and a couple of his mother's church clients, Evelyn and Barbara, were arriving. After exchanging some hellos, hugs and kisses from three of his biggest supporters, Danny gets back in the car and rushes off with his dad, leaving an anxious Jo to quiz Shelly about her nephew's sudden appearance in town.

"Has Danny seen Mark yet?" Jo asked.

Knowing that this was not the time to discuss this sensitive subject, Shelly said, "No, but he will tomorrow, he's having a paternity test done."

"Well, I'll be damn," Jo said. "Denise has finally trapped him."

"Danny perhaps has trapped himself, Jo," Shelly said with disappointment.

"So, you still think Pam is going to be civilized?" Jo asked.

Reluctant to respond, Shelly says, "Danny didn't even know about this child when he met Pam, Jo—that's got to account for something."

"Yeah, it counts for somethin alright…a butt whooping," Jo said giggling.

Shelly slightly grins as she continues styling her client's hair. Nevertheless, both Evelyn and Barbara's faces seemed shocked by Jo's comment. They knew of Pam but had never met her. And again, neither of them knew nothing about his situation with some kid named Mark, which prompts one of them to ask, "Who is Mark?"

Shelly looks at Jo while working on Evelyn's head, as if to say, again, this is not the time, Jo. But Jo pushes right ahead with the gossip.

"Mark is this local four-year old kid *alleged* as being Danny's son," Jo replied.

"What!" Evelyn said with surprise. And Barbara just sat there with big eyes, speechless. Again, Danny was her boy.

"Well—we don't know that to be completely true," Shelly said, "So he came down to check it out and get a paternity test run."

"Well—I'm tellin you, if this foolishness this woman is alleging is true, his wife gon test run his tail—and hers too, if she clowns!" Jo said, making fun of this serious matter.

"My goodness," Barbara said.

"Pam is alright, Barbara. Jo just joking," Shelly calmly shoots back.

"Okay, I'm tellin y'all, Pam is for real when it come to her man," Jo fired back.

"Well, I don't think she is right for him, but she's got some really good qualities that I've noticed," Shelly replied.

"Like what?" Jo asked

"Jo!" Shelly shot back.

"You know Pam is half-crazy, Shelly," as she continues to joke.

And as Shelly is about to express just how unfunny Jo's comments were, the doorbell rings. Jo gets up to answer it as she continues to establish Pam's unstableness. And as she opens the door, she's screams and says, "You got to be kidding me.... It's Pam Beasley-Bradley! Jo shouts.

Shelly suddenly froze, as did Barbara and Evelyn, and said to herself, *Pam?!*

"Yeah—it's me! Open the door, hell, I'm here to support my husband," Pam says, delightfully, as Jo looks over at her sister wearing that infamous expression—***the drama is about to begin.***

The Explosion

7

From the minute Grandma Shelly learned of the possibility that I might really be her grandson, she was aware of "The Pam Factor." Everyone in the family knew that Pam was a very attractive, polished, fairly articulate woman, capable of holding her own in most business environments, but owned the show in all social ones. To know Pam Beasley-Bradley was to know that she could go from boardroom classy to barroom sassy—cussing you completely out every step of the way if she thought you've crossed her in anyway. Not exactly unheard of in the black community, so it's fair to say, you don't want to get cross-wired with any black woman about her man.

And this reality perhaps explained why Jo felt such camaraderie with Pam. Jo didn't take no prisoners from anybody, either, when it came to her man. Because if this had been Jo's situation, *the cops would have already come running.*

It's about 8:30 p.m. when Pam makes this entrance.

"What's up," Pam says, for which Shelly realizes her own facial expression could betray her thoughts, as she quickly smiles, "Hey, girl," Shelly replied. "Ladies, this is my daughter-in-law Pam—Pam, these are my friends from church, Evelyn, under the dryer and this is Barbara."

"Hello Pam," they both replied.

"She's as gorgeous as I said she was, isn't she?" Shelly remarked.

What Shelly had momentarily forgotten was that Barbara and Evelyn were now up to speed as to what has brought Danny and Pam to town. So, they had been unexpectedly briefed about this woman, including her butt-whooping capabilities. Therefore, Barbara wouldn't quite make much eye contact with her as she replied, "Yeah—she is pretty," while Evelyn did what many women do when they're under a dryer to avoid talking at the salon—pretend to be falling asleep.

"Pam is a fox," Jo says. "And she knows it, too," as Pam smiles. "Let me take that bag, girl, sit down—sit down," Jo said. "Where did you get that outfit girl—you bout the most coordinated woman I've ever met," Jo added, as Pam thanks her.

But Pam was on a mission, and got straight to the point, "Where's my husband—and what's this emergency?" She asked bluntly, while still wearing her *it's no big deal smile,* looking directly at her mother-in-law, Shelly.

"I think he left with JB," Shelly replied.

Being the instigator she is, Jo says, "No, we saw him leave with his dad.... You want something to drink, girl?"

"Hell, it depends on what I'm about to hear," Pam replied with a giggle.

Pam was sharp enough to know something was going on they perhaps didn't want her to know just yet, or just didn't want to discuss the details in front of her clients. So, her mind began to race about possibilities. As she looked around the room, it was obvious Barbara appeared to be a lil nervous; Evelyn wasn't ***even*** asleep; and if Shelly combed Barb's head in the same place any longer, the poor woman would need a wig!

"Yeah, that's right, they should be back shortly. I think Duke took him to grab a bite to eat with one of the counselors from the church," Shelly adds, as she put the finishing touches on Barbara's hairdo, and suddenly regrets exposing that bit of info.

"Counselor from the church!" Pam said, looking perplexed. "What's going on with him that would require a counselor from the church?" She asked, while giggling in an effort to maintain her cool.

"Hang on a minute, Pam," Shelly replied.

She shuts the hair dryer down, forcing Evelyn to come out of her "sleep," which gives Shelly the opportunity to establish her stall till she could get both her clients out the door. As soon as the door clicked shut, Pam was ready for some answers.

"Is somebody ready to tell me what's this family emergency and why my husband is talking to the church counselor, in Pine Bluff?" She asked.

With Jo sitting at one end of the kitchen table and Pam at the other, Shelly sat in between the two of them. *There was no other way to say it but to just say it,* she thought herself. *But, then again, it is not my place to inform Pam about this situation—but on the other hand, maybe it's best if I try to explain this chaotic situation to ease her concerns, which I'm sure are many at this point.*

Shelly takes a deep breath, pauses, and said, "There's this local girl, whom Danny knew back in high school is now claiming that he is the father of her son."

Pam tilted her head, and calmly said, "Really."

"Unfortunately," Shelly said. "This lil boy is about four years old now, an incident which apparently took place while they were still in school about May of '81—right before he left for OU. So, after leaving him a message regarding her claim and this kid's *allegedly* self-inflicted gunshot wound, which happened several weeks ago, he decided to come have a paternity test performed to make sure her claim is, not true."

"You serious?!" Pam asked suspiciously as the wheels in her head began to spin.

"Regrettably, yes," Shelly replied.

"So, who is this heifa?" Pam asked bluntly.

"Denise Ann Davis," Jo said as matter of fact.

To be sure, Pam asked, "How old is this kid, again?"

"About four years old," Shelly responded.

Pam thought, *is this the same woman he mentioned a while back.*

"How well do y'all know this traveler?" Pam asked.

Almost in unison, they both replied, "Apparently, not well enough!"

Pam, who is now not feeling this conversation at all, remains cool, calm and collected as she continues on with her investigation, "So, y'all think this trip is telling the truth?"

"We don't know," Jo said. "Denise has been infatuated with Danny for a long time—and with women like that you just can't put any thing pass them."

Pam, then, turns to her-mother-in-law expecting a response from her too. And Shelly accommodates: "After seeing the lil boy a few times, Pam, this just might be true. Is Denise questionable, yes! But this particular claim may really be true. They actually had another encounter, which she also claims to have gotten pregnant." Shelly shares.

"So, he's got two kids by this woman?!" Pam asked.

"If her first claim was also true, then, yes, he's has *allegedly* had two kids with this woman. But, unfortunately, she aborted that one as far we know," Shelly sadly replied. "She wasn't really being as open and forthright about the first one, so we don't really know about that claim, but this one may have some merit."

"And apparently she hasn't been as forthright about this one either," Jo shot out.

"And with all that—y'all still believe this trip?" Pam asked, again.

"As I said, the one she aborted—not sure, but this one, possibly," Shelly answered.

"So, what's this kid's name?" Pam asked.

"Mark Mayberry," Shelly replied.

"And who is Mayberry," Pam sarcastically asked, "if her last name is Davis?"

"Amazingly, Mayberry is the child's current *alleged* father," Jo replied.

So, how bad was this kid's injury?" Pam asked with interest.

"Not too bad from what we can gather," Shelly replied. "He lost a lil blood, we hear, but he's doing fine from what we've been told."

Leaning back in her chair, Pam tries to digest everything she'd just heard and says while shaking her head disgustedly, "This is crazy.... This is the kind of silliness you see at the damn movies!"

Jo and Shelly nod in agreement, knowing the implications.

"Y'all do realize that this woman waited until this man has become a national headliner and NFL Drafted, right?" Pam asked.

"Clearly, we realize her timing is suspect, Pam," Shelly replied.

"And you telling me that this is not just a lil alarming?"

"It's very alarming, if you ask me," Jo said frankly.

Shelly gives Jo that look which said, 'shut your trap.'

But Jo gets serious and continues. "However, Pam, it doesn't change the reality of this kid possibly being Danny's son. But it does indeed shed light as to whether she would've ever confessed 'if' it had not been for his accomplishments."

"Which says she perhaps had a motive, Pam,".... Pam politely cuts her off, "Perhaps! Its obvious what this woman is after, Ms. Bradley."

"Understood, but if this is true, don't you think its better she come forth now rather than later?"

"Yes, but it depends on the game Denise is intending to play," Pam shot back. "If its just about making this right for her son, then, absolutely; but if this is about using her son to get paid, then, no, she gon have an issue, Ms. B.... But, hell, Danny might have known all along."

"I don't think so, Pam, not based on my conversation with Denise," Jo said in defense of her nephew.

There was a sudden pause in the discussion as Pam says with a giggle, "Hell, I think I need that drink now, Jo" thinking to herself, *I did not sign up for this crap.*

Jo, then, gets up and makes her way to the fridge as Shelly watched her daughter-in-law's face for signs that would indicate the possibility of a meltdown. And although Pam maintained her cool, this was the first time in her relationship with Danny that her marriage could be seriously threatened. But Pam continued to smile, laugh and joke, ensuring that all was still well.

However, Jo knew from experience that *you could never let a cool face like Pam's—fool you.* Still, Shelly sincerely wanted to believe the opposite, despite knowing Pam's uncompromising personality. So, as Jo was fixing her drink—a glass of cranberry juice, not wine, Shelly took the opportunity to make a much-needed point, "Well, Pam, you mentioned you were here to support your husband, and I hope you meant that, because he's going to need his wife to get through this, if this paternity test comes back positive."

Before Pam could respond, JB walked through the door and registered his surprise at seeing his sister-in-law. He reached out and hugged her, looking over her shoulder at his mother. After he releases her, he compliments her on her attire. And she thanks him as they make small talk. And simultaneously, Duke ambled in through the side door and likewise greets her, “Hey, Pam, how are you?”

“Fine, Mr. Bradley,” she says as she reaches over to hug him.

“Good—and your parents, how are they?” Duke asked.

“They’re doing fine, too, thanks for asking,” she replied.

Pam suddenly realizes her husband is not with him, asked, “Where is Danny?

“He’ll be on shortly, he went to eat with one of the guys from the church,” he replied, as she glances at the clock on the wall that now read 9:30 p.m.

Shelly had now moved from the middle to the far end of the kitchen table to better observe her family in action, and Pam’s reaction to it all. And thus far, as she had hoped, there was no need to be concerned. This kitchen was filled with jokes and laughter as the time began to fly by. But Duke, after visiting for about thirty-minutes, headed to his bedroom to relax and usually watch a little TV in his favorite recliner. But, this time, he decided to trade his television for a little prayer time on behalf of his son..

At times he would listen in on the conversations going on up front inside this small three-bedroom house, prepared to intervene if need be. He knew Danny was dealing with a very sensitive and dangerous situation, which was primed for disaster.

And Shelly, who’s doing more smiling and acknowledging than talking, keeps her eye on that same clock that she keeps catching her daughter-in-law scoping. At such point, she notices that it’s near 11 p.m., *and where is Danny?* She thought, too.

But Pam, under the circumstances, seemed to be going with the flow, not once asking JB what he might know about Danny’s possible son—Mark. And fortunately, JB and Jo were doing everything they could to keep her mind occupied on everything but that. And they were having a good time when suddenly the side door opens and BAM—Danny walks in.

Seeing his wife momentarily stuns him, but the lighthearted atmosphere allows him to play it off. Nevertheless, he makes his way over to Pam to greet her with a kiss. And just as he was about to connect, she slightly turns her face causing his lips to land on her left cheek. Nevertheless, she did manage to give him what appeared to be, a meaningful hug from Shelly’s perspective—proving partially that all was perhaps still well. But unfortunately Pam decides to rejoin the family’s conversation about Hollywood and life in Los Angeles, instead of giving attention to her husband.

Meanwhile, Danny made his way to the back of the house to his old bedroom, to ponder how to deal with his wife’s sudden arrival on the scene, while Pam’s behavior kept Shelly's nerves temporarily at ease and JB clueless as the conversation turns toward track and field.

JB continues on with the joke, "I forgot you were on OU's sprint relay teams."

Jo shouts, "Hell, he can't run or hide, huh, Pam!"

And I guess if you really think about it, they were probably right. He couldn't either run nor hide from this woman. She was smarter, more attractive, and just as athletic. And mind you, he wasn't too shabby himself.

Nonetheless, as they enjoyed Pam Beasley-Bradley and her conversation, it was time to call it a night—it was now midnight. So, as they were beginning to say their good-byes, Danny knew the time had come, and said to himself, *this is not the first time I've shared this possibility with her—she should be cool.*

But unbeknownst to Danny, Pam had already been informed as to why he would abruptly leave his high-profile NFL gig and rush home, in her mind, to play father to some *long lost* kid.

So, as they close it down, Halle Berry herself couldn't have worked this room and family any better than Pam Beasley-Bradley. This was an Oscar like performance. Pam was smooth and on-point. She was animated, funny and captivating. But Danny, who reappeared to say good-night to JB, and Jo, wasn't quite sure if he was ready to face the inevitable.

Pam took advantage of the activity and slipped off into one of the guest bedrooms near the front of the house to get prepared for bed. She grabs her overnight bag and heads for the shower, while Danny hugs his mother, who quietly reassures him that Pam is going to be fine.

"Pam is a pretty sharp girl—a little feisty but sharp.... and she married a decent man," Shelly whispered. "She said she was here to support her husband, so, let's give her the benefit of the doubt. In the meantime, chat with her but get yourself some rest and let's see how the test results turn out."

Danny nods as he hear the shower heads turn off. He, then, turns and heads toward the bedroom with still a look of concern, but, yet, relaxed—ready to have that discussion he was unwilling to have in LA the previous night. And despite the multitude of pressure situations he's had to endure, this, by far, was the most challenging. He understood that this could bring about a whole new level of confusion with so much to lose. After surveying the kitchen to see that everything was in order, Shelly turned off the light and made her way to her room to prepare for bed, too.

And Duke, who was already in bed, asked, "How is he doing?"

"He's fine—and believe it or not, Pam appears to be fine too," she replied.

"Was he aware that she was coming?"

"Apparently not." Shelly said with certainty.

"Umm—I don't like the sound of that," Duke said with concern.

Meanwhile, as Danny waits for his wife to enter the bedroom, he practices his intro over and over again. But unfortunately, when Pam exits the bathroom, she heads for the guest bedroom up-front, where Jo had parked her bags. So, Danny decides to stay put until he realizes that she had decided to stay put, in the other bedroom. But once he saw the light dim, he made his move.

As he stepped into the room, she was stepping out of the room.

"Babe—we need to talk," Danny says.

"Okay," she replied calmly and politely, "Let me grab a glass of water."

He then takes a seat on the edge of the bed waiting for her return, dreading the idea of having this discussion. She re-enters the room, drinking from that glass of water, as she grabs the remote and sits the water on the lamp stand. She then turns off the TV, gets in bed, and pulls the covers up, positioning herself for a sound sleep, as if he was not even there.

Danny, then, gets up and closes the door to the bedroom in an effort to gain a little bit of privacy before saying, again, "Pam, honey, we need to talk, babe," as he slowly sits back down at the foot edge of the bed. But there's no response from Pam, which causes Danny to pause and regroup his thoughts before attempting to broach the conversation once more, but to no avail. He might as well have been talking to the walls. Pam was completely ignoring him.

He then crawls over and lays next to her, leaning on one elbow, hoping his persistence would win out, but Pam reaches up and turns off the lamp stand light and turns her back to him without uttering a word.

"Pam," he says.

"Go to bed Danny," she replied with composure.

Choosing not to force the situation, he pauses again and then leans over her back and kisses her on the side of her forehead. Now discouraged and concerned, Danny lies back with his hands behind his head, gazing up at the ceiling. He begins to think about the paternity test and all the what-ifs.... *what if this kid is indeed my biological son.... what if this dude Mayberry trips, if the results exclude him as the father.... could this costs me my marriage, my career.... what if Denise is really lying about all this?*

With his mind racing with all of these negative possibilities, it was now nearly 2:30 a.m. before he finally began drifting off into a light daze himself when suddenly, with every light, radio and TV in the house off, Pam sits straight up in bed, thrusting herself back against the headboard, abruptly waking Danny, who then reaches over and turns on the bedroom lamp, which revealed Pam with folded arms across her chest and a look of grief on her face.

"You okay?" He groggily asked with concern.

"Your mother told me you had a son," she says bluntly.

Danny pauses and takes a deep breath at a loss for words, as he sits up and leans back against the headboard, too, staring up at the ceiling with disappointment.

"I SAID your mother told me you had a son," she said firmly. "Why didn't you tell me you had a son, Danny?"

"Pam, honey, I don't know if I do or don't," he replied.

"Is she lying?!" Pam asked as her voice rose, which meant he had to remain cool headed. So, he paused again not knowing just how to respond.

"Answer Me! Is she lying?! She shouts again.

"Honey, I don't know if its true or not, sweetie—I came to town to take a paternity test in an effort to determine if such is the case. This is the same girl and same situation I mentioned awhile back." Danny calmly replied.

"I'm gonna ask you one more damn time, do you have a son or not?!"

Danny knew by now, his parents were able to hear her every word but he was determined to do his best to defuse this situation.

"Pam will you please calm down—as of this very minute, I don't know," as he slides to the edge of the bed.

"Don't tell me to calm the hell down!" Pam fired back as she gets out of bed and stood over him. "Answer me!" She screamed with her hands on her hips.

"Pam, I came to town to take a paternity test—a blood test to determine if these allegations are true of false—I will know the results in a few weeks." He calmly replied.

She turned her head slightly, as if in thought. When her gaze again found his, she spoke now in an accusatory tone. "Oh really," she said suspiciously. "You sure you're not here to give some damn blood?!"

Stunned by her line of questioning, Danny asked,"What are you talking about?"

"Didn't *your son* have a freaking gunshot accident?!" She asked.

"Pam—I said I'm here for a blood test. A blood test! That's it! Come on now—we're in my parent's house!"

"I know one thing—you better start talkin before I explode up in this…!

"Pam!" He yelled, cutting her off.

So, to minimize the rising tension, Danny decided to disengage from the conversation. As he placed his hands on the bed to lift himself to exit the room, Pam, with as much strength as she could gather, slaps him across the face with a back hand, followed by a loud, "I didn't sign up for this ---! I'm done!"

Maybe it was the force of the blow, or the fact that the hand that struck him had a ring on it, but Danny could feel a little blood beginning to trickle down the side of his face. He gets up to check his forehead in the bathroom mirror, while his wife is *spewing expletives* and snatching clothes from the closet, angrily folding and then stuffing them into her duffle bag.

Feeling a slight burn from this small cut, he goes to the kitchen to get some ice, places the cubes in a plastic storage bag and presses it near the eye. He grabs a chair in the kitchen area, while she begins to change her clothes. As she exits the room headed towards the side door through the kitchen, she stops and looks at him with one bag over one shoulder and a handheld: "Now, get your butt up and take me to the damn airport, now!…. I'm out!"

He had tried patience. He had remained calm. He had tried to talk it out like adults, and now he was nursing a bruised head, and a bruised ego while his parents were being highly disrespected despite attempting to do this right. So, he finally snaps.

"Pam—damn it, I told you to stop yelling and using that kind of language in my parent's house! And I'm not gonna be called to many more damn names! Do you understand me!"

This time it was Danny's voice that pierced the night silence. At that, Pam stopped all movement as she was exiting the house, turned and looked her husband straight in the eye and said with more venom and volume, "Damn you and your parents…. get me to the airport—now!"

And just as if it looks like Danny would make a move toward her, Duke, who had now entered the kitchen, grabs him by the arm as Pam opens the front door while keeping her eyes on him, acting as if she was wished he would jump.

Once out the door, she then slams it behind her as if she was attempting to pull it off the hinges. Danny turns and grabs a glass from the counter and throws it against the wall and shatters it. "This girl has lost her freaking mind!"

Pam apparently hears him, opens the door, leans back inside and shouts, "Yes I have, and if you don't get me to the damn airport, everybody in this town will find out just how crazy I am!"

She steps back outside the door and slams it again with authority! Danny looks at his dad, who in his younger days would have hospitalized a woman for such behavior, but this renewed father looked at his son and said,"Just keep your cool."

Danny then dropped his head, again, out of disgust and complete embarrassment, as a tear fell from his eyes. He checks his hands for cuts while he heads to the bedroom to get dressed as Duke slowly trails him. As he entered the hallway, he noticed his mother, Shelly, standing outside her bedroom door with a flush look on her face.

"I'm so sorry, Danny, I was just trying to help, baby," she said as she begins to cry.

Feeling defeated, he walks right by his mom and says, "Yeah—you helped alright."

Suddenly he hears a loud thump from the hallway. The next sound is that of his Dad saying, "Oh Lord.... Shelly…. Shelly…. Danny, I need your help, son!"

Danny rushes back out into the hallway and sees his mom passed out on the floor.

"What happened?" He asks as he urgently begins to assist his Dad.

Duke, then, rushes off to the kitchen as Danny tries to revive her. "Mother, mother—talk to me mother!"

Just as Duke returned with ice and smelling salts, they hear the sound of the front door reopen, "Danny Bradley!" Pam yells, and BOOM, she re-slams the door.

Danny pauses as if on the verge of snapping again but keeps his composure.

"Do we need to call an ambulance?!" He asks, as he ignores his wife's conduct.

"No, no, I think she'll be fine…. Shelly.... Honey," Duke said as he cracked opened one of the vials of smelling salts and waved it past her nose. Shelly then begins to slowly regain consciousness.

Duke then began applying ice to her forehead as Danny takes a deep-deep breath while shaking his head is disappointment, "Dad—I'm so sorry…. I just didn't see any of this coming."

Duke cradled Shelly in his arms and leans back up against the hallway wall and said, "It's okay, son—sometimes life throws us a curve. Pam will be aright. She's just hurt, angry and afraid right now. So, be patient and *keep trusting in the Lord* and this thing will work itself out."

"Danny Bradley!" Pam yelled again, this time leaving the door open.

"Go, son. Your mother will be just fine.... The car keys are on the kitchen table."

Danny pauses and then leans over and kisses his mom on the cheek. As he rose and started towards the door, Duke says, "Whatever you do, son—don't hit her.... *The heart is willing, but remember the flesh is weak."*

Danny stops, pauses, again, and without even turning around, said, "Pray for me."

In less than thirty seconds, Danny was out the door and at the car. Wordlessly he opened the passenger side for Pam, as if to say, yes, please let me get you to the airport. And in response, she pulled the door shut with such force that she nearly closed his hand in it, which again caused him to pause in an effort to control the anger already raging inside of him.

For the next forty minutes, they made their way toward the Little Rock Airport in silence while Pam sat with her back to Danny, looking out the window, as Danny drove with his back slightly turned to her.

Once at the airport, Pam opens her door before he could come to a complete stop. She then opens the back door, grabs her bags and slams it, leaving the front one open. Danny just sits there, amazed by her behavior, and watches her walk away defiantly, as he looks at his watch—it's 4:00 a.m., and thought to himself, *Lord, I can't leave this women at a deserted airport, alone.*

So, he reluctantly parks and went inside to hang out until the airport comes alive.

Walking from the parking area to the terminal, Danny was trying to wrap his mind around the events of the past twenty-four hours. Last night he'd been in Los Angeles, having dinner at an exclusive restaurant with this beautiful wife, living a blessed life as an NFL player. Now he's watched his mother faint, his dad disrespected, and his wife threatening to divorce him. *I guess when it rains it pours*, he thought to himself.

Once inside the terminal, it took Danny about ten minutes to find Pam, who was sitting on a bench near one of the ticket counters with one of the airport maintenance crew members waxing the floors. He slowly makes his way over to her and sits down beside her. Pam immediately gets up and walked across the concourse to another bench.

And for the next couple of hours, they quietly sat separately waiting for the airport to open. It was pointless trying to make eye contact with her—she simply avoided his gaze. Mercifully, the gate agents arrived just before 5:30 a.m., and Pam got up to purchase a ticket for the 6:30 a.m. flight back to Dallas/Fort Worth.

Comfortable with leaving her now, he approaches her space, tells her he loves her—and then turns and heads for the exit in an effort to make it to his appointment to put to bed this freaking rumor and accusation that Denise Davis's son *was not* his son.

The Repercussions

8

It was nearly 6:30 a.m. when he left the Little Rock airport, and with the blood test scheduled for 8:30 at Jefferson Regional, he wanted to get back in time to shower, shave, and check for bruises. As he arrived at the house, he only had about thirty-minutes before he could expect Denise and company to be at his parents' front door.

Entering the house, he immediately asked about his mother, as Duke gave his son a once over before he answered, "She's fine; are you aright?"

"I've been better," Danny replied, as he takes a seat at the kitchen table where he found his dad. Duke had never seen Danny so distraught, disoriented, and exhausted.

"How did it go with Pam?" He asked.

"It didn't.... there was no conversation, no eye contact, no apologies—just silence."

Duke could tell that his middle son was just about broken. So, he did what any concerned father would do, encourage him to be strong and hang tough. He went on to share where he felt Shelly made her mistake with Pam, that it was not her duty to inform his wife of these allegations and accusations.

And Danny appreciated his support but made clear that Pam's actions was way out of bounds.... And that he was surprised and embarrassed. Duke decides to dig a lil deeper. "Have she ever shown signs of this kind of behavior." He asked.

"I've had a few fallouts with Pam, dad, but nothing nowhere near this kind of craziness," Danny said with mixed emotions. "Disrespecting my parents like this in their house, at 2:30 a.m., over a rumor that we don't even know if it's even true—is unimaginable," Danny replied disgustedly.

Duke's next comment, in no particular order, explained why perhaps so many young men make the wrong decisions when the find themselves trapped in conflict, domestically.

"Unfortunately, son, Pam doesn't have the mind-set spiritually, just yet, to handle something this heavy, even if this incident did take place before her time. All she see's is an invasion of privacy by another woman who might have valid reason to be around; one she knows is probably up to no good. And when jealousy and envy get control of our thoughts, strife becomes a way of life—anything could happen at anytime. As you well know, I know this from experience. But thank God he spared my life and kept me from perhaps life in the penitentiary," He says, as Danny listens patiently.

"I understand that *words have power,"* Danny softly replied.

"Absolutely, tremendous power," Duke replied. "And enough of the wrong words in the right situation can lead a man to kill, if his mind is not strong enough to handle that level of verbal abuse. And quite frankly, I don't know many preachers that could've withstood this kind of verbal abuse from their spouse. Which might explain why so many of our young men are incarcerated, from simply not being able to restrain themselves—and I, sad to say, use to be one of them," Duke said with concern.

"But still, dad," Danny said dejectedly, as he rose from his chair in agony. "This is not the woman I married."

"Unfortunately, son, I'm afraid that it is." Duke calmly replied.

The phone rings, breaking this much needed heart-to-heart session, as Danny heads toward the showers. He sees his mother and hugs her and kisses her. She apologizes again as did he, too, for his wife's behavior. But she assured him that all was well and wanted to attend the testing with him for support. He hugs her again and reluctantly accepts her request.

Then he rushes into the shower in an effort to redeem the time, as he had been accustomed of doing after a hard fought football game. Only this time, it wasn't a quote "crazy media" waiting for him on the other side of the door, it was a high school acquaintance claiming he was the father of her baby boy.

He had just slipped his shoes on when he heard the doorbell. Suddenly his head is flooded again with images: *Denise's phone call; His mom fainting; Pam slapping him across the face yelling expletives; and the slamming of doors.*

Simultaneously, his dad steps inside the room and says, "I think they're here," as Danny snaps out of it. He gets up to finish buttoning his shirt, but suddenly feels the room move under his feet. Duke notices the unstableness and asks him if he was okay?

Before he knew it, he could feel his Dad's arm around his waist, assisting him as he attempted to sit back down. The doorbell rings again, snapping Danny out of his disoriented state. He looks at his dad, and with as much confidence as he can summon says, "I'm good.... I just got dizzy for some strange reason," which was the second time he felt this unstableness when this kid entered his space.

Shelly, who was on the phone confirming the appointment, rushes to the door.

She greets Denise and Mark and gets them situated in the living room area while Danny takes another deep breath as he finishes buttoning that shirt before exiting the bedroom. Duke, who did not know this woman by face, glances in and introduces himself and quickly exits. And with Danny now making his way up the hallway, Denise is the first face he sees but can only see half of her because of the swinging shutter doors that separate the living room from the hallway.

He had decided while in the shower that he was going to be civil, and would avoid any arguments and/or debates that could turn this get-together south, especially in the presence of this already confused four-year-old-kid. Furthermore, it wasn't his style.

As he entered the room, Danny began to recall a good biblical verse to lean on in this time of trouble. And the one that came to mind, encouraged him. *"Though you will have tribulations, be of good cheer, for I have overcome the world."*

"Denise," he says, with a serious business-like tone, sporting a fake-like smile.

"Hey—how are you?" She replied, as she reached out her right arm to hug him, as Mark hangs on to her left arm and leg, hiding his face. And as Danny responded with a pleasant and cordial half-hug, without warning, Mark steps out from behind her leg and punches him right square in the left knee-cap and shouts, "Leave my mama alone!"

Danny quickly grabs his knee and bends over in a little bit of pain.

"Mark!" Denise shouts. "Apologize right now!"

Meanwhile Danny is thinking, *you gotta be kidding me.... my wife just slaps me about this kid, whom I don't know; my dad informs me I'm married to a woman, I might not know; and now, this kid is punching me in the knees about a woman, I definitely don't know; who else might I expect to kick me—the doggone nurse?!*

"Are you okay?" She asked with concern. "Apologize now, Mark!"

"Yeah—I'm cool," Danny says calmly, as he attempts regroup quickly in an effort to keep her from further scolding him.

"I said apologize Mark—now!" She said with a stern tone.

"I'm sorry," he whispers.

But as Danny stood trying to shake the pain running through his not-so-long-ago, *surgically repaired knee,* he realizes that this was the first time he'd seen Mark's face.

"So—this is Mark?" He asked.

Denise smiles and steers Mark from behind her leg so that he is now standing in front of her, and says, "Yes, this is my not-so-good-son-today, Mark."

"What's up, Mark?" Danny politely said. "Nice punch you got there young fella."

"This is the guy we see playing football on TV," Denise says.

Danny had no expectation of what Mark might look like, however, he did see the slight resemblance of himself at that age. But not enough to be certain on sight. So, as he gathers his thoughts and emotions, he gets down on the opposite knee, the good knee, to get eye level with Mark and just maybe, while he's down there, a glimpse of this *so called* gunshot wound.

"Hi, I'm Danny—your Mom and I are old friends from high school, I'm just saying hello to her, is that cool?"

Mark didn't respond.

"Maybe boxing is your sport—you got nice form." Danny said, as he tries to loosen Mark up a bit. But still no response for Mark.

It was now 8:30 a.m. They could hear footsteps coming up the hall. "Dee, Danny, we got to get going, unfortunately, the hospital is not going to be able to administer this test today if we are not there in the next fifteen minutes—and I'm sure we don't want to reschedule," Shelly said.

At that Danny asked Mark, "You ready to go see the nurse?"

Without missing a beat, Mark replied, "I'm not sick."

"Of course not," Danny replied. "Studs don't get sick, but the nurse is going to check you out to see how strong and healthy you are—is that cool?"

"Say yes, Mister Bradley," Dee said.

"Dee, we're taking separate cars, so you'll have to follow us out," Shelly said. "Danny has a flight to catch afterwards."

"Oh, okay," Dee replied.

As soon as they arrive at JRC, a nurse leads them to a room with two blood-drawing chairs. They were interchangeable and adjustable, allowing for any patient, of any size. One armrest even pivoted, enabling Denise to sit in one, with Mark on her lap, as she filled out one of the paternity test forms. As they do so, another nurse entered the room. She was holding a clipboard and had a stethoscope around her neck. Because Shelly had given the hospital information necessary to set up the blood test, the nurse knew Danny was coming, "I assume you are Danny Bradley, here to determine if you are Mark's father—correct?"

"Correct," he responded.

The nurse then paused and said, "So, you're the guy that upset all us folk here in Hog Heaven—by going to Oklahoma."

"Yep—I guess that would also be me," Danny says, with a light smile as if to say, this is not the time for a lynching; he's had enough of that the past twenty-four hours.

"Well—we are still so proud of you. You have inspired so many people in this town.… I hear you are now with the pro team in Los Angeles?"

"I am," Danny lightheartedly replied.

"Well—congratulations! It's a pleasure to meet you."

"Likewise—thanks."

"Okay—back to work," she replied.

After checking the form attached to her clipboard, again, she turned to Dee and asked, "Are you Mark's mother, Denise.... Davis?"

"Yes, I am," Dee answered, while handing her now completed form to the nurse.

As she placed Dee's form on her clipboard, she begins to explain the process.

"We'll be sending the blood samples off to a lab for testing and it will take anywhere from thirty to ninety days for results to get back, depending on the number of tests the lab is administering at the time. But we'll tag this test as priority and perhaps we should know the results within a week or so, does that sound good?"

Danny and Denise nod in acceptance.

"So, once we get the results, you'll be both notified in writing."

Having drawn blood from several children, she decided to draw Mark first since it would possibly be the most challenging. Pulling a stool up to Dee's chair, she reached into one of the armrest drawers and took out a rubber band, two cotton pads, Band-Aides, and shielding it with her entire hand, a syringe. She gently places his arm on the arm rest and told him to look at his mother and count to twenty.

As he begins to try counting, Mark can hear her rubber gloves snap as he feels the rubber band being strapped around his arm. This immediately causes him to snap his head back to see what the nurse was doing. Motioning with her head, she signals Dee to turn Mark's head to prevent him from seeing the process. And in seconds, she has swabbed his arm and inserted the needle.

Once the nurse untied the rubber band, allowing the blood to be drawn, Mark jerked his head free of Dee's grasp again. He sees his blood filling the syringe, and he rapidly starts to go limp in his Mom's arms, losing consciousness.

"Hold on, baby," Dee says. "She's almost done."

Beads of sweat begin to form on Mark's forehead, as he is virtually dead weight.

When she's finished, the nurse directs Denise to take Mark into an adjoining room and lay him on the table. Shelly, who had been quietly observing everything from across the room, now sprang into action as her own nurse's training skills kick in, trained by the same medical staff at JRC. She was at the door first, opening it as Denise carried a now semi-conscious Mark into the next room and laid him on the table, leaving a concerned Danny to wonder if the kid is going to be aright.

A couple of minutes later, the nurse returns and says, “I see this kind of stuff happen all the time, Danny. He’s going to be okay.”

As she began the blood drawing process on him, he, thought to himself, *will I be the next one to lose consciousness.*

About fifteen minutes pass the hour of ten o’clock, Danny was waiting in the lobby when Mark, Denise and his mother emerge from the examining room. Mark’s legs appeared a bit rubbery and his arm had a small Band-Aid just above his forearm, the only souvenir of his brief ordeal. Walking over to him, Danny tried to boost his spirits by giving him a high five, but Mark turned away from him. Denise picks him up which affords Danny the opportunity to finally see the *scar* that might be evidence of that gunshot incident. And Denise was barely out of the parking lot before Mark began bombarding his mother with questions.

“Mama, is that man my daddy?”

Surprised by his question, Dee curiously asked, “No, why you asked?”

“That lady said he is my daddy—I thought Mayberry was my daddy?”

“Mayberry is your daddy, Mark—and always will be,” she replied.

“Did he get stuck with the needle too?” He asked.

“Yes, he did.... He had to give blood, too.”

Denise knew, at some point, she would have to face the truth about this issue sooner or later, and needed to address it before Mark started hearing it from someone else.

As she pulled up to the Davis’s house, a family friend was driving by, as Mark and Denise were exiting the car. “Hey Dee.... is that Mark?”

“Yeah—that’s Mark,” Dee replied.

“Lord, that boy look just like his daddy Mayberry!”

Dee, who was once very comfortable with the Mayberry comparisons suddenly felt uncomfortable, replied, “He hears that a lot,” as the friend waves and drives off.

Mark stretches his neck to follow the friend’s car as it pulls away, then turns to his mom and says, “Mayberry IS my daddy, mama.”

Entering the house through the kitchen, Mark immediately runs toward the living room, ready to plop down in front of the TV. Dee, thoroughly frustrated, throws her purse down on the counter. *It’s time to deal with this, Dee, now,* she says to herself.

As Mark was caught up in an episode of *“Fat Albert and the Cosby Kids,”* Denise steps past him, turned off the television and reached for his hand, “Come here baby, I need to talk with you.”

Knowing that her mother, Leola, was within earshot, Dee called out to her, as she led Mark over to the sofa. She sat down and positioned him directly in front of her. Thirty seconds had passed, Leola still hadn't responded, and Mark had turned to look longingly at the blank TV for the twentieth time.

She thought to herself, *Might as well get it over with, Dee.*

"Mark, you asked me a question that I didn't quite give you the correct answer to."

Denise, then, paused and took a deep breath and said, "Mayberry **is not** your father, son.... The man you met at the hospital today is your real father—not Mayberry."

Mark appeared to think for a moment about what his mom was saying, confused, as expected, then asked, "Mayberry ain't my daddy?"

Denise took another deep breath and slightly reversed her answer, "Yes, Mayberry is your daddy, but he's not your father, son. The guy from the hospital today is your real father. I know it's hard to understand, but I'll explain when you get a lil older, okay."

"But why Mayberry ain't my daddy, mama?" Mark ask, as he begins to get emotional.

Dee, paused again, and replied, "Mayberry is still your daddy, Mark, and he will always be your daddy, son.... Your real father ran off to play football and didn't want you or anything to do with me," Dee shot back. So, Mayberry stepped in so you wouldn't be without a dad."

Mark, then, exploded in tears, crying uncontrollably. Dee takes him in her arms, in an effort to console him. As she does, she hears movement behind her. Turning to look over her shoulder, she sees her mom, Leola, leaning against the wall wearing a look of major disappointment.

Dee gently lifts Mark's head from her shoulder and says, "It's gonna be alright, son.... Go to your room and don't come out till I call you—okay?".

Nodding in agreement, Mark heads down the hall towards his bedroom, but he stops just far enough not to be seen, but close enough to hear their discussion. Leola settles into one of the armchairs across from her daughter, and said, "Talk."

"I had planned to tell you and daddy but I didn't know how," Dee softly replied.

"Dee, please! You've had every chance to tell one of us, so I suggest you start talking!"

Denise pauses and then says, "I had an encounter with Danny in May of 1981, before the '83 incident—right before he went off to college.... I didn't have sex with Mayberry until about August of '81. Mark was carried nine full months, which clearly tagged Danny as his father—not Mayberry."

"Dee, you couldn't have gone three months and not know you were pregnant!"

"I took a pregnancy test after missing my cycle the second month, but didn't find out for sure until about month three that I was already about thirteen weeks pregnant."

"So, if you knew, at that point, Mayberry was not Mark's father, why in the world did you lead him to believe that he was, Dee?!"

"Because Danny didn't want to have anything to do with me or Mark, mama. He knew I was pregnant, but clearly denied being the father—so I didn't want my child to be without a dad, so I decided to tell Mayberry I was pregnant."

"So, why are you *forcing* Danny into this equation now, Dee—if he doesn't want to have anything to do with this child?" Leola asked with great concern.

Dee's tone suddenly becomes somewhat colder and less timid.

"I'm not forcing him into anything.... I made a decision to tell Danny, after the *gunshot* incident, because my conscience had begun to bother me.... And, yes, I wanted Mark to know who his real father really was—that's it," Denise replied. "So, I challenged him to take a paternity test to prove that Mark is indeed his son. He came to town and took the challenge and in a few weeks the results will prove such is the case."

Leola knew her child all too well, and knew that there was something not quite right about this tale her daughter appears to be spinning.

"Do you understand what this means, and how this will affect Mark, Mayberry and this entire family?"

Suddenly, Dee started to weep, as if a dam had broken. Her sobs punctuating everything she said, "I didn't know what else to do—I know I made a mistake.... I just didn't want my son to grow up without a father, mama!"

Mark had been listening the whole time, not understanding the ramifications of all that was being said, yet smart enough to know, he had "a daddy" problem. And the sound of his mom's voice almost made him compromise his position a few times. But he remained quiet and put.

"Does Mayberry know?"

"No, he doesn't," Dee replied.

Mark hears someone entering through the side door of the house. He recognizes the footsteps as those of his granddad, Odell.

"What's going on?" Odell asks, after seeing his daughter crying and stressed.

Leola, who is beginning to regain some of her composure, says, "Why don't you go check on Mark and let me bring your father up to speed on what's going on here."

Like a little young ninja, Mark jumped up and ran to his room, closing the door softly, knowing on other occasions, the noise he made gave him away, and he'd get a swat on the butt for being in grown folks' business. But this time, he managed to escape without being heard.

Back in Los Angeles

Meanwhile, a week or so later, Danny opens his walk-in closet in another effort to get dressed for work, after taking advantage of another evening break from camp, the phone rings. He answers, not knowing that Pam has picked up the phone downstairs at the same time, which allows her the privilege of listening in on this all important phone call with her hand over the mouthpiece.

It's a Lab director from JRC in Pine Bluff, with the results of the paternity test. After confirming Danny's identity, he says, "Mister Bradley, normally we don't give this kind of information out over the phone, but we know your family and we understand the circumstances. Therefore, we made an exception."

"Thank you sir," Danny nervously replied, as he closes his eyes and takes a deep breath, knowing his life was about to change, forever, if the results were positive.

"Your test results score came back 98.9% positive, Mister Bradley, which means you cannot, under any circumstances, be excluded as the father of the child in question."

Danny disappointedly drops his head in deflation, pulls the phone away from his ear, takes another deep sigh before calmly asking a question he already knew the answer too, "Sir, I hear what you're saying, but in layman's terms, what does the phrase *cannot be excluded, under any circumstances,* exactly mean?"

"Well, in laymen's terms, at 98.9%, you are perhaps officially the biological father of Mark Anthony Mayberry," he replied. "It's probably not likely that anyone else will test higher than this percentage. So, congratulations if that's what you were expecting to hear, sir. And we have already mailed out the written results to your Pine Bluff address as you requested in your documents."

Danny, in shock, slowly hangs up the phone without even saying good-bye, while saying to himself, *Un-freakin-believable.... This kid Mark Anthony Mayberry is indeed my son.... You gotta be kiddin me!*

Bowing his head, Danny begins to pray asking God to give him the strength to share this truth with his wife and the courage to deal with whatever happens. As he starts towards the stairs he's stopped in his tracks as he sees Pam sitting at the bottom of the staircase, holding the cordless phone like a piece of incriminating evidence.

"No need to explain, Mister Bradley," she calmly said. "You knew all along that this boy was your son!"

"Pam—that's not true, honey."

"And you conveniently chose not to tell me the total truth about Mark, why?"

Danny, not knowing what else to say or how to convince his beloved wife he had not lied to her, slowly takes a seat at the top of the stairs.

"Why couldn't you tell me, Danny.... Why did you put your mother up to do it for you?" Pam asked, as a matter of fact.

Speechless, not because he had lied, but he just didn't know how to convince his wife that he simply didn't know any more than what he had already shared with her from day one, including the rumor. But just as he was about to respond, Pam abruptly yells, "Answer Me!"

"Babe," Danny says, as he gets up to step down the stairs to go comfort her.

Pam, then, jumps up from her position and rushes past him up the stairs and on into their bedroom. She slams the door behind her and locks it. She paces for a second or two and then calls a taxi and makes reservations to be taken to the airport immediately as she begins to, once again, pack her things.

Danny likewise paused to absorb and reassess his situation and his approach. After knowing her plans, he begins to plead with her calmly through the locked door.

"Pam, I love you honey. I did not lie to you about this baby.... Come on baby, open the door—this is not what it looks like—we can make it through this, sweetie."

"Make it through what?!" She yelled back through the door while she continued packing her things. "The only thing you better hope to make it through is this divorce I'm about to file against your lying trifling - - -!

He could hear the sound of drawers and closet doors being slammed and shut—as suitcases were being opened and locked.

"Pam," he says, "open the door baby, divorce is not an option for me."

That comment causes Pam to stop in her tracks, "Baby! I'm not yo damn baby!" She shouts back with force. And that response causes Danny to step away from the bedroom door. He takes a seat on the floor, near the top of stairs with his back against the wall, *in more ways than one.*

Moments later, his thoughts were interrupted by the sound of the door being yanked opened. Looking up from his position, he saw Pam, luggage in hand, standing menacingly over him and said, "I told you once before, I didn't sign up for this crap!"

She stormed down the stairs and out the front door, leaving a telltale indention as she had done to the master bedroom door/wall—one that would require a lil putty to repair. Danny sat in a state of utter disbelief, once again, of his wife's behavior..

Suddenly, the front door, which was half closed, flew open again with Pam standing in the foyer, reaching for her set of keys, looks up at Danny with a look of pure resentment, and says, "You'll be alright—there are plenty of women out there that will take yo trifling lying....!"

And once again, she spun on her heels, grabbed the handle of the door and slammed it behind her. Danny suddenly began to see flashes of his dad beating his mother as the anger began to build, a tear fell from his eye. He then tries to recall the advice of his counselor to off-set these negative and destructive thoughts, but was hard pressed to do so. All he could remember was *'Always pray.... Keep the faith.... Love never fails.'"*

The phone rings and snaps him out of this trance. Tempted not to answer it, he does so after this caller calls twice. And wouldn't you know it—it's Denise!

"Danny—this is Dee. I suppose you've heard about the test results?" She asked.

"Yeah—I did," he said dejectedly.

"I understand you needed proof. I didn't expect you to just take my word alone. But now that you know Mark is indeed your son, you need to call him and come spend some time with him—you need to get to know your son, Danny," Dee said directly.

"You serious?" He calmly but sarcastically asked.

"Its time you get to know your son, Danny. He is nearly five now," Dee replied.

Danny removes the phone from his ear, amazed at what he was really hearing from this woman, and said to himself, *its so much easier to be a hearer than a doer.*

He regroups as best he could, and says, "Dee, how dare you call me trying to coach me up on anything, let alone on how to be a responsible parent!"

"Excuse me?!" She said.

"My entire world has been turned upside down behind this nonsense—and you got the audacity to call me trying to coach me up on how to proceed next as a father—please! If it took you near three damn years to tell me the truth, then you shouldn't expect anything less than three damn years for me to accept the freakin truth!"

Not waiting for a response, Danny slams the phone on its cradle so hard that it breaks part of the receiver in his hand. As he takes a minute to gather himself, the phone rings again. He takes offense at the idea of her calling back. So he rushes into the next room to answer.

"What!" He yells through the receiver.

But it's not Denise—it's Rams teammate and best friend, RB. "What?! What's with all the hostility?!

Danny pauses, trying to gather himself, and said, “Sorry man, I apologize.... Having some marital issues,” as he takes a deep sigh.

“Well, I suggest put it in check, reconcile, and get your butt back to camp grounds, check in and handle your business, money. You missed a treatment and about to miss a workout this morning—partna.”

Without saying another word, Danny quickly hangs up, sprints down stairs, grabs his keys and rushes off to camp, disoriented and in disarray.

9

The Consequences

Back in Pine Bluff, Denise, with the phone still in her hand from the conversation with Danny, moves towards the kitchen, where Mark, Leola and Odell were having a late breakfast. Feigning exasperation, Dee plopped down in an empty kitchen chair, and with a forlorn expression which said to no one in particular, *"He still doesn't want anything to do with Mark."*

Odell, after spearing the last morsels of eggs and sausage on his plate, says, "Dee, I don't know why you brought that boy into this in the first place. But now that you have, child support would be the next best move to make since he still doesn't want to take on any responsibility."

All the while, Mark had been like a spectator at a tennis match, his eyes darting from his Mom to his granddad and back. As he watched Odell angrily chew the last of his food, he turned to his mother and asked, "What's child support?"

"To force your daddy Danny to take care of you," Dee replied sternly

Shaking his head no-no, Mark shot back, "My daddy is Mayberry!"

"You got that right and don't you ever forget it," Odell said as a matter of fact.

The doorbell rings. It's a relative of the family. He can feel the tension in the air.

"What's going on up in here," he asked? "Wait—don't tell me, y'all talkin bout Pine Bluff's newest irresponsible father, right?"

Dee looked over at her mom with suspicion as if to ask, *How did he know this?*

The phone rings in Denise's hand, she answers it. It's one of her best friends, with whom she had shared some, but not all, of her secrets about Mark and his biological father. Now that the blood test results were in, this friend was anxious to hear the latest. And to accommodate her request, Dee gets up and exits the room in an effort to talk in private about this hot topic which now seems to be spreading through her family and perhaps the town like wildfire.... Mark tags along.

"What's going on girl? Did you call and read that clown his rights?"

Dee inhaled then exhaled before she spoke, "I did—and told him its about time he get to know his son—it's been fours plus years now."

"What did he say?" She asked.

"Quite frankly, nothing. But he tripped as usual.... And even had the nerve to say, *'if it took three damn years for you to tell him the freakin truth, then, you shouldn't expect any less than three damn years for me to accept the freakin truth.'*"

"Whaaatt?!"

"Yeah girl, he ain't gonna do right.... He didn't want Mark then, and apparently, he's not interested in him now."

"Girl please—file child support against that clown, now, Dee!"

"Yeah, I may have too. But I was trying to give him a chance to man up, girl.

"Dee, four-five years?! He needs to start writing checks like in the next 4-5 days!"

"Hey, trust me, I get that," Dee replied.

"And by the way, when are you planning on tellin Mayberry?"

Dee pauses, not knowing if she wants to have that conversation around Mark as she watches him play with his toys on the floor, says, "I'm not sure, but I gotta do it soon, before he hears it in the streets."

"For real! Especially not knowing how Bozo might act, now that he has proof-proof that he is Mark's father. You don't need both of yo baby's daddy's trippin, Dee Davis."

"Girl please! Danny, I'm not concerned about, but Mayberry, yes, need to handle that with the quick," Dee replied.

"But ain't you dating some new good looking fine military guy?"

The sound of a car door being slammed caused Dee to pause before saying, "Girl, I can't get nothing pass you."

"That's right, you know I'm the skirt with the dirt—so what's up?"

"We've been on a few dates," Dee answered.

"A few dates?" Her friend suspiciously asked.

"Just a few dates." Dee replied.

"Um huh.... Well, protect yourself, girl! Remember, that's how Mark got here!"

Dee hears the front door open and then a familiar voice. Mark jumps up and runs to the front. Denise quickly said, "Hey, I gotta go, Mayberry just showed up."

Dee disconnected the call and headed to the kitchen. She sees he has a couple of shopping bags as Mark rushes his dad. Pulling items out of the bags, Mark gets excited as he pulls off his shoes to try on the new ones. Mayberry is oblivious to the tension, which is now free flowing through this house, but he has yet to speak to Dee, which causes her to wonder if he, too, already knows.

Suddenly, Mayberry makes a move that perhaps answered Dee's question. Just as quickly as Mayberry walked in, he walks out, without much explanation at all. And as he slowly makes his way out the door, Dee looks at her parents with a look of concern, before following him out. He hears her footsteps, but doesn't turn or look at her until he was behind the wheel of his car. Mark, out of curiosity, trails his mom, too, stopping a few feet behind her, knowing something was wrong. Mayberry, then, backs out of the driveway and rushes off.

"What's wrong with my Daddy, Mama?" Mark asked.

Dee snapped back, "Stop asking so many doggone questions, Mark!"

Los Angeles

Danny is sitting in his position coaches office, and he's getting an earful.

"Let me get straight to the point. I understand that you have a pressing family issue, but if you don't get your act together, soon, you'll be dealing with another kind of issue, the unemployment line," coach said.

Danny drops his head as his coach continued, "Its my understanding that you've missed a treatment and was late for workout today—and Coach Rob is not happy. And you look tired, rundown, and stressed out. The trainer says you've lost nearly ten pounds in just a few days, which tells me you're not eating or sleeping.... There is no question this staff likes you, DB, we drafted you.... but we will not tolerate this kind of behavior, especially with someone with your kind of leadership skills.

Danny leans forward and places his face in the palms of his hands.

"You're considered a character guy around here with a lot of potential. But you still gotta prove you belong.... Until then, you're just another guy on the bubble, fighting to make this roster every single year," the coach said, with concern.

"I understand," Danny replied.

"Okay," the coach said. "You'll be alright, if we can keep you healthy—if not, it's going to be a tough road to hoe."

"Thanks for the heads up," Danny replied with humility and appreciation.

After exiting the office, Danny knew just how blessed he was to be on an NFL roster, but he had also become aware of just how serious his circumstances were with this organization. He clearly understood at this point that this NFL thing truly does stands for ***Not For Long***—if you lose your focus.

But unfortunately, despite his sincere effort, Danny's off-the-field-issues were now clearly affecting his game on the field. And, yes, he still wasn't eating much or sleeping much. It was obvious to this organization that whatever was going on in his personal life had gotten the best of him, which was just another issue he just didn't need, especially having spent his Rookie Year on injured reserve following arthroscopic knee surgery. So, as practice concludes, RB pulls him aside during a stretch drill.

"DB, Pam got you way too twisted homie. You can't afford to lose your spot."

"I'm cool," Danny replied. "I'm working through it."

Another teammate, Charles White, the '79 Heisman Trophy winner out of Southern Cal, who knew this coaching staff well, had also noticed Danny's struggles and decided to make an attempt to encourage him too. He takes the treatment table next to his in the training room.

"You good?" Charles asked.

"I'm hangin tough," Danny replied.

"You sure?"

"Just a few family issues."

"I understand. Trying to do both can be tough at times, but you must find a way to deal and still come and handle your business everyday, DB," he said.

"I appreciate it, C-Dub.... I'm fighting though it," Danny responded.

"Not trying to get in your business, just wanted to encourage you.... you can play this game, D, and they know you can play this game, but you got to come focused every day to stay in the game."

Danny held Charles White in high regard, too, and had great respect for him. So, he listened intently to his words of advice.

"I've known the majority of this coaching staff since my days at SC, and anytime they look to create special plays for any player, who is not a starter, as they contemplated doing with you during the playoffs last year, says that you may have a lil job security, *if* you come out and handle your business—every day."

Fortunately, the advice from RB and C-Dub sparked Danny, and he began to focus, perform, and ball again. But having to deal with being separated from his wife, and his four-year-old son's life, made battling for a roster spot for this second year pro indeed a tough row to hoe.

But while in the midst of making his presence known again, he re-aggravates his hamstring due to stress and lack of rest. Nevertheless, he continues to push and practice on it. But on this day, as the team meeting adjourns, Danny, along with fellow teammates Ron Brown and Henry Ellard were headed to their receivers meeting, a Rams staff member caught up with him and pulls him aside, "Coach Robinson wants to see you," he said. "And bring your playbook."

This can't be good, Danny thought to himself.

Turning to see if Ellard or Brown had overheard the Rams runner, he then slipped away and made his way to Head Coach John Robinson's office, still dressed in his Rams team attire. NFL players have always feared *The Turk*, the nickname for whatever staff member is given the task during training camp of delivering the message that ends with, *"bring your playbook."*

Even though Coach's door is open, Danny chooses to knock first, as a gentleman would. JR looks up from his paperwork with a grim expression as he says, "Come in and have a seat," as Danny does so politely.

Coach leans back into his chair, pauses, and then said in general and in no particular order, these words: "These are the really tough decisions that an NFL head coach has to make. And its never comfortable having to make them, but we drafted you because of your ability to play multiple positions. Not many quarterbacks have the natural ability to switch to another skill position and be productive, competing with players whom have perfected their games at these positions most of their career. And you've been able to do just that, leaving no question that you can play receiver at this level. But over the past few weeks, we've become concerned about your health.... I am aware that you have some personal family issues, which has affected your focus, and we understand that those things can happen.... You guys are not robots, you have lives to live outside of football.... But unfortunately, this game can place an even greater demand on your life, despite what your life might be like at home. So, at this point, though divided about this decision, we've decided to go in a different direction. And if I can express my opinion, don't let this decision further discourage you from pursuing this dream—use this as an opportunity to resolve your personal issues and reposition yourself—best wishes," JR said, in general, as he stood up and extended his hand to shake the hand of a now *even more* broken young man.

Being a class act, knowing there was nothing to debate, Danny stood up, likewise extended his hand, looked his now former skipper right square in the eye, and said, "Thanks for the opportunity, coach, it's been a great experience."

Heading back to the locker room, Danny hoped his teammates were still in position meetings so he wouldn't have to face them as the *Turk* leads him to the training room first, to get an exit exam, and then on to the locker room to gather his personal items.

The exit physical was fairly short. Danny had a history of being healthy over the course of his career, only missing one game due to a sprained ankle until the knee scope of his rookie year.

After the exam, the team physician presented the injury release papers to Danny to sign, but this educated student of the game chose not to provide his signature, being that he wasn't quite healthy enough to pass a physical with another team. He was always the player rep type, and often studied the business side of the game, in this case the

Collective Bargaining Agreement (CBA). So, he was well aware that he was entitled to a second opinion, as this particular team doctor winks as if to say, "Good decision." Danny then steps down off the table and heads to the locker room where *the Turk* was waiting at the entrance for which he says, "As the old saying goes—you can't make the club in the tub."

But surprisingly *the Turk* replied, "Yeah—but according to the rules, they're not suppose to cut a man in the tub."

Another Rams employee sees Danny pack up his items and walks over and encourages him to keep his head up. Danny thanks him and turned to follow *the Turk* to the exit doors leading to the employee parking area. And once outside the doors of the facility, *the Turk* says, "Here's your flight ticket back to Dallas to be used anytime in the next thirty to ninety days—best wishes."

They shake hands as Danny heads toward his car.

As soon as he was inside the car he took another big sigh in as many days, and began to pray a piece of an old but yet very fitting 'Serenity Prayer' written by theologian, Reinhold Niebuhr. *"God, grant me the serenity to accept these things I cannot change; courage to change the things I can; and the wisdom to know the difference."*

Settling into the driver's seat, he wrestles to hold his emotions in check. Hurt, broken and confused, he starts the car, not knowing what direction his life might go from here.

Pulling away from the Rams training facility one last time, he flirts with the speed limit, hoping to get home and maybe find his wife there with a change of heart about divorcing him, too. But the closer he got to his place of refuge, the more he began to feel the effects of these new consequences and repercussions.

10

The Debacle

Danny arrives at his condo in record time, no speeding ticket, and as soon as he opens the door he shouts , "Pam…. Pam," but gets no answer. He tosses the keys onto his desk and sinks into his office chair, lost in a sea of thoughts…. *I just got cut…. my hamstring may need to be cut…. I'm headed for divorce court…. child-support court…. and under the circumstances, I may have to take the Rams to court—unbelievable!*

The ringing of the phone snaps him out of his daze, but over the past few weeks, there's been nothing but bad news on the other end of the line, so he chose not to answer.

He gets up and begins to walk trancelike before he slumps down onto the living room sofa, with his head down reminiscing about his life. He sees himself walking to church as a little boy; his dad beating his mother; the signing of his scholarship at OU; his graduation; draft day; his first rookie camp; his wedding day and honeymoon.

For about ten straight days, Danny laid on his sofa, stressed, without having any food, water, or sleep. He didn't change his clothes, shower, or answer any calls. He would pick up his Bible, periodically, and thumb through it with tears dampening the pages. And for the first time in his life, football had been taken away from him.

You'd think, under the circumstances, my wife would be more considerate, Denise more sensitive, and the Rams a little more patient. But such wasn't the case with this situation as he began to think to himself, *How could one act of fornication, where a child is conceived, affect so many people's lives, especially a child I didn't even know.*

Consequently, for several days, Danny sat around staring at the walls, reading his bible, and asking God for forgiveness. He needed the strength to forgive Denise for withholding such a serious life-changing piece of evidence from him. He could not remember ever being at a lower point in all his twenty-three years, except having to endure the domestic violence his father brought home to his mom during his early years. And all he could think of, now, was a safe haven to get away from all this chaos that had become his life. He was on autopilot. So, he, too, dialed the airline considering where to escape on what money he had left.

And with nowhere to turn, he decided to go home—to Pine Bluff. He books a flight to Little Rock, packing his duffle bag, and takes a taxi from Anaheim over to Long Beach Airport. Once on board, it was evident that the depression had set in. This broken passenger just wanted to be left alone. He only spoke when spoken too and avoided making eye contact with any would be talker. He was in a zombie like trance. Once in the cab, in Little Rock, he gave his driver the address and settled into the back seat in a state of complete weariness. The only words spoken the entire trip came at the end when the driver announced the fare.

And as usual, he was prepared to use his own key, since he hadn't told his parents he was coming. But once again, before he could open the door, his mother suddenly appeared at the door, after hearing slammed doors of a car. Not being surprised to see him after having seen the news about his release, his parents were relieved that he had come home. But as soon as Danny looked into his mother's eyes, he collapsed into her arms right there on the spot.

"Oh my God, Danny!" Shelly shouts as she cradled her son's head in her arms. Duke rushes over to assist her, as she places her hand on Danny's forehead.

"He's burning up Duke.... Lord have mercy, Danny.... Danny! We got to get him to the hospital, go start the car," she said. "And come back to help me carry him out.... Danny.... Danny!" She pleads.

It was as if all the strength that had allowed him to remain stoic throughout the past several weeks was all tapped out. He had been broken completely down, whipped emotionally, mentally and now physically.

As Duke returned, Shelly says, "He's not responding, let's get him to the car, now!"

Shelly runs to the phone and calls Dr. Jensen, the family doctor who was also a family friend. He agreed to meet them at the ER. Once they managed to get Danny to the car, he lets out a loud sigh! Shelly began to cry as Duke becomes extremely concerned. This was a scary moment for the Bradley's. Danny had been their hope to a better life and had become one of the State of Arkansas's most recognized people.

Upon being admitted to Jefferson Hospital, Danny is diagnosed with a severe case of the flu, dehydration, and sleep deprivation, according to the family physician, low in everything, including potassium and magnesium. His body was in complete pain, due to an extremely high fever, accompanied by a rapid heart beat. So, Dr. Jensen decided to keep him for a while to observe his progress and more importantly give him a chance to get some "uninterrupted rest."

Being relieved that their son is going to be fine in time, Shelly asks Dr. Jensen for a favor, as he was exiting the room, "Would you call Pam and tell her what's going on?"

"Sure," he replied. "Is she still giving him a hard time behind this situation with Denise?" He asked.

"Yeah—it's gotten to be pretty ugly between them," Shelly said with sadness, as she passes him all of Pam's numbers.

Doc steps into an ER office and makes the call to Pam at her parents house first and actually got a chance to talk to Pam. He gives her an update of the situation and Danny's soon-to-be-private room number, but sensed that this newly wed didn't sound concerned about her husband—at all.

Two days go by and there is still no phone call from Pam, and Danny indeed had been getting plenty of rest. But, on day three, she finally reaches out, and it's Shelly who answers the phone.

"I got a call from Dr. Jensen, what's up?" Pam asked frankly and directly.

"Well, Pam, it appears that all of this nonsense has taken a toll on him," Shelly said.

"Ms. Bradley, Danny brought this on himself," Pam replied disinterestedly.

"Yes, he did lay it down with her, if that's what you mean, Pam. But don't you think you're being just a lil too hard on him about this? Is it possible you could be completely wrong about what he knew and when he knew it?"

"I could, but I'm not, so I don't have to worry about that," she replied mercilessly.

"Even though this incident happened before he even met you? Shelly asked.

"That's irrelevant," Pam sarcastically replied.

"Okay, if that's how you feel about it. But he's still your husband, Pam. I'll tell him you called," Shelly said kindly, but yet disgusted with her daughter-in-law's behavior.

"Let me speak to my *so-called* husband," Pam said.

"He's asleep right now," Shelly replies.

Duke, who has been listening, shakes Danny and tells him that Pam is in the phone wanting to talk. Still groggy from the sedatives, but aware, he reaches for the phone, while Shelly, perturbed, gives Duke a, *what the hell you do that for,* look, and hands the phone over to her son, reluctantly.

"Hello," Danny says, with the meds making two syllable words sound like three.

Without a drop of sympathy in her voice, Pam asked, "What's wrong with you? And why you in the hospital in Pine Bluff and not LA?"

Danny pauses at her comment before saying, "I got released."

"Released from what?" Pam asked pitilessly.

At that, Danny handed the phone back to his Mom.

"He's not feeling well Pam," Shelly said with a bit of anger. "He'll have to call you back after he gets himself together," Shelly said, ready to hang up on her. But Pam interrupted her close.

"He said he got released, when did that happen?"

"Yes, Pam, the Rams let him go—he's lost that, too, a week or so ago. You would know that if...." But Pam interrupts again.

"Well, I hope y'all not blaming me for all this!" She said arrogantly.

"We're not," Shelly replied. "He brought this on himself, right?

"I'd say so," Pam shot back.

"Well, if he made the bed, he's the one that has to sleep in it," Shelly sarcastically replied. "But I'm sure, at some point, he'll get back to you," as Shelly abruptly hung up and Shelly turns to Duke and says, "I know I've done some naive stupid stuff over the course of my life, but Pam is about the most inconsiderate selfish young lady I've ever met.... Not one time did she mention anything about coming to see her *hospitalized* husband!" Shelly angrily shouts.

In the meantime, word has traveled around Pine Bluff that Danny Bradley, the local luminary, was cut by the Los Angeles Rams and was in Jefferson Hospital recovering from a heart attack. The story makes its way to Denise Davis' doorstep, so she calls the hospital to check it out, and is transferred to the room Danny now occupies, despite the protocols put in place to guard this particular patient at all cost. It was Shelly that answers this call, too.

"Ms. Bradley—this is Dee. What happened to Danny? I got a call that he had been cut from the Rams and had a heart attack?"

The exasperation evident in her voice, Shelly replied, "Heart attack! Girl, Danny ain't had no damn heart attack! Who told you that?!

"Its all over town," Dee replied.

"All over town!" Shelly said, as she looks at Duke again, who is holding up the whisper finger to his lips. Shelly was heated and was beginning to get loud.

"Yeah," Denise replied. "I've gotten a few calls tonight about it."

"Child, Danny ain't had no heart attack.... Yes, he did get released from the team, but he hasn't had a heart attack, honey—Danny is just stressed the hell out about all this craziness going on, which perhaps led to his release, Denise.... He wasn't eating, sleeping or drinking; he's lost a ton of weight with now a severe case of the flu, dehydration and fever that's nearly off the charts," Shelly said defensively. "But I'll tell him you called," as she rushes Denise off the phone, too.

Danny, who heard this particular conversation, says to himself, once again, *Man, when it rains, it pours.*

Meanwhile, Dee wasn't really sure what to believe, so she decided to check this out for herself. Despite the request that no one but family-family would be allowed to see

Danny. And about an hour later, Denise knocks on his door and slowly enters the room. Duke and Shelly turn to see what nurse this might be and were suddenly surprised to see this visitor. Shelly thinks to herself, *Well, I'll be.... The woman that's married to him, won't come see him, but the one who's been lying to him, will.*

"Hi," Dee says softly.

Duke immediately gets up to give up his chair, and said, "How you, Dee?"

"Fine," Denise replied, with caution.

Danny, with his back to the door, opened his eyes and looked at his mom who was sitting in a chair diagonally facing the door, wondering as to how she got through, which prompted Shelly to ask, "How did you get pass the nurses desk?"

"I have a friend that works in ICU, who brought me back," Denise said reluctantly, as Danny turns over on his back, which allows him a chance to make brief eye contact with her. She waves, and said, "I just stopped by to check on you. How are you doing?"

"He's on his way back," Shelly said, as Danny tries to sit up and clear his head.

"Denise, then, began looking around the bed area for all the wires and hookups that would validate the rumors of a heart attack.

Duke then politely says, "We're headed to the cafeteria—we'll be right back, son?"

Shelly gives Duke another unpleasant, *look*, as to say, *I'm not going anywhere.* But Duke motions for her to join him, as Dee watches as his parents exit the room.

She calmly places her purse on the night stand and then sits on the edge middle-ways of the bed and leaned across his body with her left arm.

"You had me concerned there for a minute," she says. "After hearing the rumor that you were in a local hospital after having a heart attack, I got worried and thought I'd come see for myself.... And, yes, I see that such is not the case," she added. "But I should have known, with all the envy some people in this town have towards you."

"I'll be alright," he subtly replied, looking straight ahead.

"Well—if I had anything to do with you being here, Danny, I am truly sorry. I never meant to cause you harm in anyway," Denise said, as she kisses him on the forehead.

Danny had no response.

"You were always a good friend to me, and I've failed to be that to you," she said. "If I could do this all over again, I would have certainly did it totally different.

But despite his weakened state, and the need for tranquility, he decided to engage.

"Why didn't you tell me from the start I had a son, Denise?"

Denise paused, wondering if he had heard anything she just said, says, "Well, Danny, everything was going so well for you—and I didn't want to hurt you," she replied.

Not buying that story, he asked, again, "Why didn't you tell me I had a son, Dee?"

"I thought it would hurt what you were trying to accomplish, Danny. And I didn't want to get in the way of your dreams."

Danny pauses as his temp begins to rise, says, "Let me get this straight, you decided not to tell me I had a son, a human life, because you didn't want to get in the way of my career? You did this to protect me, from me? You tag an innocent man as the father of my son, granting him all privileges and naming rights simply because you didn't want to hurt me?" Danny asked frankly.

Denise, not knowing how to respond, drops her head as she removed her arm from across his chest in obvious deep thought, thinking, *This is not going the way I had planned,* but Danny pressed on, "Has it ever occurred to you that-that's exactly what you've done—hurt me. I've lost my wife, my job, and perhaps my career; and from the looks of things I could have lost my life behind this nonsense had I not come home."

Still no response from Denise, who sat there with her head down.

"And I'm sure this guy Mayberry is not what you call casually hot, if he truly knows what's really going on here.... If not, maybe I need to have a chat with him, too."

Dee is speechless, as the look on her face said it all. The door suddenly opens, Danny's parents are back.

Denise gets up and calmly grabs her purse with a light smile on her face, as she re-greet his parents, and then said, "Thanks for letting me visit," as she strolls out the door.

Before his Mom could inquire about what Dee said, Danny's brother JB enters the room, passing Denise on his way in. He had the same question. "What she doing here?"

But he quickly notices the anguish on Danny's face and moved toward the positives.

"You look pretty good for a man that supposed to have had a heart attack," JB says.

Feeling a lil more alert," Danny replied, as he propped himself up in the bed a lil more to engage in this much needed chat. "So, what's the 411 on Mayberry?" He asked.

"I talked to a few guys from around town that went to school with him…. and they said, interestingly, that Mayberry told them over six months ago that he, too, had heard the rumor that Mark was not his son—but yours. So, it's out there, and it appears that Mayberry already know, even long before the lil gun incident Mark had, if that's when Denise is claiming she came clean with him."

While Danny weighed the latest information, Dr. Jensen entered the room. After greeting everyone he stood at the foot of Danny's bed looking at his chart, and said, "It appears that your fluid levels are back to normal, fever is still a little high, but your blood pressure is fine, air passages are clear, vitals good, potassium and magnesium levels are good, and you look well rested—though you could stand to put on about ten to fifteen pounds. I'm going to let you go home, but eat well and get plenty of rest, son."

Doc exits the room as Shelly and Duke follow him out, again.

"Is he ready? Shelly asked. "You don't think he needs a lil bit more rest in isolation?"

"He's going to be fine," Dr. Jensen said. "Just make sure he eats, stays hydrated, and as much as you can, stress free…. To be honest with you, the Rams decision to release Danny, may have been a blessing in disguise.... It was probably in his best interest given the circumstances. He needed some time off to get himself together physically and emotionally," Doc says, with concern.

Within a couple of hours, on this Sunday afternoon, Danny and his family were halfway to the house by the time Denise makes it back home. And she finds her dad, son and a few relatives watching an NFL game while her mom is cooking dinner.

"Where have you been?" She asked.

And before she could answer, another relative says, "Word on the street is that your boy is out at JRC suffering from a heart attack after being cut by the Rams."

A third relative replied, "I'd have one too, after losing all that dough."

Under any other circumstance, Denise's silence would have prompted her family to press her for a response, but they were too engrossed in the game to notice, so she eased into the kitchen to assist her mom, just as the phone rang.

"Denise, its for you—its Mayberry," Leola says, with that look of a concerned mother.

Not really wanting to deal with the inevitable, right now, especially with the whole family within earshot, Dee decides to take the call in her bedroom, as Mark trails with one of his favorite toys in hand. However, she decides to send him back up front to have this conversation in private. Once he was out of range, Denise closes her bedroom door, picks up the phone, and tells her mother she's got it. And Mayberry gets straight to the point, as Leola only pretends to hang up.

"What's this I hear about Mark not being my son?"

Denise slightly paused and asked, "Where did you hear that?"

"This is a small town, Dee, is it true or not?"

Denise pulled the phone away from her ear for a moment and then said, "Mark is your son, Mayberry," Dee shot back after a brief pause.

"You didn't answer my question, Dee," he said more sternly.

Dee pulls the phone away from her ear again, in deep thought and after placing it back, she then replied, "After the gunshot incident, I contacted Danny and asked if he would take a blood test to make certain that he ***was not*** Mark's biological father. And since he was so sure that he ***wasn't*** the father, he agreed to be tested. So, about a month or so ago, he came to town and took a paternity test.... and weeks later the results validated that Danny was indeed Mark's biological father."

"You gotta be kiddin me!" Mayberry replied.

"When Mark was born, I was pretty sure you were the father, Mayberry, until I discovered right before I delivered him, Mark was carried nine full months, instead of the seven months I previously stated, which would've made Mark your son," Dee said.

As Mayberry sat in silence, Dee continued to explain this insanity, "But, as I told Danny, we didn't want anything from him and didn't need anything from him, and that nothing is going to change between you and Mark's relationship.... He is your son and will always be your son, Mayberry.... Plus, Danny doesn't want anything to do with Mark anyway. So, to answer your question, yes, Danny is Mark's biological father, but, no, he **is not** Mark's Dad, you are.... And that, I assure you, will never change."

"Dee, I see you and your family in church every Sunday. Couldn't somebody in the family have told me?"

"Nobody knew Mayberry, my parents didn't know to tell you." Dee replied.

"If no one knew, Dee, then, how am I hearing it out here in the streets?" He asked.

Think fast Dee.... "I don't know, maybe Danny or his folks are talking about it."

"But I heard this over a year or so ago, Dee.... And if Danny and his folks just found out, then, how could they be the ones talking?!"

Denise didn't have an answer except to say, "Mark is your son, Mayberry. You're the only daddy he knows, and I repeat, nothing is going to change that."

"Where is Mark?" Mayberry asked poignantly. "Let me speak to my son."

Dee, sensing she was losing control of the situation reiterates, "Your relationship with Mark will never change, Mayberry."

She yells out for Mark, as the phone beeps. She puts Mayberry on hold to answer the call—its Shelly. Dee's facial expression was that of surprise and concern.

"Danny is home from the hospital, and he wants to know if he could stop by to see Mark tomorrow, before he leaves town?"

As she talks, Shelly motions to Danny to pick up the other phone to silently listen in. Trying not to sound as flustered as she really was, Dee replied, "Not tomorrow, maybe when he comes back to town."

Odell is now standing behind her with Mark, both waiting to talk to Mayberry.

"It's probably going to be a while before he's back in Pine Bluff, Dee," Shelly replied.

"Tomorrow won't work. But I'll bring Mark by when he comes back," Dee responded.

Suddenly Mark asked, "Is that my daddy?"

Dee, is suddenly reminded that Mayberry is on the other line holding, which she then abruptly says, "I have another call," and quickly clicks back to only a dial tone. Gripping the phone with both hands, Dee turns to see her father, who has caught some of the exchange with Shelly, and is now waiting for some answers.

"What's going on, Denise?" Odell asked.

"That was Ms. Bradley—saying that Danny wants to see Mark and I forgot I had Mayberry holding who is also asking to talk to Mark. But, by the time I clicked back, he had already hung up."

"Go back up front, Mark," Odell says.

"I thought I was gonna talk to my daddy," Mark replied.

"We'll call him back in a few minutes, son," Odell said, while Denise was trying to get her thoughts together.

As soon as Mark stepped away, they didn't notice that he was only about five feet just outside the door, once again, eavesdropping.

And now Odell gets straight to the point, "Dee, you are not taking Mark to see nobody that didn't want anything to do with him. Do you understand me? Now, I don't know why you got Danny and his folks involved in this in the first damn place," as he turns exits the room and sees Mark standing nearby, "Come on son—everything is going to be just fine."

As he hoists Mark into his arms and heads out the room and shouts, "If Danny didn't want him, he needs to stay the hell away from him!" Odell shouts out at Dee.

Mark and Odell reenter the family room, and as they do, the side doorbell rings—it's Mayberry, who gets an even warmer than usual greeting, as Mark jumps down from his grandfather's arms and into Mayberry's.

Odell, then, slaps him affectionately on the shoulder, "Where you been boy—Mark's been asking about you?"

Leola joins in, too, as the other relatives also speak and wave, too, giving Mayberry the sense that they now all knew about this scandalous situation. As he makes his way deeper into the house, Denise slowly eases into the room as she watches her family shower Mayberry with love. Not knowing how to press into the space, she suddenly decides to send Mark away for a week or so to spend some personal time with his daddy Mayberry. And Mayberry couldn't have agreed with that decision more, especially knowing that Danny was indeed in town. Denise went to pack Mark's duffle bag, while Odell, Leola and the rest of the family continued to entertain him.

They could all see the anguish that now seemed to easily beset him so they worked overtime to keep the conversations cordially lighthearted. But it was time to go and Mayberry is more than ready to exit, perhaps after feeling betrayed by the entire family.

Dee hands Mark's duffle bag to him, as he picked him up to head out the side door of the kitchen. And once they were outside the ear range of her parents, Denise looks him in the eye and said, "Listen Mayberry, Mark will always be your son. You've been there for him since day one. He carries your last name and you've been a good father to him. So, I'll say it again, your relationship with Mark will never change."

Mayberry opens the driver's side door to his car and allows Mark to crawl over to the passenger side. He tosses the duffle bag in the rear seat, as Denise continues, "You are the only daddy he knows."

Mayberry, then, gets in the car, shuts the door, starts the engine, and asked, "Who's the new military guy?"

"Military guy—what military guy, and where did you hear that?!" She asked.

Putting the car in gear, he looks at Dee, shakes his head, and says again, "It's a small town, Denise.... People talk—just checking to see who else might be *next* in line claiming to be the father of my son," as he pulls off while Mark waves happily, bye-bye.

11

The Responsibility

A week later, after not hearing from Denise, or seeing Mark, Danny decided to depart, knowing he had a host of issues to deal with both in Los Angeles and Dallas/Forth Worth. However, none, in his mind, was bigger than the issue he was leaving behind, in Pine Bluff. So, as he stood in the concourse waiting to board his flight back to LA, his mother is trying to encourage him as he shares his thoughts, still feeling distressed.

"If I had believed her, mom, I would have tried to pursue this paternity test a year ago, but I really didn't buy her story despite knowing the possibilities.... And the way she's got this thing set, is just ugly. But I understand the consequences—I laid it down with her and I take full responsibility for my actions.... But, it is extremely unfair for Denise to place another man in this kids life knowing, all along, from day one, that he **was not** this kids father," Danny said, as a tear begin to well up in his eyes.

"Honey, I can only imagine how you feel, but despite this ready made life this child seems to already have, Mark needs his real father.... And just in case you've forgotten, *you've been forgiven..... None of us are perfect, son.... We have all come short of His glory, but you serve a perfect God, who has not failed you; He's given you the victory through Christ...* So, hold your head up and keep the faith," Shelly said with love.

The gate agent makes her final boarding call. Danny gathers himself, hugs his mother and begins trying to redirect all these negative thoughts rumbling in his mind, as Shelly continued: "And you can rest assure," she said, as she steps back from their embrace, "regardless of how much Denise might try to fight you regarding your biological rights, just keep in mind, Mark is "your son"; he is "your seed", and according to scripture, baby, that makes the two of you—**inseparable!"**

What a strong message this loving mother of three gives to her confused, distressed, and broken son. Nevertheless, life for me, at this juncture, still seemed normal. Although, I began to hear a lot more chatter around the house about this guy Danny Bradley, but none of it affected my day-to-day routine with my daddy Mayberry. And even though I was too young to understand the significance of this new chapter that was about to unfold in my life, I did recognize the "added" attention I was starting to receive from my family. I was a Davis/Mayberry, and my granddad, Odell, was going to make sure that everybody understood that regardless of the results of some paternity test.

A year goes by, and Danny and his agent had mutually decided to go separate ways. He had moved from LA to Dallas in an effort to, once again, repair the damage with his wife stemming from this unexpected son. No, it wasn't the only reason, but it was definitely the top reason. And Pam, surprisingly, was willing to listen, but only on her terms. She had started working for an airline based at D/FW Airport in their Administration department, and Danny takes a job at a local fitness center in an effort to learn more about the health club business to which he aspired to own someday. And he uses this facility to rehab as he awaits his chance to get back into the league.

So, after a brief stay with Pam and her parents, they moved into a condo near the airport to accommodate Pam's drive to work. However, still torn between the love for his wife and his desire to be a positive example in his son's life, weighed heavy on him daily. And, at this point with Pam, it was a silent ultimatum: it was either her or him but he couldn't have both. And Danny, knowing that Denise was uncooperative, used this time in an attempt to change his wife's position on Mark. And if successful, she could work in concert with him to gain unlimited access to his son, who was in the possession of an obviously unaccommodating mother.

So, in his quest to bring these things to fruition, he changed his approach. He began using his mother as a go-between, since that's what Denise seemed to prefer, which would also keep his wife from knowing how often he attempted to reach out to his son.

And yes, Pam, at this point, monitored his calls and had made clear that he was not to visit any parts of Arkansas without being accompanied by her. But Denise, too, had terms he had to abide by, if he was to establish any kind of relationship with *her son.*

Nonetheless, in the midst of it all, Danny finally gets the call he had been waiting for—a call from an NFL team, the Detroit Lions. And despite not having an agent, he agrees to a contract to join the team. But, unfortunately, it would come on the heels of another blow to his career—the NFL union strike.

Most teams at the close of training camp were beginning to round up talent that they had previous interest in or had just released. And Danny was on a few teams' radar after being released by the Rams, but was not able to pass a physical exam, which had forced him to file a grievance against his former team to ensure he would receive, at least, his 1986 contractual salary. But Detroit, despite this filed grievance, wanted to give him a second chance. And it certainly didn't hurt that one of Detroit's coaches, Rex Norris, was the Defensive Co-coordinator at Oklahoma during Danny's first two years with the Sooners.

Detroit, Michigan

While at the team hotel, and with just a few hours before game time, Danny decides to respond to a message he received from his Mom, stating that Mark wants to talk with him, which is at least a start as far as he was concerned. After making the call, Dee puts Mark on the phone and in a whiny voice, sounding almost as if he was on the verge of crying, said, “My Mama said I need some clothes.”

Before Danny could respond, Mark indeed begins to cry.

Danny pauses, and said, “It’s okay, son—don’t cry. When do you need them?”

Between sobs Mark replied, “I don’t know.”

Danny suddenly felt both anger and empathy as he listened to the son he barely knew asking this stranger to buy him clothing. And calmly Danny replied, “Sure, I got you covered baby—it’s going to be alright—okay.”

Mark’s sobbing then became sniffles.

“Hang in there, son, let me talk to your mother.”

He could hear the phone changing hands, followed by Denise saying, “Yeah—what’s up?” And her tone was not lost on Danny, but he was determined not to let it get in the way of the point he needed to make with her.

“Dee, don’t you think he’s a lil too young and disconnected to be calling me asking for money.... This kid doesn’t know me like that.... And it’s not his duty to make that call—its yours.”

“But he’s only asking his father for clothing,” she shot back.

“I understand, Denise, but he doesn’t know me like that just yet. So, don’t push him to call me about money or clothes, or even gifts right now—you pick up the phone and call me, cool?”

“Okay,” Denise said nonchalantly.

“But I gotta get going—call my mother, give her your address, I’ll send some cash.”

“Thanks,” she said, as neither one of them was sure what to make of that discussion.

Danny immediately dials his mom back to update her on the latest conversation with Denise. He had learned over time that documentation beats conversation 24 hours a day, 7 days a week. So, he intended to keep his mother informed every step of the way regarding his dealings with Denise.

After recounting, verbatim, what happened on the call with Dee, Shelly could hear the frustration in Danny’s voice starting to build again. Suddenly, there’s a knock at his hotel door. It’s one of the teammates warning him he’s about to be late for the buses to the stadium. They exchanged I love you's and hung up. Danny grabbed his bag and headed to the elevators.

Thirty minutes later, as the team buses pulled up to the Pontiac Silverdome, the scene was chaotic. Striking players and sports media are all over the place. Current NFL players with picket signs are shouting obscenities, while television cameramen are dodging foot and vehicular traffic, trying to capture the faces of the striking players as well as those of Danny and the other replacements players who was once one of them.

Inside the buses, you could have heard a pin drop. Watching this scene, Danny pondered if he was doing the right thing. He believed in the cause his NFL colleagues were striking for, knowing that working conditions and pay scales had to change, but he was separated from his wife, disconnected from his son's life, and in need of an opportunity to fiscally bounce back somehow. And Detroit became the team of choice, since they seemed committed to keep him around, if he stayed healthy. But despite his skepticism, he decided to play through the strike and work on his game and try to recover from a year of NFL lost wages.

After about three weeks, the strike ended. And despite the circumstances, Danny performed well as a kick-returner and receiver. He scored two touchdowns against the Seattle Seahawks with a nice average on punt returns. He likewise faired well in all categories against Tampa Bay and Green Bay. His play drew rave reviews from the coaches, the media, and from NFL Hall of Fame Quarterback, Kenny Stabler, who served as color commentator for the Lions games.

The next day, Danny and his fellow replacement teammates are exiting a team meeting when Lions management announced the end of the strike. Unexpectedly, one of the Player Personnel runners pulls him aside. "You're presence is requested upstairs by Coach Rodgers."

Here we go again, Danny thought as he replied, "Sure," he said to the gentlemen.

Turning the corner to enter the locker room, Danny notices the players lockers were now cleaned out, including his. And said to himself, *This is not promising.*

As he made his way upstairs to the Head Coaches office, he runs into another replacement teammate, who Danny thought, *for sure, would be retained but had just been let go*. Now he's really confused as he's approaching the Head Coaches office. Suddenly, another team administrative guy calls him into his office, "Coach is still in a meeting. Why don't you have a seat and I'll be with you in a few minutes?"

"No problem," Danny says with a nod.

Taking a seat at the meeting table in the office, Danny asked if he could use his phone to call home."Absolutely," they guy said, before he exited the room. Danny thanks him and dials his mother.

"Hey, baby, how's it goin in Detroit this week?" She asked.

"Crazy and Cold," he said. "But the strike is over, I'm waiting to see what's next."

"Well, how's it goin with Pam, did she come to the game this week?"

"She came last week, but she's still not quite with it.... She doesn't seem to know what she wants to do.... She's really struggling with the whole situation with Mark."

"Why do you allow her to keep running in and out?" Shelly asked, with empathy.

"I don't know mother.... I guess because I love her." Danny replied with sadness.

"Baby, unfortunately, sometimes in life we just have to let some things go. And if Pam wants to go, maybe you should let her go, son."

Exhaling as he spoke, Danny said, "Maybe so, but keep praying for me—the weight of trying to please her, re-establish my career, and not being able to see my son without having to fight with both Pam and Denise is weighing heavy on me."

The team's Admin guy reenters the office, and Danny says his good-byes, "I'll hit you later and don't forget to check on Mark and see if he received that money."

Danny rose from his seat at the meeting table, hangs up the phone and moves to one of the chairs directly in front of the team reps desk. While busily thumbing through file folders in a two-drawer cabinet, Danny is wondering which shoe is about to drop now.

The rep removes some papers from the folder and extends them across his desk towards Danny and said, "We like the way you handled yourself during the strike, we felt that your performance proved that you are not only healthy, but can still play at a high level. Therefore, we decided to keep our promise and offer you a two year contract, which will run through the '88 and '89 seasons. I will need you to sign here and here."

Picking up the contracts, Danny replied, "Unfortunately, sir, I'm going to need a minute to read through this. I don't have a traditional agent anymore—I'm represent myself, at this point."

"Sure—go right ahead. I'll be back in about ten-fifteen minutes. So if you have any questions, I'll be right down the hall."

No sooner had he walked out of his office, Danny discovered the sticking point in the contracts. There was no page for the remainder of the '87 season. He got up and walked to the office doorway, getting the attention of the Administrative assistant, seconds later, the rep returns with a somewhat puzzled look on his face, and said, "That was quick—maybe you should be my agent!"

"Yeah, right," Danny replied with a smile, and then said, "As I viewed paragraph 5, I didn't see any language covering the remainder of this season—the '87 season."

His face told Danny that he was about to find out why his locker was cleaned out.

"Oh, I'm sorry if I didn't make myself clear—these contracts cover seasons year '88 through season year '89—not the remainder of this season—'87.... This is not an extension of your current contract—that contract has been terminated.... Management decided that they didn't want to mix a strike player into the locker room with our regular players out of fear of confrontation, even if that player was previously on our roster. So the couple of replacement players we believe deserved a spot on our current roster, we're offering them immediate contracts for the next season, in your case, two."

"Understood, but if I sign these contracts, today, I would be prevented from signing a contract with another team tomorrow."

"Yes—that would be correct, and I apologize for not making that clear."

Danny pauses to think, knowing that his next move could decide the fate of his already short-lived football career, "Sir, I think I'll take my chances in the free market."

"I understand, but you do realize it's not likely another team, at this juncture, will be in the free agent market, especially given the fact we just concluded a strike at week three of the regular season.... What we're offering you, under the circumstances, gives you that same opportunity to re-establish your career here in Detroit, with a franchise that understands your situation," he replied.

Danny pauses to ponder his comments, once more, realizing, again, that his entire football future and family life would ride on his response to this life-altering proposal. He thought to himself, again, *I have a marriage in trouble; a son in trouble; and a bank account that reflects trouble. Can I really afford to stay in Detroit and pursue a league that appears to be in a lil trouble?*

He takes a deep breath and said, "Sir, I appreciate the interest, but I'm gonna have to pass," as he extended his hand across the desk to the team's rep, who replied, "I respect your decision, and I'll inform Coach Rodgers of your decision, as he, likewise, reached across to shake Danny's hand.

Danny leaves this office very disappointed but definitely knowing that he had made the right choice. He believed that he had finally gained control of his situation, instead of the situation being in control of him. He knew his time would be better served by focusing on his relationship with his disgruntled wife, estranged son, and perhaps, a new career.

12

The Priority

After leaving the complex, Danny rushes to his in-laws house where he had been staying until the strike was over. He packed his things, said his good-byes and headed off to the airport in his rented car. Once he arrived in Dallas, he takes his wife to dinner at a nice five-star restaurant to discuss their relationship regarding love, life, and marriage. He informs her of his intent to retire and his desire to truly put family first.

He shared his plans of opening up a health and fitness club and thought that a really good Bible study group for couples, would be good for them to restore their marriage. And all seemed well until he decided to address the hottest topic—his son. Then the wheels began to slowly come off at this well-planned romantic dinner.

He explained that he could not continue to ignore the fact that he had a son, and did not want to operate irresponsibly as his dad had done with he and his brothers. He reassured her of his love for her and his hope to do this as a family, together. And expressed how *spiritually wrong* it would be if he neglected his fatherly responsibility to this kid, and how he once longed for his father during his childhood but was often left disappointed and dejected. So, he asked her again if she would help him in his quest to deal with the multitude of challenges that Denise had already begun to present.

And for the first time since the announcement, Pam listened and appeared to be enjoying her dinner, the wine, and these things he still had on his mind. But suddenly, her emotions begin to change, and Pam, then, expressed herself right there on the spot.

"Danny, I understand that you want to be a father to your son, and I realize that Denise has robbed you of that opportunity, but for the last damn time, I am not interested in being a stepmother to some kid you had with some other trick!" She said, as she begins to raise her voice. "I told you once—I didn't sign up for this nonsense!"

But knowing that time was not on his side, Danny pressed a little and tried reasoning with her before she cuts off.... "I said no!" Pam shot back. "In fact, its time you make a decision—it's either me or Mark.... And if you struggling, let me help you—Divorce," she says, as she gets up from the table and walks out.

Danny, not being surprised, is still taken aback by her irate and compulsive attitude about these issues, as he watches her exit the restaurant. *Perhaps his dad was right,* he thought, *He didn't really even know this woman, the way he should.*

Moments later, he leaves cash on the table to cover the meal and makes his way to the valet stand where she stood.

The valet guy pulls the car up, she gets in before the other attendant could open her door. Danny tips the valet guys and steps into the car too. He pauses and looks over at his wife, who immediately said, "Get me to the house, please!"

"Pam, divorce is not an option for me—I married you for better or for worse."

"Well, I didn't marry you for better or for worse—I'm done! So, in the meantime, its just best we stay separated until the divorce is final."

"Until the divorce is final, what are you really saying, Pam?"

"That I might like you better, not being married to you," she shot back.

Danny pauses, puts the car in gear and drives off, knowing that this is not going the way he'd hoped. And for the next fifteen minutes there was complete silence before Danny says, "Pam, you've walked out over four or five times at this point. You've had plenty of time to file for a divorce, but you haven't. This whole separation thing sounds like an excuse to go play."

"Excuse me! Please! I don't need a freaking excuse to leave you, *Danny. I have reasons—ReaSons Mister Bradley—with a capital R and S—to opt out."*

"Pam," he said, but she cuts him off again. "So, don't expect me to abide by anything from this point forward.... the hell with the marriage vows.... you do your parenting thing while I do my thing—single."

And for the next twelve months, they indeed separate again. Danny had come to the end of his rope, he realized that he had failed to successfully reach his wife, which meant he had to go solo in dealing with Denise and her family if, what he's been hearing in the streets from Pine Bluff is true. So, to deal with the inevitable, he didn't turn to drugs, or alcohol, or women, he turned once again to a spiritual counselor in hopes of making sense of what his life had quickly become.

By the beginning of 1989, Danny had not seen his son since the summer of 1986—and had only had opportunities to talk to him a few times over that same course of time. Denise was not going to allow him the right to freely spend time with his son without requiring he give up something in return. And Pam was just not having it at all. It was a life with just her or nothing; and with Denise, it appeared to be divvy it out, or stay out

Consequently, as much as he didn't want to divorce his wife, he knew it was perhaps the only possible solution if he was ever going to be in a position to develop a relationship with his son. And unfortunately, as much as he would have loved to work with Denise, in the raising of "their son," he knew that his bond with Mark was going to have to be built *independent* of her help.

So, after receiving a call in the spring that Denise was about to marry her military friend, Danny decided to take a trip to Pine Bluff to explore the possibility of relocating Mark to Texas to live with him. He was just not liking the idea of another man either, making claims to an already distant son, who already had two daddies. But Denise, surprised to see Danny, wasn't having such discussion. She simply evaded him and his questions while she anchored Mark down deeper into his relationship with his daddy Mayberry. However, he got Denise to, at least, commit to allowing his son to visit him the up coming summer—in Texas.

After returning to Dallas, he pondered his options. With a divorce imminent, he thought about making a return to the game one more time to be liquid enough to launch his health club business venture, and better care for his son. Having learned how the banking system worked as a pro-athlete, he decided to seek conventional financing—but to no avail. And after receiving no after no after no, returning to the NFL was his only option to earn the cash needed to launch his project.

Jimmy Johnson had just been hired as the Dallas Cowboys head coach, and was previously the head coach at Oklahoma State, which carried a staff of coaches that were very familiar with Danny's skill sets after having recruited him out of high school to attend O-State in '81.

As you are well aware, he chose OU instead and became Coach Johnson's in state conference nemesis. Nonetheless, Danny contacts Coach Johnson and one of his closest assistants, Butch Davis, and explained his situation and his desire to revitalize his defunct football career. And without much hesitation, coach Davis was assigned to the task of evaluating Danny by way of a workout. And Danny thought there was a chance he'd get an offer, after a respectable showing. But unfortunately, a couple of weeks later the Cowboys said, "No can do—best wishes."

Now knowing, without a doubt, that his football career was indeed over, Danny took a job as a Career Development Counselor, at, of all places, the Aviation Travel Academy in Arlington, Texas, which trained and prepared airline personnel for the industry. He understood that he was never going to make enough money to fund the health club venture working *for* a health club, so he took on this additional new gig and opportunities in hopes of saving enough money to launch his dream project.

Meanwhile, it's a blustery summer day in Pine Bluff, Arkansas, in '89. Family and friends are gathered at a small church to witness the union of one Denise Ann Davis and her new hubby, Braylon Terry, with seven-year-old Mark Mayberry as the ring bearer. They exchange vows, kiss and are showered with rice and applause as they exit the church doors headed towards a waiting limousine with Mark trailing behind. As they drive off, Mark turns to his Grandma Leola and asks, "Do I have to go to Texas and see my Daddy Danny?"

She looked down at him, smiles, and says, "I'll see if I can get you out of it."

Odell joins them and the three begin walking to the car. And Leola, holding Mark's hand turns to Odell to finish a previous conversation, "I'm gonna say this again, Denise got way too much going on in her life, and Mark's got way too many daddies involved in his life, at this point."

"I'll take care of Mark," Odell replied.

Leola paused and then asked, "With what, Odell? Your meddling only adds to this damn problem—he doesn't need daddy number four muddling up the waters even more!" Leola said with conviction. "And what about his real father?

"Aw hell, Leo, Danny ain't even involved and don't want to be," Odell shot back.

"Well—I wonder why—is it by choice or force?"

"By choice, hell, you know that!" Odell said.

"If so, why has he been trying so hard to get Mark to move to Texas, O? That doesn't sound like someone that doesn't want to be involved!"

"As I said, I'll take care of Mark—he's not going to Texas to see no-damn-body that didn't want him," Odell said, as he opened the driver's side car door and gets in, which prompts Mark to smile, Grandpa Odell was singing his tune.

Leola then slides inside the car and said, "Odell, this child is not your son, nor can you afford to take care of him. So stop bumping your gums about what you gon do!"

That comment upset Odell a bit, who was known to boast and brag a little, setting off an argument between the two of them after having slammed their respective car doors. All Mark could think about as he let down his back door window is how much he didn't want to go to Texas to see his *so-called* real daddy, a man he really didn't even know. *Grandma Leo is right,* he thought to himself. *I do have too many daddies! And why would my mom agree to let me go see the only one she says didn't even want me?! The only dad I want to spend time with is my Granddaddy O and Daddy Mayberry.*

A few weeks later, on the other side of town, Duke and Shelly Bradley are at home watching TV when the doorbell rings. Surprisingly, Odell Davis and Mark is at the door.

Shelly opens as Odell politely says, "Hey, Shelly, just stopped by on account of Mark going to Texas tomorrow to see Danny. Dee asked me to bring him by before he flies out to try to help him get a lil bit more comfortable."

"Sure—come on in. I told Dee we wanted to see Mark before he left," she says.

"Yeah, this whole thing is such a mess," Odell said as Duke enters the room.

"Hey Duke."

"Mr. Davis, how are you, sir?"

"Not bad for an old man—and you?" Odell replied.

"I'm just out in the deep end trying to stay above water," Duke replied.

"I know that's right," Odell said, as he wasted no time getting right into it. "Boy, I tell ya, Duke, I knew when Mark was born that this child wasn't Mayberry's.... Dee had that boy running in-and-out the house in the wee hours of the morning rubbing her stomach and bringing her ice cream—and I told Leola when Mark was born that this was not Mayberry's boy! And as soon as the truth came out, I said to myself, there it is—that's it right there! That's who this boy resembles, Danny Bradley—not Mayberry. And I told Dee, at that point, she needs to clean up what she messed up."

"Well, the first time I heard about Mark," Duke said, "was when my nephew Bo brought him by here. Mark had to be about two or three years old, and he told us that Danny had been accused of being the father. But went on to say that he'd promised the child's mother that he wouldn't expose who she was unless she failed to tell us herself."

"Is that right!" Odell said.

"But as Bo talked and we listened, I, too, thought to myself, now this boy does resemble Danny quite a bit when he was this age. Gazing lovingly across the coffee table at her grandson, Shelly then said, "Well I guess we're family now, which means you need to come visit us sometimes, Mark?"

Mark had been silent the entire time and he was not about to speak up now. And with that comment, Shelly senses Odell was not ready for Mark to spend much time at his new grandparents' house and suddenly appeared ready to go. They say their good-byes as Odell guides Mark out the door with Shelly and Duke standing in the doorway, watching as they drive off.

The next day, Denise and Mark are at Little Rock airport, standing in line at the airline ticket counter. When it's their turn, they step up to be helped, and what happens next only validated Leola's concerns.

"May I help you?" The agent asked.

"Pre-paid ticket for Mark Mayberry to Dallas/Fort Worth." Dee answered.

The ticket agent looks down at Mark, who is looking everywhere but at her, as he takes in all the activity of the busy airport, as she asks, "Can I see some ID for both you and Mark please?"

Dee hands the ticket agent their identification. After checking each, she says, "I need you to fill out this *Unaccompanied Minor* form, since he will be flying alone." Dee quickly finishes the form and hands it back, as the agent continues booking Mark's flight. She checks the form to make sure it is complete while asking, "What is your relationship to Mark ma'am?"

"His mother," Denise replied.

"It says here that Mark Mayberry will be picked up by Danny Bradley, is that correct?"

"Yes—that's correct," Dee replied.

"And what is Mister Bradley's relationship to Mark?"

"He's Mark's father," Dee responded.

The ticket agent pauses a moment while reviewing the form, then says to Dee, "Well, ma'am your ID says Denise Terry, but the kids last name is Mayberry, and you're saying that he's being picked up by a Mister Bradley, is that correct?"

"That would be correct," Denise said.

"Okay, so, your maiden name perhaps was once Mayberry?" The agent asked.

Denise now pauses a bit at the sound of that and wondered *what's up with all these questions,* but replied with an answer that further confused this agent, "No—my maiden name was formerly Davis—not Mayberry."

"Okay, so, Mayberry was not your maiden name prior to your married name, Terry?"

"Correct," Denise replied.

"Just so we're on the same page here, we have Mark Mayberry, an Unaccompanied Minor, traveling non-stop to Dallas/Fort Worth, signed off by Denise Terry, his mother, whose maiden name was once Davis, who also consents for a Danny Bradley, his father, to pick him up at DFW airport, is that correct?"

"You got it," Dee replied.

"Ma'am, do you realize that the names Davis, Bradley and Terry are three different names, none of which reflect a direct relationship with Mark Mayberry?"

In nearly eight years, Dee had become increasingly comfortable with the stories she'd been weaving in explaining Mark's conception, birth and parental tree. Even hearing her mother harp on about the absurdity of Mark having too many daddies, was annoying—but manageable. But now that a total stranger was exposing her foolishness, in front of a few other complete strangers, was starting to tick her off a little.

Attempting to remain composed, Dee kept her response simple: "It's a long story, but I am indeed Mark's mother, and Danny Bradley is indeed his father."

"Okay—I'll be right back," the ticket agent said.

Suddenly the agent returns with apparently her superior, who steps outside the counter and approaches Mark and Denise, introducing himself to Dee first and then kneels to talk at eye level with Mark. “Hey kiddo, I understand you’re headed to Dallas today,” he says while the ticket agent gets back on the monitor appearing to book the ticket. And Mark nods, “yes.”

“Do you know who’s picking you up when you in Dallas?”

“Danny,” Mark replies softly, as he looks up at his mother.

“Danny who?” He asks.

“Danny Bradley,” Dee replied for Mark, as she shook her head in slight disgust. All the while, the supervisor has been watching Mark and kind of ignoring Denise. After she blurts out Danny’s name, he resumed questioning him. “I noticed that your last name is Mayberry, who is Mister Mayberry?”

“My daddy,” Mark said confidently.

“And Danny is your daddy too?” He asked.

Mark looks up at his Mom, who obviously didn’t want to be there, let alone answering interrogatories about how jacked up this situation was, suddenly says, “Sir, Mayberry is Mark’s Godfather, Danny is Mark’s biological father, and Terry is his stepfather and my husband.... and far as I can recall, I’ve been his mother since I went into labor over eight years ago, is there any other questions.”

The supervisor looked up at Denise and said, “Thanks for your patience, ma’am. It’s our job to make sure we know who’s who when kids are traveling alone.”

The ticket agent hands her boss the *Unaccompanied Minors Badge*, who then drapes it around Mark’s neck and tells him to keep the badge around the neck at all times.

“Ms. Terry,” he says, “I am going to escort you and your handsome son to your departure gate and introduce him to the crew who will be in charge of the transport.”

They make their way to the gate, which was a reasonably a short walk. He approached the counter and asked if one of the agents would call the plane and get a crew-member to come out and review some information about an *Unaccompanied Minor,* as he writes down the instructions while waiting. And in less than a minute a *very* attractive flight attendant emerges from the plane and approached the gate agent counter, as all in the concourse appeared to take notice, including Denise.

“Hi,” the supervisor said, in awe of this flight attendants beauty, he explains the situation and hands her a note as she glances over at Mark and Denise.

The Flight Attendant looks at the instructions, folds it up and places it inside the jacket pocket of her uniform, as she prepares to take Mark aboard. The supervisor says his good-byes to Mark and Denise, while continuing to admire the beauty of his colleague. Denise then gets a private moment with Mark.

"You behave on the plane and have your Daddy Danny call me as soon as you get there, you hear me," she said. Mark fearfully nods, yes, as tears begin to fall from his eyes. "But why do I have to go, mama?" Mark asked.

Dee gives him that look as if they have had this conversation already. She hugs him and hands his duffle bag to the Flight Attendant, who takes Mark's hand and leads him into the jet-bridge. And as one would expect, Mark was extremely nervous, uncertain and a lil terrified. But managed to maintain his emotions, this is also his first plane ride.

Dallas, Texas

While a tense, yet, excited Danny is in his car on his way to the airport as the gate agent announces the arrival of Mark's flight, which always prompted friends and family who were waiting for love ones to begin jockeying for position around the jet way exit. But the post terrorist attack era, friends and family must wait outside the security checkpoints. So, by the time Danny makes it to the gate, passengers were just starting to deplane. He picks a spot to be as visible as possible not knowing if Denise really put him on the plane. But suddenly, Mark appears, holding a hand of one the Flight Attendants, as Danny lets out a sigh of relief.

He walks over and kneels down in front of Mark and hugs him. "What's up champ?" Danny asked, as he could see Mark had been crying.

The Flight Attendant introduces herself, "I'm Salena, and you are?" She asked.

"I'm sorry, I'm Danny—Mark's father," he replies, as he stands to shake her extended hand. And he, too, notices that this woman is beautiful.

"I have a few instructions before I'm allowed to turn him over to you," she said.

"Understood," Danny replied.

She, then, looks down at Mark, and asked, "Do you know this gentleman?"

Tears begin to fall from Mark's eyes again as he says, "Ye—ye—yes."

"Awe, it's going to be aright," she said.

Danny kneels down again, and asked, "What's wrong, son?"

"I'm scared," Mark replied, wiping his eyes with the back of his hand as Danny reaches out and hugs him warmly again.

"I got ya covered, big-fella—we're going to have a great time, son.

The Flight Attendant, not wanting to break up a tender moment, clears her throat to get Danny's attention before saying "I have a few questions before I can release him."

"I'm sorry," Danny replied.

"It's okay—just doing my job," she said with a smile. "Is this the man coming to pick you up, Mark?"

"Yes," he answers.

Turning her attention to Danny, she asked, "May I see your ID please, sir?"

Danny takes out his ID and hands it to her, and asks, "How was he on the flight?"

"He cried a little but for the most part, he was cool—that happens a lot with kids his age flying alone for the first time.... Do you happen to know Mark's birthday?"

"Umm, January 29th, I believe," Danny responded.

"And his mother's maiden name?" She asked.

"That would be Davis—Denise Davis."

"Last question, would you happen to know Mister Mayberry's relationship to Mark?"

Danny paused and said, "Wow—that's a complex one."

"Mayberry my daddy," Mark blurts out.

They both look down at Mark, as Danny begins to chuckle at his sudden outburst and said, "Yes—I would say that Mayberry is his 'birth certificate' father."

"I think that's good enough. Godfather was the correct answer—I apologize again for all the questions, we're just doing our job—the ticket agent in Little Rock was a bit confused with all the names. So, if I can get you to sign here and here, we're set."

While Danny signs the form, she notices his championship ring. "What's the ring?"

"University of Oklahoma," he replied.

"Boomer Sooners, huh!" She says with a even brighter smile.

Handing the form back, he remarks, "What do you know about Boomer Sooners?"

"A little—may I take a closer look?"

"Sure!" Danny delightfully replied, this woman was gorgeous.

Taking the ring off and placing it in her now extended hand, Danny realized she had gone from business mode to possible "flirt zone." He watched as she placed it on her left ring finger and stretched it out to get a better view.

"That would make a great wedding band," Danny said with a smile.

"Be careful now," she replied laughingly, "if I didn't know better I would have to say you're flirting with your son's Flight Attendant."

Raising his left hand to show his wedding band, Danny says, "Actually I'm married."

Mark, who had been watching them, decides to intervene again, "My mama say you separated—she left you."

"Oops!" Salena says.

Stunned by his comment, Danny thinks to himself, while laughing, *Just a few minutes ago, you were crying—now you gossiping?*

He, then, looks down at Mark and said, “Thank you sir—but I got this big-fella.” Danny turns back to his son’s flight attendant, “As I said, I’m married.”

“Hey, my name is Bennett and I’m not in it,” she replied with her own chuckle.

Danny places Mark’s duffle bag over his right shoulder and asked, “What do you know about separation young fella?”

The Flight Attendant laughs, and after writing something on a small piece of paper attached to her clipboard, hands Danny his ring back, winks and walks away. And as she does, he notices her phone number attached. He thought, *Now, if I had played the separation divorced card, she would have shot me completely down.*

Danny, then, looks at Mark and says, “Alright matchmaker—you ready to go?”

Mark, who was more focused on what he saw change hands between Danny and the pretty lady, asked, “Is that your football ring?”

Danny smiled and said, “No sir, it’s your football ring.”

“How is it my ring?” Mark asks.

“Well, one day you’re going to be big enough to wear daddy’s championship ring, but it’s my bet that you’ll have a few championship rings someday yourself.... But until then, let’s go have some fun lil Boomer,” as they make their way out the terminal.

For the first time, since Dee’s announcement, Danny had hope, and felt more encouraged about her *willingness* to work with him in developing this much-needed tie with his son. And with Pam, thus far, having chosen to separate for the fifth time, allowed this father the opportunity to make up for some lost time.

It had been a tough couple of years for Pam, Mark, Denise; and even for Mayberry for that matter; and perhaps the families associated with this drama. But however, none had to tangle with the multitude of challenges and life changing adjustments his Dad Danny had to bear. He had gone from the top of the mountain to the bottom of the pit in every area of his life, after just months of my mother’s announcement that *her son was his son.*

And even though this father had new reasons to be hopeful, encouraged by Denise’s seeming willingness to finally support the idea of him having a meaningful relationship with his son, what he discovers next set the stage for the kind of war that he would have to endure for the next seventeen years.

13

The Unbreakable

As happy as this father was to have time with his son, Mark, on the other hand was very uncomfortable around him. Despite the fact that he took him places he'd never been, did things he'd never done, and gave him things he'd never had, this kid was still very distant. His emotions were all over the place. At times he appeared to be cordially responsive, and at other times he was distraught. This was a guy who Mark had been told on numerous occasions that he simply didn't want him, which made it extremely hard for Mark to accept this wanna-be-father, including all of the nice things this man on the outside was attempting to do for him.

At this age, being so attached to Odell and Mayberry, Mark just didn't see the need of having another dad around. And no matter what Danny did with him or for him, Mark appeared to be unreachable. From the time he arrived, when given a chance, he would sneak away inside the house and call his mom, begging her to let him come home.

Yet she would say, "No, no, Mark, stay so you can get more school clothes."

And each time, in the late night hour, Mark would just cry and cry about having to spend time with this guy. So much so, Mark decided he had-had enough. About 6 a.m. this particular morning, Danny had fallen asleep in the media room, when he was awakened by Mark, who is standing over him, fully dressed with tears just free flowing.

"What's wrong son?" Danny asked groggily.

While Danny knew the possible answer to his question, he still searched to see what might have brought on this latest episode. He knew Mark had been calling home, and he could only imagine what he might had been telling them and vice versa. But this time, Mark was ready to talk.

"I want to go home, I'm scared," he said with certainty.

Danny pauses and gathers himself before asking, "Can you hang in there for another couple of days, son? There's a lot of activities at the Boys Club—it's going to be fun."

"No! I wanna go home! I already called my mama and told her I wanted to come home," Mark shouts back.

"What did she say?" Danny asked, as he wipes his son's face.

"She said stay there until you get some more school clothes. And I told her you already bought me a lot of stuff."

"And?"

"But she said stay and maybe you'll get me more stuff."

"Okay—then why don't you?" Danny asked calmly.

"Cuz—I wanna go home, I'm scared!" Mark replied, as he cried out.

Danny gets up and sits on the edge of the bed facing him: "I'm sorry you're having such a tough time with this, Mark. But what are you so afraid of, son?"

"Why can't you move back and live with us," Mark asked.

"Unfortunately son, that's not an option. I live in Texas, I work in Texas, and your mom has a husband, and they reside in Arkansas.... And I doubt very seriously that your step-dad would go for that. But tell me again why are you so afraid?

"Becuz!" He said in fear.

"Because what, son.... Talk to me.... Why are you so afraid?"

"Becuz, my mama said you didn't want me," he cries out louder.

"She did?" Danny asked, incredulously.

"She said you went off to play football and didn't want to have anything to do with us, that's why Mayberry is my Daddy," Mark said through sobs.

Danny drops his head in disgust, as he takes a deep-deep sigh and exhaled, and calmly asked, "When did she tell you that, son?"

"She always says it…. Everybody in the family says it," Mark wails.

The patience he'd been praying for was now being brutally tested to the max.

He grabs Mark by the shoulders and looked him directly in he eye, and said, "Listen to me, son, I know I have not had the opportunity to spend much time with you, but I love you.... And what your mother and family is saying **is not** true. It's simply **not true.** I *did not* run off to play anything, knowing that I had a son.... Do you understand me?"

"She said you didn't want me!" He replied, as he continued to cry. "Can I go home?"

Danny pauses, and said, "Yes son, you can go home, as his anger begins to rise.

He then reaches for the phone, dials a number and hit the speaker button. As the phone rings, Mark begins to calm down not knowing what his father was about to do.

Danny whispers, "Be quiet and don't say anything," as he places his index finger up to Mark's mouth as they hear the sounds of the connection being made.

Denise answers, as Mark's eye expression suddenly shows major concern.

"Denise Terry—Danny."

"Hey, what's up? She said groggily. "Is Mark alright?"

"Yes and no," Danny replies.

"What's going on?" Dee asked.

"At times he's seems cool and then times he's not."

"What happened?" She asked.

"Well, he woke me up at about 6 a.m., crying wanting to know why I can't move back home and live with you guys....And I explained to him how that is not really an option."

"Mark is just trying to come home, Danny," Dee said. "I've already told Mark he needs to stay there and get to know father better. So, he's just trying to come home."

"I understand that, Dee. He doesn't really know me, so, I can see why he's uncomfortable, but he also made another very peculiar statement."

"Okay," she said cautiously.

"He said that you and the whole family keep telling him that I ran off to play football and didn't want to have anything to do with you or him—is that true?"

Anticipating Denise's response, he keeps his eye on Mark. And she immediately asked without hesitation, "What did you tell him?"

"What did I tell him?" Danny asked. "Are you serious?"

"Yeah, what did you tell him? I hope you told him the same thing for now, and when he gets a lil older I'll tell him the truth." Denise alertly replied.

Danny could tell from Mark's expression that he was confused by his mom's answer.

"Denise, why would you tell Mark that?"

"Because he's too young right now to be dealing with all this, Danny. But in due time, I'll make sure he knows the truth," she responded dismissively.

"So, for now, you thought throwing me under the bus is the best way to handle it?"

"Like I said, I will tell him the truth when he gets a lil older, Danny."

"Well, let ask you, Dee, what is the truth?" He asked.

"What do you mean?" Dee replied sheepishly.

"What I said, what is the truth. At this point, I have heard a lot of stories about this situation coming out of Pine Bluff, Denise. Do you even know?"

"And what is that suppose to mean?" She asked.

"Well, as the old saying goes," Danny says, "A person can tell a lie for so long that they start believing their own lie.... So I'm just curious, what is the truth?"

Denise paused, and said with a little bit of agitation, "The truth is, you didn't leave knowing you had a son to go play football, nor did you ever say you didn't want Mark."

"And?" Danny asked, expecting her to add to her answer.

Dee pauses, but continues, "And, I realize that I shouldn't have ever gotten Mayberry involved in this, but I can't go back and change the past and I'll make sure he knows the truth in the future."

"I'm not asking you to change the past, Dee, but I am asking you to stop lying to Mark about his father…. It's unfair to him, me, and my family. But thanks for sharing, I was starting to wonder if you still knew the truth with all the lies I've been hearing."

Without waiting for a response, Danny disconnects the call and places a hand on Mark's shoulder, he said, "I didn't run off to play football, nor have I ever said I didn't want you, son.... What your family has been saying to you is simply not true."

Before Danny could say another word, Mark bolted and ran out of the room.

"Mark!" Danny called out, as he jumped up and ran after him. Mark had made it to the front door and was fumbling with the lock when Danny caught up to him. He takes him in his arms, picks him up and hugs him tight as Mark is sobbing hysterically.

"I got ya, I got ya, it's going be alright, son," Danny says as he tries to console him

Moments later, after he gets Mark to calm down, he releases his embrace of him and places him on the floor, "I love you, Mark," as a tear now falls from his own eyes.

"There is never a reason for you to run away, son—do you understand me?

Through tears Mark replies, "But nobody wants me!"

Danny fought to hold back more tears himself as he said, "Baby, that's not true, son.

"Yes it is.... My mother doesn't want me either," Mark surprisingly said.

"Your mother loves you, son! She loves you! She made a few mistakes but she loves you, Mark," as he continue to wail. "And I'm sure Mayberry has been a really good daddy to you, also, right?"

Mark shakes his head, *yes,* through sobs while wiping his eyes.

"And then you have your granddaddy Odell, grandma Leola, and even your new step-dad probably loves you a bunch too," Danny said, as Mark shakes his head, *yes, again.*

"And most important son, the good Lord, who created us all, loves you more than life itself.... And you are the apple of His eye, Mark Anthony.... So, you have plenty of love big-fella," Danny says, as he hugs him again and begins to pray.

Once he was done, he agreed to send Mark home. And that immediately made Mark happy. But at this juncture, Mark didn't quite know what to make of this man. He didn't know what to expect when he arrived in Texas, but he knew, even at this tender age, that this guy didn't quite appear to be the person his mother made him out to be.

Meanwhile in Pine Bluff, Dee and her parents were having a town hall meeting discussing the call she received from Danny. And as expected, a stressful Denise and agitated Odell were circling the family wagons, as Leola tried to stay calm and neutral.

"Dee I told you not to let that boy go to see Danny from the git-go! You should have known that conversation was going to come up at some point! And you had to know Danny was going to deny any and eveything," Odell said.

"I understand all that daddy but, you have also said, on many occasions, that Danny needs to take on his fair share of this responsibility, too. And I agreed, Mayberry and I shouldn't be the only one's providing for Mark."

"But the young man seems to be willing to do something, Dee," Leola said.

"But if we allow Danny the freedom to spend this kind of time with Mark, there is no tellin what else he might try to fill his head up with," Odell shot back.

Dee takes a deep breath regretting her decision to allow Mark to make this trip.

Leola chimed in, again, "I think its just a way too early to be making these assumptions. The young man seems to be making an honest attempt to be a father."

"Mama, Danny left me hangin for seven or eight years with Mark! It's past time for him make an honest attempt!" Dee said with conviction. "But that's not the problem right now, I agree with daddy, if we don't control Danny's access to Mark, who knows how many other lies he may have already filled Mark's head with."

"Where has Danny been the past couple of years, Leo?" Odell asked.

"Invisible and disinterested," Denise replied in between.

With neither of them taking into account the number of years it took Denise to reveal the truth to Mark's father, Odell takes his insensitivity to a whole new level.

"Dee, it's time for Mark to come home. This is too much for a kid his age—I don't wanna have to go see Danny about my grandson!"

"Oh, stop, O!" Leola said. "We don't know anything just yet, accept he's trying."

"We will this evening, because he's coming home," Odell said sternly.

Dee then places a call to Shelly asking that she have Danny call her, it was time to send Mark back home. Without letting Dee know about Danny's plans to do just that, she simply agrees to pass on the message.

As she hangs up the phone, Odell gets up to leave and makes his final remark, "Dee, I highly suggest you keep Mark out of Texas for a while—if Danny wants to see him, make him come to Pine Bluff to see him."

And from that point forward, the Davis family declares *all out* war against my father, before he even had a chance to prove up, with my grandfather acting as commander-in-chief. And as any good educated military soldier would, my father responded with patience. He didn't retaliate with vengeance, he remained focused on the overriding mission of being that responsible father to me that he never had growing up.

So, he relents to the idea of me coming to see him, he started coming more often to see me—in Pine Bluff. And one of the first events he takes me to was a fund-raiser, hosted by college teammate Keith Jackson—a celebrity charity basketball game in Little Rock. And there were a lot of kids at this event, but very few got to go back stage in the locker rooms and meet the NFL great Reggie White (Philadelphia Eagles); NBA All-star Kevin Johnson (Phoenix Suns); and (Hollywood actor) Allen Payne, just to name a few. He was working it but my family just wasn't feeling it. He believed I needed more exposure, but they felt he should just sign *a stay away* disclosure.

Nevertheless, a lot happened that changed the lives of my parents between 1986 and 1989. Despite Danny's attempt to return to the game, the Los Angeles Rams, in 1990, were forced by arbitration, to pay him his full salary from the grievance he filed against them back in '86.

And by 1991, he had the distinct honor of being presented the key to the city of Pine Bluff by Mayor Carolyn Robinson; and he finally purchases that 50,000 square foot multi-purpose health and fitness center in Dallas/Fort Worth. And this time it was not Ron Brown, but Keith Jackson that teamed up with him as a minority owner. And the two of them hosted events that brought out the who's who in the sports and entertainment world.

With Danny at the helm, Bedford Professional Athletic Club was thriving with revenues averaging six-figures per month. Financially, life was good again, in fact, better than it's ever been. Even though it cost him about seventy-five percent per month to operate this business, he still managed to profit well as majority owner.

During that same four-five year period, my mom, with the support of her family, stuck to her guns and had only allowed me to go visit my father in Texas, twice. And to be honest, that was still just fine with me. As far as I was concerned, Mayberry was still my dad with grandpa Odell filling in the gaps. And anything outside of that was really no interest of mine, even though this man went out of his way to get to know me.

But unfortunately, because of all the negative things my family constantly said about him, I had grown into not even liking the man, which made it easier for them to control how we spend time together, when we spent time together, and where we would spent time together.

So, Christmases, and occasionally my birthday, was all he was allotted. Along with, of course phone access, but even that was closely monitored under high security. And despite his efforts and holiday moments, they still treated him as an outsider, while Mayberry was the beloved insider.

But, however, what became very interesting to me was whenever I needed anything, my mother would always push me to call, *not* my Daddy Mayberry, but *rather* my Daddy Danny, which always made me angry. And I would just weep, asking why?

And her answer was always, "Because I said so, Mark!"

I just didn't understand. But nonetheless, despite all this man had to endure, whatever I needed and even *wanted,* if I made the request, he *always* came through without hesitation. He never said no. But with the rest of the family, my mom would always pretend as if he never did anything. Consequently, my family despised my father while, at the same time, they praised Mayberry.

But suddenly, Danny plants a seed in my head that would begin to keep me up at night. *"Son, if we're going to ever have a strong relationship that the good Lord desires for us, we're going to have to build it ourselves, independent of anybody else's help."*

Now what in the world does a ten-year-old do with that? Especially, when his entire family is totally against his relationship with this man? Answer: You stay put and trust the people around you. But seeing the injustice, even at that age, bothered me. Causing me to often wonder why was it so hard for my family to forgive this man. Not that I understood forgiveness either, at ten, but I saw them make a ton of mistakes everyday with each other, but, yet, they didn't seem to have a problem forgiving one another, why not him. Which made me start wondering, what did he really do?

By late January of '92, after multiple stints of separation, Danny finally threw in the towel and filed for divorce from his beloved wife, Pam. He moved out of their condo, and took up residence at his business partner and college teammate, Keith Jackson's, who had just purchased an off-season home just miles from Danny's condo.

And by March of 1992, their marriage was dissolved. Despite his commitment and desire to the do right thing by me, my mother's motives and behavior had perhaps cost him almost everything.

But by the spring of '93, the threat of divorce begins to knock on her door. My step-dad, who had married into a world of selfishness and confusion decided he, too, had-had enough. He walks out, leaving my mom with two dependents, me and my sister, Cassie, who was two or three at the time. And to make ends meet, of all people, my mom decides to call my Daddy Danny, collect.

As I watched her make this call, I recall feeling a little betrayed. This was the last person I thought my Mom would call about anything like this. He was the enemy! An enemy whom "they say" I needed to stay away from unless otherwise given permission. And surprisingly, she conveniently apologizes for avoiding his calls and promises to be more supportive regarding his relationship with me, which causes me to go into an even deeper level of confusions about all of this situation.

And with Dee's credibility at just about zero, she still gets right to the point.

"Braylon left about two weeks ago and it doesn't look like we're gonna stay together…. We hardly ever talk anymore and when we do, it's just crazy…. One of us will file for divorce, and I'm hoping it's him because I can't afford to file…. So, I was wondering if you would help me pay the bills until this is over."

Amazingly, this *allegedly* irresponsible guy asked her what kind of help were she talking about. She tells him she needed about everything that Braylon was paying, which was about seventy percent of their total bills.

And as disappointed he was at the very thought of her making this call under these circumstances, Danny actually thought about doing it, but in the midst saw an even better way to help her and me. But he had to ask a few other questions, first.

"Have you thought about getting an attorney involved? Legally, he can't just walk out on you and his daughter without providing some kind of temporary support."

"No, I haven't. I can't afford it.... He says he's not taking on no more financial responsibility. So, I guess I'll let him be the one to file and spend the money, while I try to survive until it's over. But right now, I can't make it with two kids on one income."

Here comes his 64 dollar question: "Well, Dee, why don't you send Mark to me?"

Denise pauses, shakes he head in disappointment, and then replied with an slight attitude, "It's not that easy to do, Danny. Besides, I don't know if that helps resolve my problem—I'll still have these bills!"

Danny, then, backs off thinking, *Yeah, bills that I can't spend a dime on, especially if I can't spend any time with my own son, Dee,* and then asked to keep hope alive, "Have you considered moving back in with your parents?"

But unfortunately, Dee's next comment ends the call. She shot back quickly, "No, I can't do that. In fact, I won't do that," She replied. "That's exactly what he's hoping I'll do—quit and give up.... And if I do that, he wins, I lose.... And I will not give him that luxury..... I want to prove to him that I can make it without him."

Danny, knowing the pangs of divorce, empathized with Denise but could not fathom idea of possibly getting involved in her state of affairs, especially financially at this point. So, he makes it plainly clear: "Dee, under the circumstances, I pass."

Instead of seeing the conventional wisdom of moving back in with her parents, my mother exited this conversation seemingly even more frustrated and discontent with my father for not supporting this *spirit of competition* thing she had going with her husband.

After they hang-up, five minutes later he calls back. My Mom was bathing Cassie, so I decided to answer.

"What in the world is going, son?" He asked. "Can you talk?"

"Yeah," I replied hesitantly, wondering if I was doing the right thing.

"What's happening—talk to me?" He asked again.

"Well, from what I can see, they been arguing a lot lately and it appears that some of their fights are about you."

"Really," Danny asked. "What are they saying?

"Well, I don't know the whole story because I'm usually over at my grandparents house but, it sounds like he's always fussing about what you do and don't do."

"Did you get the monies I sent a month or so ago for the summer gear?"

"Yeah, but I only got a couple of things, she spent the rest."

"On what?" He asked.

"Stuff for her."

"So, she's not using the cash towards things you need?"

"Some, but not all," I replied, as my Mom suddenly reenters the room and I abruptly had to hang up. And he must have known because he tried calling back.

However, by the fall of '93, my mother and step-dad reconciled and he moved back in, but the arguments and disagreements about dad over the next several years continued. And now looking for more of a reason to discredit my father, my mother takes advantage of a slip-up. After making arrangements with him for me to visit Texas the summer of '94, he fails to make good on it, and she goes off. A mistake she seemed to never let him live down around our house, without ever even knowing his reasons as to why the trip fail through.

"Mark packed all his things to come visit you, Danny, and he didn't even hear from you! Don't you ever put my son in that situation again! Don't tell him you are going to do something and don't!"

And BAM! She hung up, and then says to me, "Danny may be your father but Mayberry is your daddy! "You didn't need to go any 'damn' way.... All he's doing is brainwashing you!

Now, mind you, in my house, my mom and family made commitments to do things for me and with me all the time and failed to do them—with amnesia! So, why call this man and just go off like that! And after finally talking to him about the situation, once they let him through, I discovered that the reason the trip fail through was simply because he and Pam were flirting with the idea of getting back together and Pam, suddenly reverted back to her previous stance about the idea of being a step-mother, the day before I was to arrive. And since she was in and out of his condo, still, he chose to cancel the trip rather than have me walk into a situation that gone south again. A fallout that I would still get the terrifying experience of viewing live and in living color later that same summer, at an Arlington, Texas, water park known as *Wet-n-Wild*.

So, trust me, I clearly understood on that day, why he chose not to make good on my visit to Dallas earlier that summer. But it had become obvious to me, at this juncture, it appeared that my father was losing this war, on both sides, badly.

14

The Entanglement

By spring of 1995, Danny had decided to change careers. He was hired as Director of Player Programs for the Dallas Cowboys. A hire that was easy for this franchise to make. All of the front office management team knew Danny and knew him well. Barry Switzer was now the Head Coach. Larry Lacewell, the Player Personnel Director, and the Joneses were all from Arkansas. And Troy Aikman, the NFL's most prolific quarterback, during this time, gave a thumbs up on this hiring. Danny had the privilege of playing with Troy at OU, and had consulted Troy before interviewing for the job.

Again, the health club business was good but this entrepreneur was inspired by the idea of becoming the first black front office executive for, arguably, the most storied franchise in all of sports. So, he decided to sell the health club in an effort to fulfill his entire duty to the Cowboys.

The next day, the Pine Bluff Commercial and the Arkansas Gazette headlines this special Cowboys hiring. The locals wrote about his accomplishments, achievements and accolades. And as usual, there came subtle negativity from my family regarding this appointment. In their eyes, this man was damned if he did, and damned if he didn't—he could do no right, privately, personally, or professionally.

As I laid in bed, this night, pondering my life and the people in it, and all the whys, I started asking myself, again, *what did this man really do? Is there something more my mother is not telling me that would explain why they are so unfair to him?*

And knowing that I was not going to get an answer from her, or them, I began to push against the grain about visiting him in Texas. I was too guarded at home. I needed space and time with him to get these questions answered. But each time I would make my push, she would instead send me to my Daddy Mayberry in Alabama, which is where he now lived. This made me even more curious about this man and his previous relationship with my mother. Their treatment of him just wasn't right.

It appeared that I was in the middle of a *stupid* family warfare, which they had started but didn't want to admit that she, and now they, had thrown the first punch. They all keep saying that he really doesn't want me, but on the other hand, the man kept trying to spend time with me. So, the week I was scheduled to go to Alabama, I made one last attempt to get out of it, during dinner, hoping to go to Texas.

"Why can't Mayberry come here, mom—y'all make Danny come here?"

As you might imagine, that was a huge mistake. My mother snapped.

"Excuse me!" She said with fire in her eyes. "Mayberry is your damn Daddy, Mark! Danny ain't done a damn thing for you, son, but mess with your head—brainwashing you with all his lies!"

"What lies, Mama?!"

"Stop lying!" She shouted.

"But I'm telling you he hasn't said anything about you, Mama!"

"I said stop lying, Mark!" She shouted louder.

"I just don't understand what he did?" I said underneath my breath.

"And you won't at your age, Mark! You too young to understand, son!

"Dee!" Leola said, as she attempts to calm her daughter.

"No, Mama, let me finish—this is why I refuse to allow him to go to Texas; every time he comes back he's got some new theory he's concocted in his head!" She said, as I look at her confused as if to say, "I have."

"Don't look at me like that," she fire back. "I hear you talkin to ya lil friends! But let me remind you, son, Danny may bc your father, but Mayberry is your daddy!"

"And don't you ever forget it," Odell adds, as he breaks his silence.

At this point, I just broke down in tears, which made my mom even angrier.

"And stop all that crying," she yelled.

"That's enough, Denise," Leola said, as she reaches over to console me.

This was a battle I had no way of winning nor was I going to discover anything new about this situation. They just have it out for this guy. And not wanting to go to see Mayberry, I asked, "So, how long do I have to stay in Alabama?"

"Until your Daddy Mayberry decides to send you back!" She said firmly. "And, no, you're not going to Texas when you return!" She added.

"She's right Mark," Odell said. "Danny disowned you for nearly seven-eight years before he was willing to even acknowledge you as his son," Odell threw in. Followed by, "So, get your stuff together! It's time to go!

Now I'm listening to all of this stuff, knowing that most of it, if not all of it wasn't true, I wanted to make known so bad what I heard her say the truth was years earlier during my first visit to Texas. But I didn't. I held it. Because if I had shared that, you think they're against him now, this would've literally made it impossible for this man to have any access to me, making his suggested way for us to deal more real: *'Son, if we are going to ever have a strong relationship—we're going to have to build it ourselves, independent of anybody else's help,'"* he would often say.

Defeated, perplexed, and mystified, I walked with head down, shoulders slumped to grab my bag as they rushed me on out the door. And I was off to the Alabama to go play son to my *chosen* Dad, who is obviously *being played*—by my mother, while being prevented from visiting my *real* Dad, because he wouldn't *be played*—by my beloved mother. It was completely obvious to me, at this stage, that if there was not more to this story, I was simply being used as a pawn between these two men to *pacify* her personal agenda. And by the time I neared my 14th birthday, despite not having answers to a host of questions, I began to grow tired of being forced into the middle of my mother's *unnecessary* warfare against *my father*—who wasn't, by the way, "*my daddy,*" they would often shout.

Finally, by mid-fall, I got that chance to go to Dallas to see him. He was persistent, and that disturbed my family a bit. He was unwilling to quit and they didn't really know to deal with that. They knew he wanted to spend more time with me across the Arkansas boarder, at this point. His new job just wouldn't allow him the luxury of traveling as the health club business had afforded him. But yet, they didn't care. It was either come to Arkansas, or nothing.

But every time I needed anything, I was told to call my Daddy Danny. They wanted me to have access to his money, but they didn't want him to really have access to me. And to validate her fears, while waiting for my flight, my mom spent her entire good-byes promoting another trip to Alabama, which she scheduled for the second half of the fall, in an effort to trump my trip to Texas.

On arrival, I had no idea that I would get the chance to hang out with him for a half-a-day, and get a tour of Valley Ranch. It was a work day for him. And the drive from the D/FW airport to the Cowboys practice facility was much shorter than expected. Salena, my father's new girlfriend, the flight attendant, picked me up, which was cool. I had gotten to know her fairly well over the past couple of years when she would accompany him during his holiday visits to Pine Bluff.

As we enter the building my father was waiting at the receptionist desk. He and Salena make small talk, hug, kiss, and then she exits. And as we turn the corner to head to his office. I noticed the Cowboys *Wall of Fame,* which was covered with pictures of the great Cowboys teams. I was especially interested in the '92, '93 and '94 teams, as I stared at pictures of Aikman and Michael Irvin; Emmitt Smith and Darren Woodson; Charles Haley, Darryl Johnston and Jay Novacek. And as we started walking down the glassed-in hallway, a gentleman approaches going the opposite direction. "Danny, what's up, who's this handsome young guy?"

"Coach, this is my son, Mark—Mark, say hello to Coach Switzer."

Before I could get a word out, Coach Switzer said, "Son—I didn't know you had a son. Hell, he's much better looking than you!" He says, as he shakes my hand.

"Well, it's a long story coach," Danny replied.

Switzer's secretary came out and said, "The lunch buffet is ready."

"Mark, you hungry?" Switzer immediately asks.

I'd just eaten almost a batch of cookies on the plane, so, no, I really wasn't, but yes sounded like the right answer to give.

"Yes sir," I replied.

"Great, come on back and have a burger—meet a few players," Switzer says.

On our way to the lunch buffet, we run into assistant coaches John Blake and Dave Campo, and head trainer Kevin O'Neill. They too complimented me on my attire and Coach Campo invited me to come out to watch practice. Blake was funny. He looked at me and said, "What's happnin—you look like you can get out the blocks like a gazelle.... What's your forty time?"

My dad just laughed while I stood there very confused as to what the heck a forty-time out the blocks meant, nor had I ever thought of myself as a gazelle. I look over at my Dad as we moved on, he says "Its a compliment. Gazelles are quick and fast."

Nevertheless, despite being depressed, I was amazed with all the cool people my father worked with and how they all treated him. I recall saying to myself, '*how could my family not like this guy. There has to be a lot more my mom is not telling me.*'

Before heading to the locker room area where the buffet tables were, my dad decided to drop off my duffle bag in his office. This was a nice-nice office. But hey, this was the facility of the World Champion Dallas Cowboys. But for some reason I still couldn't quite enjoy this moment. I was nervous, sad and stressed with everything going on in my life. Most kids perhaps would be overwhelmingly ecstatic to hang out with the four-time World Champions, but not me. I was struggling. And the main purpose of this trip was to get some answers.

Thinking of a way to ask him these all important questions, he notices my discomfort, asked what was going on.... And if I was okay, as we take a seat.

I suddenly get a lil choked up, but I held it. "I'm just tired of being in the middle of all this fighting in my family."

"Is there anything new going on you'd like to share?" He asked.

"No, just the same old stuff."

"Your sure?

Yeah, I'm sure," I replied, as my nerves took over my thoughts.

"Okay—but understand, I want you to always be able to share your feelings, cool?"

"I understand" I softly replied.

"Let's call your mom and let her know you made it safely."

It was this kind of behavior that made me question my mother's motives *even more* about this man. He was always considerate of her and them, while they often bashed him. And I just didn't understand this dynamic. One parent was positive and kind while the other seemed to always be negative and angry. One parent wants to hear and listen, while the other just wants to be heard, disinterested in anything I had to say. And calling her, at the moment, was not what I wanted to do. But, before I could tell him that he was already handing me the phone and dialing her number.

As it rings, he turn to his computer, as I waited for my mother to answer, hoping she wouldn't. While he couldn't hear what she was saying on her end, he could surmise some of it from what I said on my end.

"I haven't had a chance to tell him, Mama. I just got here.... Mama, I just got here."

About fifteen seconds later, I just hung up. Danny snaps his head around, and asked "Did you just hang up on your mother?"

"No, she hung up on me, daddy," I replied with a look of frustration. "She's always fussin at me about somethin dealing you!"

Danny paused to take in the word—Daddy. He has never heard his son call him—Daddy. He leans back and asks as a proud father would, "What did she say, son?"

"All she thinks about is clothes, shoes, money, daddy! That's the only reason she allows me to come to Texas.... It seems like she's always looking to get somethin from you," I answered, as I began to cry a little.

"Well, that is one of my responsibility as your father, son."

"But it's always about gettin somethin from you," I replied. "And I told her before I don't like asking you for money and clothes all the time, daddy.... They don't do that with Mayberry.... And you do more for me than he does and her for that matter. That's why I don't stay at home much anymore, I stay over at my grandads. But they are against you, too.... But I think my grandparents don't like you because my mom has filled their heads up with a bunch a junk." Mark said, as Danny takes it all in. "Every Christmas and Father's Day and even birthdays, she always makes sure that Mayberry, Braylon and my Granddad received a gift from me, using money that you sent me.... But you—she never even mentions your name."

"Well—thanks for that update, but, tell me, what kind of relationship do you have with your step-dad?" He asked.

"He doesn't say much to me. I don't think he really likes me either. He seems to just tolerate me because he's married to my Mom."

"And Mayberry, how's your relationship with him these days?"

"I think she's doing the same things to him with the money thing. She's not telling him the truth about you or me. Mayberry doesn't really know what's going on. I've heard her tell him you don't do anything and don't want to do anything."

"Really?"

"Yeah, often tells me what to say to you and him if certain questions are asked."

Danny thought, *how any man could be strung along like this just didn't seem to make any sense.* But before he drew any conclusions, he had to gather more info.

"How often do you see Mayberry? Danny asked.

"Not much. He moved to Alabama a couple of summers ago. But they still pushing me towards him. Last summer, they forced me to go visit him instead of coming to Texas as planned, and told me to tell you that I went to Ohio to visit a relative."

"What does Mayberry have to say about all this?" He asked.

"He doesn't say anything about you to me, he only talks to my Mom about the situation.... I'm just tired of lying to you and him. I'm fourteen years old, daddy, and my mom still treats and talks to me like I'm five!"

Danny grabs a tissue from a wall cabinet above his desk, as Mark tears got heavier.

"Have you tried telling her how you feel?"

"She cares less about how I feel.... My mom thinks I'm clueless."

Danny takes a deep breath, leans forward and said these words in no particular order: "Son, sit up straight.... I heard everything you've said and I can see your pain and even feel your pain, but there is hope.... I'm very sorry that you've been placed in the middle of an adult war, having to deal with adult issues, with grown-ups who are acting like kids.... I don't confess to have all the answers, son, but I'm gonna keep asking the good Lord to help us get through this.... And I believe somehow someway, we're going to overcome this, together, as a family.... So, hang on in there with Pops, this too shall pass, cool?"

Mark nods his head in agreement as Danny continued: "In the meantime, I'll keep trying to reach out to your mom and see if she'll finally sit down and discuss these issues with the both of us."

"She ain't gon talk to you."

"At some point, she got to talk to me, son." He confidently replied. "But even if she didn't, what's our slogan, Mark? Come on," he said, *"that if we are going to ever have a strong relationship—we're going to have to build it ourselves, independent of anybody else's help,* right?"

Mark shakes his head in agreement as he regroups.

"Last question," he said, "would you consider moving to Texas?"

"Dad—you do most everything anyway, why not? Plus, they too negative for me.

"Understood—but prayer is the key to the kingdom and faith unlocks the gate," Danny says as he bows his head and begins to pray right there in the middle of our conversation. Shortly thereafter, we rise to head toward the lunch buffet.

The closer we get, I begin to hear a familiar voice down the hall as we made our way—it's Nate Newton's booming voice over everyone; Larry Brown laughing, and Woodson responding to a Nate joke. I guess you can say at this point, I got a lil excited. I am about to enter the locker room of the World Champion Dallas Cowboys at Valley Ranch! But, unfortunately, my own world was anything but triumphant. I was just too broken to really enjoy it.

Nevertheless, as we round another corner, I see all of the Cowboy greats, face-to-face, and out of uniform. Once we enter the actual locker room, I then felt like we stepped into Hollywood. I didn't know what Hollywood felt like or looked like—but this had to be it. It was a Wednesday, or as I discovered, media day, and there were cameras everywhere.

I know, I should have been at school, right? But folks, this was school. There wasn't a high school class in the country that could provide this kind of education. And my Dad was going to take any opportunity he could to spend time with me even if it was in the middle of the week during a school day.

And he took me to straight to his favorite, the man, Troy Aikman—and then Michael Irvin, Emmitt Smith and Deion Sanders. This should have been one of the most amazing experiences of my life, but instead, I was simply trying to understand my situation in life while still wondering, *how could my family not like this guy. What did he do to them? What do they have against him? He seems to have a great life, a great job, and work with some great people. It just didn't make sense to me.*

So while I watched players, coaches and staff personnel show their respect toward this not-so-popular-guy in my household, I decided first chance I got, I'd just go ahead and ask him, straight up. After all, again, this was one of my main reasons for pushing to come to Texas the previous summer, to get answers.

The next day, after he takes me on a shopping spree at the Galleria Mall, for which I'm sure made my mom happy, we were in the parking garage loading up the shopping bags, the moment had come. He noticed during the two hour spree, I was still down and under, pretending to be okay. But once we both strapped on our seat belts, I was ready to talk.

He slid a Maze CD, featuring Frankie Beverly, and soon *"Happy Feelings"* was softly pumping through the speakers of his drop-top 500SL, Benz, headed toward one of my favorite restaurants in town, the Rainforest Cafe.

As he pulled out of the parking lot, he looks over at me, as I kept my eyes on the Dallas Parkway traffic, and asked, "Is there more you want to discuss, I'm all ears?"

Looking out the passenger side window, at nothing in particular, I froze, again, copped out and replied, "No, not really, I'm good," with a bit of nervousness.

"You sure?" He asked.

"Yeah, I'm sure," I replied, again, not really certain, at this point, if I really wanted to know what he might have done. But I knew if I straight up asked him, he would tell me the truth, whether I wanted to hear it or not. He had been that kind of guy with me.

And to no surprise, he didn't buy my answer, but let me off the hook, for now.

"I received your report card last night. Are you satisfied with a 'C' average?"

"I can do better," I replied, while still gazing out the passenger side window.

"Well, it would be reasonably responsible if you start doing better, son.... This education business—is serious business," he said. "I've seen a lot of black men denied a lot of opportunities because they didn't respect the value of an education."

"I understand," I replied soberly, while still gazing out my window, knowing that my demeanor spoke volumes as to the pressure I was under.

And being the focused father, he opened the door, again,"Mark, talk to me?"

Mark then paused and said, "I just wish things were different."

"Different in what way?" He asked.

"I just wish my mom could get along with my Dad better."

"You have any suggestions?"

"No—I'm just confused why it has to be like this."

"What are you most confused about?" He asked.

"Well, she said you didn't want me, I discovered that not to be true.... She says I'm better off with Mayberry, I can't see how that could be true.... And she keeps saying, all you're doing is brainwashing me, and I hope that's not true.... So, I'm just trying to figure out what really is the truth—what does she really have against you?"

Danny paused, knowing that his son has been thinking about these questions for a while, as Mark finally makes eye contact, "Well—have you asked her that question?"

"Yeah, I have.... But she keeps saying the same old thing."

"Which is?"

"That you left me and didn't want me, and one day I'll understand why she did what she did, period, end of discussion."

Danny takes another pause, before replying, "Well—quite frankly, son, I'm not really sure why your mother has been so against me…. I didn't meet Dee until I was about a junior in high school and I never did get to know her family to well. So, I don't really know their family story but, we became friends our senior year, and right before I went off to college, and that's all we really were—just friends."

"Well—if y'all was just friends—how did I get here, then?"

Danny smiles but recognizes that his son was dead serious.

"Well—big fella, you don't regret being here do you?"

"No—I'm not exactly saying that," Mark replied.

"Okay—just checking," he said, as he pauses to ponder his response, as Mark braced himself awaiting his answer.

And Danny generally said in no particular order these words: "Sex outside of marriage is sin, son.... And its not God's best plan when it comes to having children. There are just so many obstacles to overcome when parents are in separate homes, seeing different things, and some cases operating by different beliefs.... *A house divided against itself will fall....* And unfortunately, such has been the case for your mother and me.... You were indeed born out of an act of sin, but you *are not* sin itself, son.... *You are fearfully and wonderfully made*, a gift from God, according to scripture, despite the sin that brought you in.... God doesn't mix the child with the mess.... *God is a good God, faithful and willing to forgive if we confess our failures, and cleanse us from all the mess we often find ourselves in....* I believe I'm walking in that forgiveness, but it appears that perhaps your mom is not.... And the one thing that might be bothering her, still, is the way I responded when she informed me that *her son was my son.* Which is also probably when she began to shoot me down as this deadbeat dad before I ever had a chance to be your father."

"How did you respond?" I asked, cautiously.

"Not knowing if any of it was really true, I was slow to pursue her claim until I knew more about you, her and this guy Mayberry. After all, you carried the name of another man, whom had been your father from the start. And at that time, a lot was going on with me; the NFL draft was just months away, and it appeared that I might make a lil money. So, I honestly thought her motives were wrapped around her trying to cash in on my accomplishments. You read about these kind of stories, but never do think it could really happen to you. Plus, I was about to get married, so, there was a lot of things that made me question her claim. But, I believe she thought I was just flipping her off."

"Were you?" I asked.

"Well, in some ways, yes—I was a lil upset about it. But it wasn't because I was trying to simply ignore her claim, hoping it would just go away, but for all the reasons I just mentioned. I don't believe your mom took into account of how suspicious her timing was, or the readjustment I would have had to make to be a father to a kid I didn't even know existed. So, since I didn't just drop everything and rush back into Pine Bluff to play father to her child, especially the way she had this thing set up with Mayberry, she took it personal," he said, as he pulled up to the Rainforest Cafe. "So, after the gunshot incident took place, I then decided to come to town and see if I could talk her into allowing you to take part in a paternity test, knowing that Mayberry had legal rights to say no, which is when we met up at JRC.... And after the test results came back positive, the damage to your Dad's character had already been done.... Your Mom and perhaps her family had already beaten me down around that small town."

"But that's wrong, Daddy!"

"Well, yes, son—it is.... But forgiveness is necessary if we want to live life free from anger and resentment, son," he humbly said with concern.

"Man, this is crazy, its just not right daddy."

"She made a mistake, son. Let's try to love her through it, not beat her up about it."

"And you sure there's nothin else she's not telling me about this whole situation?"

"Nothing that I'm aware of, son. And if there is, if I can ever get her to sit down and chat with us, together, we'll just ask her that very question, cool? My Dad said, reassuringly. "But, in the meantime, don't be so hard on your mother.... We all make a few mistakes in life, son.... And yes, she still seems to have an issue, but at the end of the day, Mark, your mother loves you. So, lets give her chance to make this right."

I just shook my head in disbelief, not wanting to truly believe my own mother could be so unfair toward someone that seemed to be more than fair to her, making this family warfare, not only trifling, but insanely, senseless.

15

The Jealousy

A few days later, on Sunday, I was supposed to fly back to Little Rock, but there was one more event on the list of things to do before I was to head back. Yes, he hooked me up with a seat right behind the Cowboys bench at the 40-yard line accompanied with a sideline pass. The pass read, in bold print, **Game 10, November 6, 1995, Dallas versus Philadelphia, Texas Stadium**.

As I watched these Pro-Bowl and Hall of Fame players play this game Americans enjoy so much, I finally felt alive. Maybe perhaps it was the talk we had over the past few days, which allowed me to get a lot of things off my chest and some answers to a few questions I desperately needed his input on, but this moment felt good. And what made it even more enjoyable was the attention my father expressed toward me.

Despite this big-big world he lived in, full of excitement and anticipation, I never felt neglected, which flies in the face of all the things my family keeps saying about him. And yeah, it was kind of cool to watch the Cowboys practice and meet a few of these incredible people behind the scenes. But, at this moment, it was my Dad I suddenly found to be the most fascinating person of them all. He was the center of attraction in my world of both the good and the bad. I was now starting to decipher the truth about this man, which began changing this distorted perception my family had instilled in me.

As the final gun sounded—and the Cowboys had manhandled the Eagles 34-12—I started doing what every other Cowboys fan in the stadium did—talk Super Bowl! It was apparent that this team could end up winning their third Championship in four years. So, as my Dad lifted me up over the wall and onto the field for a trip to the postgame locker room and press conferences, I decided to ask the sixty-four dollar question, as we entered the tunnel: "if Dallas makes it to the Super Bowl, can I go too?"

He smiled, as if I read his mind, and said, "Yes—it was always the plan, the game is on your birthday weekend, January 28th - 29th, so, yes, we're going to the Super Bowl!"

I remember thinking, *Wow, I really should move to Texas.*

Later that night, after a post-game dinner with Coach Switzer in the West End of downtown Dallas, Danny was on Hwy 114 headed home. He calls Mark to see if he made it home safely. And he could immediately tell in his voice that all the joy he left Dallas with, was now gone. He couldn't really talk openly, his mom was sitting near by, for they had just had a not-so-comfortable discussion about his trip to Dallas.

Danny figured this was as good a time as any to talk to Denise about a number of things, including the Super Bowl trip he had planned for Mark.

"What's going on with Mark, Dee?" Danny asked.

"Nothing that I'm aware of—Mark is fine," Dee shot back.

"Mark is fine?" Danny said sarcastically, repeating her answer.

"Yeah, as far as I know.... Why, what's up?" She too asked, sarcastically

"Dee, every time I try to talk to you about our son, you seem to be reluctant to talk. You either always busy or nonchalantly brush it off with this lame laissez-faire type of attitude—what's up with that?"

"I don't have a problem discussing Mark, Danny, but there's nothing to really talk about," Dee replied, with a note of finality in her voice. "But if you'll call me at work tomorrow, we can chat then."

"At work—why not now?" Danny asked.

"Now is not a good time for me," she replied.

"Dee—if you don't stop this foolishness, while you have time, you will regret this later.... He won't always be thirteen-fourteen years old, Ms. Terry.... One day he'll grow up and you'll have ***a ton*** of questions to answer. So, I'm warning you now, don't risk losing your son, Denise, trying to cover up the past.... This nonsense won't be funny down the road—*God is not mocked; whatever a man sow that he shall also reap*."

"Boy, please, Mark ain't going nowhere, but I gotta go—I'll talk to you tomorrow, at work, if you want to finish this discussion," she replied and hung up.

Danny, now sitting in his driveway, began seriously thinking about how to get his son out of that environment and unfortunately away from his own mother.

The next day, I was having lunch with my friend, Tanisha, at one of the school's picnic tables, filling her in on all that happened during my trip to Dallas.... the complex, the players, coaches, the practices, and the game—the whole nine yards. Compliments of my dad, who nobody in my family likes, I added. But while we were talking, three of my own football teammates walked up and decided to intrude.

"Yo, Mark, what's up, we heard you went to the Cowboys game this weekend, playa!"

"Yeah, as a matter of fact, I did," I replied.

Another teammate asked, "How you get tickets?"

"His dad works for the Cowboys!" Tanisha shot back.

Almost in one voice, the three of them waved her off, and said, "The Cowboys—Yo dad don't work for the Cowboys!"

I smiled and said, "Yeah, he does."

Still not buying it, one of them shouted, "Well, prove it then!"

I went into my book bag and pulled out an article from the Arkansas Democrat Gazette, held it up, and said, "This is my dad—Dallas Cowboys headliner."

They each stepped closer to view the article for as long as it took to determine whom the article was about, and then one of them said sarcastically, "That ain't your dad!"

Mark, sensing a little hostility, decided not to respond.

"If that's your Dad, why is his name Bradley, Mayberry?" One said, as they begin to laugh, thinking they had caught me lying.

My frustrations of having to explain this complicated and complex situation slightly embarrassed me. No one understood how confusing my circumstances were more than me, so I decided to retreat, "Aright, okay, he's not my dad, then."

Tanisha, who have always had my back, looked at the three of them with contempt, took me by the arm, and said, "Come on Mark, they're just jealous. Don't let them get next to you."

As we walked away, I said, "We'll see who gets the last laugh after I come back from the Super Bowl with pictures of me and Prime Time, playa's!"

"Yeah right!" The three of them shouted, giving each other hi-fives.

Tanisha then says, as we headed back towards our next class, "Is your dad really gonna take you to the Super Bowl?

"Yeah—if they make it. He's taking me for my birthday." I replied.

"For real! That's awesome! I wanna go too!" She excitedly said, as the bell rings.

"I'll check and let you know what he says," as we go in separate directions to class.

A couple of months later, Tanisha and I were in one the few classes we had together, passing notes back and forth, discussing the upcoming Super Bowl and my jealous teammates who are waiting to bust my chops, if I don't come back with Super Bowl pics. And the bell sounded, just as Tanisha was handing me her last note, the teacher's voice carried over those of her twenty-five rowdy and often obnoxious students, "Mark Mayberry, not so fast Mister Man! Have a seat, sir, we need to talk!"

It was as if I had a communicable disorder. As soon as my classmates heard her call my name, they were like a stampede of cattle getting out of there! I then sat back down at my desk, which was already near the front of the room, as she gives me that famous, *Don't play with me,* look of hers.

She approached me with her right hand extended, "Give me the note," while snapping her fingers as she spoke.

"What note?" I replied. That earned me another, *Boy, don't lie to me,* look.

So, I handed her the note, balled up in my fist, as she opened it and read it aloud: "It's Super Bowl time, that will shut those jealous chumps up."

My teacher lowered the note and asked, "Who are the jealous chumps, Mark?"

"Some of my teammates.... They don't believe I'm going to the Super Bowl."

Sitting down at the desk next to me, she asked, "Well, are you?"

"Yes ma'am, if the Cowboys win this weekend against the Packers," I replied.

"Really? And just who might be taking you to the Super Bowl?" She asked.

For the past few weeks, everyone that I told that Danny Bradley was my real father, responded with disbelief or had questions I couldn't really answer. And since I sensed that this was going to be another Q and A session I didn't have the answers too, I started to bail, but suddenly chose not too: "My father is taking me." I replied, with my head held high chin up.

"That's a very kind gesture of your father, but you know you're only setting yourself up for further confrontation if you're not being honest about this, Mark?"

"Yeah, but I'm not lying about it," I replied confidently.

Not quite ready to totally believe my story, she asked, "Who's your father?"

And I thought, *Oh well—here we go again*, before simply saying, "Danny."

Which causes her to pause, and curiously asked, "Danny who?"

"Danny Bradley," I replied, waiting for all the negative questions to begin.

But surprisingly, she shouts unexpectedly, "What?! Danny Bradley is your Daddy! Boy, I didn't know Danny is your Daddy! I've known Craig, JB, and Danny for years.... Get out of here! Danny help put Pine Bluff on the map—he and Monte Coleman! Good for you! It's a blessing to have a father that can do those kinds of things for his son."

I didn't know what to say accept, "Thank You."

"You have some big shoes to fill Mark Mayberry," as she gets up to break the session, but suddenly had a thought, knowing who his mother was, her smile dimmed a bit. She immediately rushed to her desk as I was preparing to exit. She reached for a folder while still pretending to be enthusiastically engaged, she says, "Mark, I'm looking at my *Student/Parent* information folder, and it states here that Reginald Mayberry is your father," as she places her hands on her hips, thinking she had me trapped too.

Man, I thought. *Here we go!*

"I'm listening," she said.

"Well—it's kind of confusing."

"Well, clear it up for me? She asked with agitation.

"Mayberry is my Mom's ex-boyfriend, who acted as my father the first several years of my life, until my Mom decided to make known who my real father was…. A blood test was taken and that's when I found out that Mayberry was not my father. But that's how I ended up with the name Mayberry," I cautiously replied.

Thankfully, she chose not to ask any more questions, because I didn't have any other way to explain it. She simply smiled and said, "I understand, but no more note passing in my class, Mark Bradley!"

And with comment, I was out the door with a smile at having escaped detention, and feeling better about being a Bradley in this town.

A few weeks later, it was January 14th, 1996, and the Cowboys were playing the Green Bay Packers in the NFC Championship game. My grandparents had a watch party at their house. Hey, Arkansas, once the Joneses took over Valley Ranch, became an even bigger Dallas Cowboys state from what I've been told.

So, as the clock began to wind down and ticked off the final seconds, with Dallas leading Green Bay 38-27, I started to get excited about the chance to see the Cowboys win their 3rd Super Bowl in four years! The gun goes off, and my family was celebrating and barking a bit at those who were against the Cowboys.

And just minutes after the game ended, the phone rang—it's my dad, Danny! I could hear all the hoopla in the background through the phone. But when it came to him, around my house, I felt I was always in enemy territory. So, I had to maintain my emotions a little, as my mom hands me the phone.

"How bout them Cowboys!" He said with enthusiasm.

"Wow! That was a good game," I replied nonchalantly, looking over my shoulder.

"Did you see your boy, Keith Jackson?" Danny asked.

"Yeah, I didn't know he played for the Packers, I thought he was still with the Eagles—I know he feels bad right about now," I replied.

"I'm sure, but, hey, it looks like you're headed to the Super Bowl!"

"You serious!" I said with a soft burst of enthusiasm, too, as my mom hovers over me, paying close attention to my every word.

"Yes sir, I'll be in touch soon—I gotta get going, we're about to do our mid-field post game prayer," he said, "Tell your Mom I'll be calling her next week about your trip!"

We hang up and as soon as I placed the phone on the hook, she asked, "What are you all excited about?"

"He said he'll call you next week, he's taking me to the Super Bowl for my birthday."

"The Super Bowl?" She asked suspiciously.

"Yeah, he promised me a while back that if the Cowboys made it, he would take me with him as his guest," I replied, trying to hold in the excitement.

But the look on her face told me what her answer was going to be before he even had a chance to ask. "Mom!" I said with concern.

"I'll have to think about that," she replied.

"Mom—you gotta let me go to the Super Bowl!"

"I said I'll think about it, Mark," she shot back with a slight attitude.

Suddenly, all the excitement about going to the Super Bowl was sucked out of me, like the air out of a popped balloon.... I could feel the tears forming so strong, I just stormed out of the house, slightly slammed the door behind me. Seconds later, she rushed out to scold me for slamming the door, as she then slammed it behind her.

More hurt and angry than I've ever been, I shouted, "This is crazy!"

Dry eyed still, but angry, I started towards Tanisha's to vent my frustrations, but she was already headed to see me. And since she had no idea what she was walking into, her first words on arrival were, "Looks like we're going to the Super Bowl!"

But it only took a few seconds for her to know something was wrong.

"What? What's going on, Mark? What happened?" She asked deflated.

"I got to get away from this family!" I shouted.

"Why, what happened this time?!" She asked.

"She's not gonna let me go!"

'T' looked at me in complete disbelief, "Why?!"

"I don't know, Tanisha!" I replied as tears begins to flow.

"Why?! Your dad is trying to do something nice for you!"

"All she wants is money from him—it's the only reason she even told him about me!"

With a look of genuine shock on her face, 'T' replied, "Are you serious?!"

"If Mayberry was making an offer like this, or any offer, she wouldn't hesitate to let me go. And he doesn't nearly do as much or even in a position to do as much as my real dad does! But every time I need anything, she always says, *'Call your Daddy Danny—Call your Daddy Danny.'*"

"Wow!" Tanisha replied surprised to hear how bad things really were.

"She never push me to call Mayberry—it's always, 'call your Daddy Danny,'" and I'm just sick of it! I'm tired of calling this man for everything if I can't even spend any time with the man!" I said, as my frustrations kick into high gear.

"Man, this is wrong! You got a crazy-crazy life, Mark! Why don't you get your grandparents to talk to her?" T asked.

"They won't do it.... She got them fooled too—they don't like him either."

"Wow—I knew it was bad, but I didn't know it was that bad," she replied.

After that comment, we just sat there in silence before she broke the calm and asked the same question I've been asking for a while, "What did your Dad Danny do?"

"I really don't know. She keeps claiming that he ran off to play football and really didn't want me.... And now she claims he's brainwash me to turn me against her."

"Well—is that true?" She asked.

"I heard her say out of her own mouth, T, that it wasn't true." I replied angrily.

"You did?!

"Yes! But she doesn't know I heard her say it, but I did."

"When was that?" Tanisha asked.

"A while back—I was about eight-nine years old then."

"Well, if you heard her say it's not true, why do you still seem confused about it?"

"I don't know—I guess I don't wanna believe my own mother could be that cruel."

"But if you heard her say its not true, Mark, then she is being cruel."

This was the first time I was willing to accept that my Mom could really possibly be the villain in all of this. And this was just heartbreaking folks. This is my mother!

"What are you going to do?" She asked with concern.

"I don't know.... There are times I just feel like running away from it all."

"Come on now, Mark. You can't be running away—we're headed to the Super Bowl!

Suddenly, I heard the door open behind us, it was my mom, Braylon and Cassie, coming out of the house, headed towards her car. I wipe my face quickly and pull down my shades to cover my eyes. "Hi Tanisha," she says. "And Mark, go put your jacket on and be home by 7:30!"

Well, it was already after 7 p.m., so that ended our lil chat session.

Two days later, I'm doing homework in my room, still anxiously waiting for my dad to call her about the Super Bowl. Every time the phone rings, I'd be the first to answer it, hoping it was him. I, then, decided to call my grandma Shelly to see if she could get a message to my Dad, but got their answering machine.

Then my Mom enters my room and tells me to turn off the light, it was time to go to bed. She can tell I had been crying again, but really didn't have much sympathy.

"What's wrong now, Mark?"

"Have you talked to my Dad?" I asked.

"Who, Mayberry?" She asked with a little sarcasm in her voice.

"No, Mama," I replied. "Danny!"

"No, I haven't—why?"

"Are you gonna let me go or not?"

"Go where, Mark?

"To the Super Bowl, Mom!"

She pauses and then said, "No.... You're not going to the Super Bowl."

"But why?!" I asked.

"Because I said so!" She fired back.

"But Mama!"

"Mark, don't start with me! I said no!"

"Mom!"

"Mark, first of all, I haven't heard from Mister Bradley. And second of all, **If I can't go—you can't go!"** She said, as she exited the room.

I'm thinking, *What?!* Did she just say, *if she can't go—I can't go?!*

Suddenly, the phone rings, snapping me out of this suffocating trance. She reenters my room, tosses me the phone, and said, "It's your Daddy Danny," as she stood in the door with arms folded, glaring at me. And as usual, he noticed right off that all was not well. "What's up, son? Tell me what's going on this time?"

"She's not gonna let me go," I said with great disappointment.

"What do you mean she's not going to let you go?"

Suddenly, Dee, after hearing those words exited the room.

"She said **if she can't go—I can't go."**

"Are you serious?!" Danny replied in amazement.

"Yep, that's what she said," I replied. **"If she can't go—I can't go."**

"Let me talk to your mother, Mark!"

I walked over to her room, held out the receiver and said, "He wants to talk to you."

Shaking her head, no, emphatically, she said, "Tell him to call me at work tomorrow," as she gets up and heads to the bathroom and slightly closed the door.

"Did you hear her?" I asked.

"Put her on the phone, now, Mark!"

Suddenly, I heard the shower heads come on.

"She just got into the shower," I replied.

Danny pauses and gathers his thoughts, and said, "Hang tough, son—don't give up yet. I'll call her first thing in the morning and get this thing work out, cool?"

"She's not going to let me go, Daddy." I reconfirmed.

"Well, I say you can go, son." Danny replied sternly.

"Dad, I'm telling you, she's not going to let me go, if she can't go."

"Well, son, you can take this to the bank, she's not going. I'll be in touch."

We hang up, and as promised, the next morning, Denise is in her office reviewing some case files. She's a productive probation officer, one that carries a gun on her hip, by the way. One might ask, *why would anybody want to agitate a woman, regarding her child, with a gun on her hip?*

The phone rings—its my Dad Danny.

"Ms. Terry, it's his birthday, why can't my son go to the Super Bowl with his father?'

"I didn't tell him he couldn't go, I told him I'll think about it," she replied.

"Denise, it would be a great experience for him. It's only one of the biggest events in the entire world, Dee!"

"Danny, I told him I'll think about it."

"He said you told him he couldn't go?"

"I told him, I'll think about it.... Plus, Mark's grades aren't stable enough for me to allow him to go to an event like that."

"His grades?! Dee come on.... I've seen his report card, too, and I didn't see any thing that indicated he was close to failing, Dee!"

"He can do better." Dee shot back.

"Of course he can, and it would be nice if we all did better by each other."

"Danny, I am not trying to prevent you and Mark from spending time together."

"Well, looking at our history, I find that impossible to believe, Denise Terry.... Every fourteen year old kid in America would love to go to the Super Bowl with his father!"

"I understand, but unfortunately, I just had a client walk in. When are you coming back this way," Dee asked hurriedly.

"Maybe tonight if you don't stop all this craziness," Danny replied.

"Good, then we can chat about it then. I gotta go—bye-bye."

She hangs up on him—boom!

Danny sat back in his chair, livid. Woodson walks in, having made arrangements to talk with him about a marketing deal, sees the stress and asks, "You aright?"

"I've been better." Danny disappointedly replied.

Woodson was one of Danny's closest friends on the team and was aware of some of the issues he was dealing with regarding Mark. Danny didn't confide much, he kept this situation close to the vest.

"Ole girl still giving you a tough time about your son?"

"Yeah, she got this thing twisted up pretty bad Woody. He wants to go to the Super Bowl and she won't let him!"

"You serious! Why? That's your son, DB!" Woody said.

"She told him, **if she can't go—he can't go."**

"Come on man.... What the hell did you do to this woman?"

"I don't know, Woody, I don't know what's really going on with her," Danny replied.

"Its that bad?!"

"Unfortunately, it appears that it is."

"Can you get him out?" Woody asked.

"I'm working on it, but it's much easier said than done. There's a lot of factors involved in making that happen."

"Well—it sounds like Mark needs you more than ever," Woody said, as he then began rescheduling his appointment with his Director of Player Programs, in an effort to give this friend and father a chance to deal with an urgent domestic issue.

And while Woody's words of encouragement sunk in, Danny abruptly decides to book another flight to Little Rock, to see if he could corner his son's *beloved* mother about these deliberate, conscientious, and calculated decisions that she has continued to make to keep him separated from his son. But would it be in enough time to make good on his promise of taking him to Super Bowl XXX, or will this much needed get-together have to wait until after?

16

The Blockade

BOOM! It's Monday, January 29th, my fourteenth birthday. A day for which I was suppose to be celebrating with my dad in Phoenix, Arizona, after the Cowboys beat the Pittsburgh Steelers 27-17, but sadly, I was stuck in Pine Bluff, experiencing the lowest day of my life. It wasn't just not going to the game, but all of the craziness that lead up to the reasons why I wasn't allowed to go to the game.

However, it was lunchtime at Jack Robey Junior High, and Tanisha was trying to help me cope as we take our seats to eat in the school's cafeteria. She tried to cheer me up by giving me a birthday card that she personally crafted. And just as I was about to thank her, those same three clowns that had given me a hard time about my dad and the Super Bowl, came up behind us.

One said, "M&M, yo homeboys wanna to know, did you go to the Super Bowl?"

I tried to ignore them and continue eating, while pretending to be viewing my B-day card. But then another one barked, "Show us them pictures of Prime Time."

"Mark, don't pay them any attention.... Let it go." Tanisha says.

But then, the third guy spoke, "We called your house yesterday, you were in Pine Bluff—not Phoenix," as they make mockery out of it.

I dropped my fork and closed my eyes, trying to let it go, as they laughed mockingly at their jokes towards me. But like a volcano, I suddenly opened my eyes, as if in slow motion, I could now only read what 'T' was saying, "Don't stoop to their level, Mark," followed by my mom's voice saying repeatedly, ***if I can't go—you can't go!***

The next thing I knew I was up out of my chair ready to throw, as one of the school's administrators jumped in between us. At which such point, I was forced to leave the scene, as 'T' angrily trails me.

Once outside, I dropped my book bag and slammed an open hand against the wall and begin to shout angrily, "I can't believe she did this to me—it's not fair! All I wanted to do is go to a freaking football game with my Dad—with-my-freaking-Dad! I'm tired of this mess! I gotta get out of this town!"

Tanisha didn't know what to do or say, she then dropped her book bag and put both hands over her face to hide her own tears, and asked, "But what about me?"

I look her right square in the eye, and said, "What about you! I hate my life!"

She then picked up her book bag and rushed off as I paced back and forth.

And for the next several months, I shut completely down. I was mad at everybody, my mom, my grandparents, my step-dad, Mayberry, and even the family dog—Roxanne. I was hot! I felt like everybody had let me down, including my Dad Danny!

He should have forced her to let me go! Fight her if you had too—and everybody else in the house for that matter! Demand she let me go, I thought to myself.

As a consequence, I withdraw from everybody. A decision that would make it even harder on my Dad Danny, whom was already on the oust, but I did not care—he was now on my not-talk-to list, too. And, as you may have guessed, I didn't get any arguments from my mother. This helped her continue to promote her agenda against this man, making it nearly impossible for him to reach out to me.

And by the summer of 1996, I had calm down. I missed my father but my family made it to difficult to have a relationship with him. But after being forced to go to Alabama to visit Mayberry, again, knowing this man wasn't my father-father, I decided I wasn't taking it anymore. As I sat in my window seat on a flight, I thought about all the lying and manipulation and backbiting going on within my family regarding my Dad Danny, I knew it was time for me to step up and step out.

I loved my mother, but what she was doing was just unfair. I was done lying for her and protecting them, the family. There was just way too much drama going on regarding all these doggone daddies! Hell, at this point, I didn't want a daddy, nor could I ever see the day I would want to be a daddy! I didn't want to be Danny, Mayberry or Braylon. I really didn't know who to really believe or trust anymore. And the one who appeared to know best was the one they kept claiming initiated all this mess.

There seemed to be so much *envy* and *jealousy* among my family members towards this man, you could truly cut it with a knife! And to make their behavior so amazingly bizarre, they would act as if I was both *deaf* and *dumb.* They spoke negatively about my Dad Danny freely and often as if daring me to challenge them.

I would often think, *Where is God in all this chaos? These were church-going people, listening to the bible being preached every Sunday morning, but, yet, when we exited the doors of these church, we lived life as if God didn't exist in heaven or on earth.*

And since my father wasn't around to defend himself, they said whatever they wanted whenever they wanted to say about him. And with Mayberry, I never did quite understand his position on things. He just wouldn't question anything or didn't seem to want to really know anything. And I kind of felt kind of bad for him. He was a nice man; raised by a good family; he worked in the church; and a believer. But after he discovered that I was indeed not his son, his follow up makes you wonder what is really going on with him. What could he possibly be thinking. He just wasn't inquisitive enough to even know how to proceed with me in his new role, as daddy Mayberry.

You would think that most men after about four-five days, who find out that the son they've been raising is not theirs, would go absolutely ballistic, let alone four-five years, regardless of race, creed, or color! Its been now fourteen-fifteen years, and he still hasn't said a word to me about nothing. At least inquire beyond the facts you once trusted, my brother, to ensure that the news you're now hearing is not worse than the first fabricated story you've were told. This is crazy! He treated this ordeal as if nothing ever happened. The question is, was it because he really didn't care or did he, too, have an unknown agenda? The problem is, neither one is good. What if he was the other man, fighting a whole family just to talk, at times, to his son?

Anyway, at any rate, I'm done. If he don't care, then why should I care. He sees the injustice going on here, but he's not saying anything, either. And if his excuse is, he never knew the truth, after tossing my bag into the back seat of his car, this would be the day he'd learn the unadulterated truth.

A few hours later, as we were finishing dinner, Mayberry's wife, Dana, a really-really nice lady, started clearing the table and had instructed her two kids to go take their showers get to bed. Yep—Mayberry is now married with children.

"Mark, your room is ready," she said. "Towels and toiletries are in the same location."

I got up and head toward the guest bedroom without really saying, okay. I was zoned in on that conversation. And as expected, Mayberry follows me to the bedroom. And as soon as I entered the room, he asks, "What's going on? You've been very quiet, withdrawn and kind of standoffish—what's up?"

I thought to myself, *just tell it like it really is, Mark.* "Well—I'm just starting to get uncomfortable with this situation," I replied.

He looked surprised by my answer and asked, "What situation, son?"

"The situation with me, you and my mom."

Looking even more perplexed and curious, he asked, "What's the problem?"

"I'm just tired of being in between all the fuss?"

"What fuss, Mark? He asked.

"All the stuff going on with me, you and my dad Danny—and I'm tired of lying to you, protecting them and lying to him."

"Lying about what?" He asked, as he appear to brace himself for this conversation.

"Well, she got me telling you one thing and my Dad Danny another thing."

Mayberry then takes a seat on the edge of the bed, and by the look on his face, he appeared to be unsure if he was ready to hear what I was about to say.

"Okay," he said cautiously. "Go ahead."

"Its mainly about my relationship with my Dad Danny."

"What is your relationship with Danny?"

"Good," I said.

"Really?

"Yeah," I replied.

"Your Mom says he's been disinterested for years—is that not true?"

"No—it's not true. He's been doing things for me since I was about seven-eight."

"So, okay, he does participate?" He asked.

"Put it like this," I replied, "He does as much, if not more for me, than anybody."

I know my words might have stung him a bit, but I was tired of being the human tennis ball, volleyed back and forth between Alabama, Arkansas, and Texas.

"I didn't know that," he then replied. "But I understand if you're now uncomfortable with our relationship. I certainly don't want you lying to me, protecting them or lying to him. So, why don't we get you back home in the next day or so—cool?"

"That's fine with me," I replied nervously, as he gets up and exits the room.

And just as he did, I suddenly exhaled. *Wow,* I said to myself, as I took a deep breath. I felt close to hyperventilating. But as promised, a couple of days later, I was on a plane back to Little Rock. On arrival, it was my granddad that picked me up, not my Mom, which gave some hope that all was least half-way well. But the ride home threw me for a loop. Granddad Odell didn't have very much of anything to say, which always meant I was on my own. And sure enough, when he dropped me off at her place, instead of taking me home with him, I knew the lynching was about to begin. And the minute I walked in the door, she lit into me.

"Who do you think you are tellin Mayberry I've been lying to him?!"

"What do you mean?" I asked, backing away from her as I spoke.

"You know exactly what the hell I mean, Mark!" Her voice rising with every syllable.

"He asked me about my relationship with my Dad Danny and I told him," I replied.

Looking as if she wanted to hit me square in the mouth, she said through clenched teeth, "What did you say to your Daddy Mayberry, Mark Anthony?!"

I knew she wasn't going to like my answer, but I had to say it.

"Answer me! She screams.

"That he does spend time and money on me!" I humbly replied.

With her arms waving in front of my face she shouts, “How do you know what the hell Danny do or don’t do, Mark?”

Treating me, again, as if deaf, dumb and clueless, I just flopped on the sofa, defeated.

“You were suppose to stay with your Daddy Mayberry for at least a month!”

“I was uncomfortable, Mama,” I replied. “I told you I didn’t want to go.”

“No,” she shouted back, “You rather take your butt to Texas so Danny can continue brainwashing you. But I make the damn decisions around here Mark Anthony! Do you understand me?!

I knew I was in a lose-lose situation, so I chose not to say anything.

“Do you understand me! She repeated.... Answer me!” She yelled.

Yes,” I said softly.

“Until you start paying bills around here, what I say goes! Do you understand me?!”

“Yes, Mom!” I shouted back.

“Are you raising your voice at me?! She asked angrily. “Danny, don’t run this house, Denise does! Am I making myself clear?!”

“Yes,” I responded, as the tears begin to rush out, as she storms out of the room and then quickly reenters with her purse and keys in hand, and said, “Grab your bag, and stop all that damn crying! I’m taking you to Daddy Odell’s house! And from now on, stay the hell out of grown folks’ business, Mark! You way too young to understand all that has gone on with Daddy Danny!”

I got up, grabbed my duffle bag, which was still packed and step through the door she holding open, expecting her to perhaps swing on me at any moment.

“And I heard Mister Bradley might be in town,” she continued. “And I wish I would catch you over at Shelly’s house without my permission! You are grounded until I say otherwise! No phone, TV, video games, playgrounds—nothing! Now let’s go!”

As soon as we got to my grandparent’s house, my mom walked through the door, laying down the complete law. “Daddy, don’t let Mark leave this house to do nothing, and with nobody, including family! And I think Danny is in town wanting to take Mark back to Texas for the summer! It ain’t happening! In fact, I’m thinking about sending Mark back to Alabama! So if anybody from the Bradley’s household called, tell them Mark is out of town!”

“This is why you should have never gotten Danny involved in this, Dee.”

“I know it,” she replied. “But I gotta get back to work. I’ll call you and let you know when Mark might be *going back* to Alabama!”

The minute she walked out the door the tears rushed out again. Odell walked over to the couch, sits down and said, "It's gonna be alright, son. We'll get through this together, as a family."

On the other side of town, my Dad Danny was indeed on the scene, but left after not being able to get through to me. And as predicted, grandma Shelly called and as promised, they told her I was out of town. I didn't want to be grounded any longer than I had to so I abided by their rules and regulations.

I thought I was ready to fight this animal but I discovered on this day, that this was an elephant of a challenge to tangle with. It was simply much tougher than I could have ever imagined. However, I knew this was wrong, and my Mom knew I knew that this was wrong, but she was determined to do this her way even though she saw all the signs that said—*wrong way!*

She just kept right on driving the character of my father into the ground by continuing to mislead the family and contaminating my mind. And a part of me was *completely convinced* my granddad knew that what my mother was doing was *completely wrong.* But, he, too, seemed to be fighting to cover up this family lie, which meant they couldn't afford to let this tale about Danny's character—die.

This was not just my Mom's tall tale anymore. It had become the family's fictitious story. And by the end of the summer, they had finally managed to *completely break me.* And their method of consolation now that I have conceded, was a three weeks stay with my new AAU basketball team to Orlando, Florida.

Later that week, I was in my room doing homework, my Mom entered wanting to chat about school and my new teachers. We really hadn't talked much since the summer grounding. But she had become unusually nice, especially since she felt my Dad Danny was no longer a threat.

I told her things were cool, cool, and cool with school. But she insisted I tell her more about my new teachers. And I went on to share my concerns about my history instructor Mister Norful, Smokie Norful. Nothing major, but I informed her that it appeared to be a class that may be hard to pass. And then she suddenly changed the subject in mid-sentence, which clearly validated why she really want to chat.

"Have you talked to your Daddy Danny lately?" She asked.

Disappointed that she would even ask, I said, "You told me not to talk to the man, or anybody else in the his family, mom.... So, no, I haven't."

"Well it's time for some school clothes, son, so call him."

"Mom, I haven't returned any of his calls since April or May."

But this undeterred mother pressed the issue.

"You need school clothes, Mark, so call him."

"Come on Mom—I got enough stuff!"

"Call him Mark," she said, in an elevated tone, as she gets up to exit the room.

I'm thinking, *You gotta be kidding me! Haven't we dumped on this man enough!*

"Why can't I just wear what I got, mom? Or, why can't you get me a few things?"

"Your step-dad and I can't afford that expensive stuff your daddy buys you, son! So if you want to keep wearing those things, I suggest you call him."

"But I don't have to have all that expensive Polo stuff, mama!"

"Mark, call your daddy, end of discussion—now! You know the drill, call Shelly and have her contact Danny," she said and exits.

Minutes later, the phone rings. Guess who? It's grandma Shelly. And before mom hands me the phone, she whispers, "Money and school clothes.... And remember, you went to Ohio this past summer to visit a relative."

Then she tossed me the phone.

I spent the next few several minutes trying to explain my whereabouts with my distant, but, yet, live-around-the-corner, grandmother. Apparently I didn't sound convincing enough, because she interrupted me in mid-sentence, and said, "Come on Mark, you're a big boy now.... You know how to pick up the phone and call us.... Your Daddy has been trying to reach out to you for about five plus months now."

My Mom couldn't really hear what grandma Shelly was saying, but I knew she would be trying to anticipate it based on my responses. So, I didn't say much in return.

"The past is the past," Shelly went on to say. "There's only so much your father can do to develop a relationship with you, Mark.... This craziness has gone on way too long.... You're not giving him a chance—you gotta do a better job of staying in touch."

"Yes ma'am," I humbly replied.

"I have money here right now, sent by your Daddy—money for school clothes and even a lil pocket change to be given to you each week, but we can't catch up with you."

Yes, I thought to myself! *I didn't really have to call him—he's already done it.*

"And he instructed me to give this money directly to you—not your mom, a request he said was made by you a while back.... Is that truth?" She asked.

"Yes ma'am," I replied, feeling relieved I didn't have to make this call.

"Okay, so, when are you coming to see me?"

"I can come by tomorrow."

"Okay, Mark, it's time you take some responsibility, son."

"Yes Ma'am," I replied.

As soon as we hang up, my Mom pounced on me with questions. When I told her what grandma Shelly said about already having the money for school clothes to be given directly to me, that didn't go over well. And I kind of left my Dad hanging a bit here, because it was indeed 'I' who requested that he not give money meant for me directly to her.

"Directly to you?! She asked. "And why did he send money again through Shelly—she ain't your damn mama!" She shouted. "Your daddy is a trip—what else she say?"

"That I need to stay in touch," I said sheepishly, knowing that could tick her off more.

"For what?! So they can continue to brainwash you?! I'll have daddy to take you over there tomorrow, and you just get the money and get out of there, Mark!"

I purposely left out mentioning the other monies that were earmarked for pocket change. I was just glad I didn't have to call him once again to ask for money. We had all been pretty cruel and disrespectful to this man and it would have been *extremely embarrassing* to have to make that money call again.

Nonetheless, it was this kind of behavior exhibited by my father that represented the kind of character that my mom just didn't like. Despite it all, he just kept finding ways to rise above their slanderous attacks and innuendoes to be there for his son—regardless. Now I wasn't aware of this at the time, but this is what I believe the good Lord would call—unconditional love.

So, after picking up the dollars for school clothes and finally getting a chance to talk to my father, I was ready to make another decision that would shake up my entire family. I had decided, by the end of the fall semester, I'd take my father up on a long-standing extended offer and move to Texas!

17

The Manipulation

By Thanksgiving Day, I still hadn't found a particular time, manner or way to tell my mother I wanted out. So, as she was folding clothes and discussing my plans for Christmas, which did not include a trip to Dallas, I figured that now was better than any to share my intentions. And yes, given the timing of this request, it caught her off-guard, since she felt she had this situation, at this point, under complete control. So I took a deep breath and let it rip.

"Mom, I think wanna go live with my Dad."

"Which Dad," she asked sarcastically.

"My Dad Danny, Mom," I calmly replied.

"Boy please," she replied, disinterestedly.

"Mom, I'm serious—I wanna move to Texas to go live with my Dad," I replied again.

"Mark, let it go, son. I'm not having this conversation with you again."

"Mom!"

"Mark, I said no! You're not moving to Texas!

"I've already told him, yes, Mom!"

Mark! No! She shot back.

Not wanting to take no for an answer this time, knowing she would run from this conversation with my Dad, I decided to just tell her what my plans were this time around: "Mom, I'm moving to Texas to go stay with my Dad."

She then paused, looked over at me as in deep thought, as tears began to fall from her eyes. And I wasn't quite sure of what to do or how to react to this response. I had never really seen her cry before. As the tears got heavier and heavier, she then grabs her chest, fell to her knees, and screamed, "Lord don't let him take my baby away from me! Please Lord! He didn't even want my son! And now he's trying to take him away from me! Please Lord, don't let him do this to me! All I did was try to make this right! Please don't let him take my baby!

I, then, rush over in tears also, to help her up, "I'm sorry Mom.... Its okay."

"Don't touch me! "I'm tired of trying to please everybody!" She cried out in pain.

After she was planted, I exited the room, grabbed the cordless phone and escaped to my room to call grandma Shelly to see if she could get my Dad Danny to call me right away—its an emergency. I then hear her yell, "You gon be the death of me!"

Then my step-dad enters the house, and I could hear them discussing the matter in their bedroom. Suddenly, he was at my door, looking for answers too, which I was unwilling to give—to him. He and I had never developed a close relationship, so this had to be an even more uncomfortable conversation for him.

"Mark, you know what moving to Texas would do to your mother, after all she's been through with Danny? This will kill her, Mark!

I didn't respond. But he went on, "Your mother loves you! She's only trying to do what's best for you…and I assure you moving to Texas isn't one of them," he said, as he exited the room. I wanted to say, *I might be ignorant but I am not stupid, Braylon Terry. Moving to Texas is perhaps the best move I could make at this point!*

The phone rings seconds later, but Braylon beats me to it and doggone it, it's my Dad. He tells my father I was busy and he would have me call him back. So I had to wait once again to share with him the goings on inside this chaotic compound in PB.

The next day, I was abruptly leaving class for lunch when Tee caught up with me, matching me stride for stride, and asked, "What's going on? Why are you rushing?"

"I'm trying to get out of this building before I say somethin that may get me expelled."

We had reached the double door exit, I pushed through one, she pushed the other.

"Why, what happened?" She asked.

"Ms. Smith giving me a hard time for accidently turning off the lights."

Tanisha chuckled a bit and replied, "Don't let her get to you—everybody has problems with her.... She's just mean and controlling."

"I don't need any more controlling people in my life, got enough of that at home."

"Yeah—speaking of home, what happened last night, why were you whispering?"

Just thinking about it, made me mad all over again.

"I couldn't talk right then." I replied. "My mom was upset with me and I was waiting for my Dad to call."

'Tanisha' then asked, "What was she upset about this time?"

"It's a long story Tee."

Tee suddenly stops, and said, "Well—make it short for me, Mark."

I then stopped, paused, and replied, "I told her I wanted to move to Texas to live with my Dad, and she went off on me, falling out on the floor, crying, saying my Dad is trying to take me away from her and how I was going to be the death of her."

With a puzzled look on her face Tanisha said, "She said that?!"

"Yep.... And then my step-dad rushes me saying I was making a big mistake and this move to Texas would kill her.... Its just crazy."

"But he's your Dad, Mark!"

"She doesn't see it that way, Tanisha! Mayberry is my Dad, Danny is just my long lost disinterested father who's trying to brainwashing me; to turn me against them."

"That's what she said?"

"That's what the whole family is practically saying: *'Danny might be your father, but Mayberry is your Dad.... All he's doing is brainwashing you, Mark.'*"

"Wow, Mark, I agree, it's time you get out that house. It appears that your long lost disinterested father might be the only one who seems to be making any sense here."

"Yeah, right." I sarcastically replied.

"What's that suppose to mean?" She asked surprisingly.

"Maybe they're right—maybe he doesn't want me—maybe he is brainwashing me!"

"Brainwashing you! How?! I don't get it, Mark! When did he stop wanting you?!"

"If he wanted me, Tee, he would've already come got me out of this mess!"

"Mark, he can't do it if you won't stand up to her,"Tee calmly replied.

That comment threw me back a bit, to which I said, "I gotta go."

A week had gone by, during which Danny placed calls to Dee's house, her job and her parent's—and not one of his calls were returned. About fifteen days had now passed, but there was still no response from Denise or Mark again. So he decided in this last message, he was going to be direct and straight to the point, but surprisingly Denise decides to take his call—at work.

"Ms. Terry—Danny."

"Hey," she said, as if they talk all the time and were on good cordial terms.

Danny pauses in disbelief as to how she could be so cold, cool and controlling.

He asked, "Is there any reason why I can't get a return phone call back from you and Mark? I have called you every other day for about ten straight days. What's up?"

"Sorry, I've been busy with work. I'm not sure why Mark hasn't called you back."

"Denise, the nations president ain't that busy," Danny replied. "This craziness has been going on for fifteen years, Dee. Mark wants to move to Texas, and we need to discuss this, along with a host of other things, Denise."

"Danny, I understand your concerns, but I'm not avoiding you. Yes, we do need to talk about a lot of things going on with Mark, but unfortunately, it won't be today. And I just had a client walk in, I'll try calling you later," Dee said, and politely hung up.

Danny, in disgust decides "the hell" with phone calls. He prepares to make another trip to Pine Bluff to get to the bottom of this never-ending communication problem, with his mind focused on how he, himself, could become Denise's next client.

A couple of evenings later, Shelly, surprised, greeted her son and Salena with hugs and kisses after they enter the family's driveway. They were just in time for dinner, and Shelly was curious about this latest trip, and asked as much, as they made themselves comfortable at the kitchen table, Duke joins them.

"So, how's it going with Mark these days? As I told you, he stopped picking up the lil money you left for him.... And I still can't get him to return my calls," Shelly said.

"I'm not sure, but I'm here to get to the bottom of it," Danny replied while trying not express to much disappointment in front his parents.

"I hear he's disappeared on you again," Duke said.

"Yeah—such appears to be the case," Danny calmly replied.

"I just don't know what you could have done that is so unforgivable," Shelly said.

"It's definitely a forgiveness thing," Selena added. "And perhaps a lil resentment going on with Denise and her family."

"But Denise's issues with Danny are personal, not parental," Shelly replied. "And I've told Mark its time for him to stop letting his family keep him separated from his father," Shelly added, as Danny's cell rings.

He gets up from the table to take the call as Salena responds, "Well, I don't say much, but I've tried seeing things from Denise's point of view, being a young woman and all but, I just can't quite understand why she can't see that what she's doing is obviously wrong, even if it is personal! This man wants to be a father, trying to make all the sacrifices to be a father, has the resources to be a good father, but, yet, she just refuses to allow him to be a father to "his' son! How do you do that without even blinking."

"I see Mark around town, and it seems like he's afraid to even speak," Duke said

"He's still confused about it all," Shelly added.

"Well, excuse my french, Mister and Ms. Bradley, but what Denise is doing should be against the law.... Her behavior should be just as against the law as many of these deadbeat dads out here who refuse to take on any responsibility," Selena shot out.

"You got that right," Duke said. "Because if Danny had decided to quit like a lot of these young men do, every court and social service agent in America will want to throw his tail in jail."

"Well, of course, according to how the system works," Shelly, said. "But when I asked Mark about it, all he says is that they keep telling him that Danny didn't want him and is now trying to brainwash him with lies; trying to turn him against them.

"Brainwash him!" Duke exclaimed. "What the hell!"

"Yeah—he is being brainwashed!" Salena replied. "Brainwashed with the truth!"

"And that's the problem," Shelly added. "They don't want Mark to know the truth."

"Of course not! Salena said. "The deal is they are accusing Danny of the very thing they're guilty of themselves—brainwashing that kid. And we wonder why so many of our young men end up in jail, on drugs and dead. Or how so many young women like me grow up confused, broken and lonely looking for love in all the wrong places," Salena said as her eyes began to well up with tears."

"I know what you mean, Salena, I use to be that young man, who didn't have a father at home to teach me.... I had to teach myself about life.... But thanks be to God, who came in and cleaned me up and turned me around," Duke said as he, too, begins to tear-up, as Shelly reaches for a tissue for the three of them.

Danny, who was now off the phone, is standing in the hallway grieving a bit himself, as he listened in on this heart felt discussion.

Salena continues: "I see everyday what this does to Danny not to be able to visit or talk to his son regularly, and it's just not right. My mother had three kids by three different men, and neither one of us have any kind of meaningful relationship with our biological fathers, who, still, to this day, are disinterested in our well being," she said emotionally, wiping her eyes. "I wish I had a father that just cared enough to call, much less one that might come visit once-and-awhile."

"I understand," Shelly replied. "My father and mother abandoned me at sixteen years old, leaving me to care for six of my brothers and sisters with no money, no job and barely enough food to eat. So, I know what you're talkin about. And, for me, just thinking of a mother working at literally keeping her child away from his father, for no just cause—in this day and time, really should be against the law."

Danny decides that he had heard enough of these sad stories, wipes his own eyes, takes a deep breath and reentered the kitchen.

"Hey guys, come on now, this thing will work itself out—all is well."

"I'm sorry, son, I got a lil emotional on ya," Duke said.

"I understand, but what's the family slogan, Dad?" Danny asked.

"Prayer is the key to the kingdom and faith unlocks the gate," Duke replied.

"Well—let's trust the Lord and stay prayed up," Danny fired back with confidence.

At that Duke got up and stretched out his hands toward the center of the kitchen table and said, "Well, big-boy, we can lift this thing up right now."

They joined hands as Danny led his beloved family in a short prayer to the throne of grace, with thanksgiving.

About three weeks later, it was about 2 p.m. on December 23rd, Grandma Shelly was in the kitchen cooking Christmas dinner with her sister, Jo, on support. Duke was relaxing in the family room watching college football. After still not hearing much from Mark, Danny was back in town again, in an attempt to locate his son.

He pulled up to his parent's house in the newest two-seat model of Mercedes Benz SL500, the Christmas music in the house was playing, but Danny didn't seem to be in a jolly mood. As you may have figured, my father had a thing for cars and always sported one of the nicest Benz's on the streets anywhere, with both his E-class and SL.

He rings the doorbell, this time he's alone. Jo rushes to see who this may be, as she suddenly shouts, "Danny!"

"Merry Christmas!" He says.

"Boy, you just too much for this small town!" Jo said, "You can't drive that up in here! That's too much for these folks in this lil town, Danny!" Jo said, having fun as Danny just smiles as he hugs his mother, while Duke helps him take his bags to the back of the house, making small talk along the way.

Moments later, the doorbell rings again. Hey, it's the holidays, doorbells ring all day long during this time of the year. Jo rushes to answer. "Denise Terry! Girl, your ears must be burning" Jo said. This boy hasn't been here five minutes, and here you come. Get in here.... Merry Christmas!"

"Merry Christmas," Dee replied.

Shelly then rushed back to inform him that Dee was in the house. But being the focused father, he immediately asked, "Is Mark with her?"

"No—she's appears to be alone," Shelly replied disappointedly.

As she turns to head back up front to give her the green light to enter, Dee had already made her own way back, and was suddenly standing in the doorway, dressed to impress while Duke exits the room.

"Merry Christmas, Mister Bradley."

"Merry Christmas, Denise!" Duke replied.

Denise, then, steps into the room. "Merry Christmas, Danny," Denise says, with a gentle and humble smile as she reaches out to give him a hug-hug.

"How long are you here for?" Dee asks.

"A week or so.... How did you know I was here?

"You know how fast news travels in this town when it comes to guys like you. Besides, who else comes to town in a hundred-thousand dollar drop top Mercedes—but Danny Bradley?"

He shakes his head, “There’s just way too much gossip going on in this lil town.”

“Don’t be so hard on us, you never know what you might have missed in this town.”

“Oh really?” Danny asked.

“Yes, really,” she replied.

“Well, my experience has been more of a headache—not a place I’d find a helpmate.”

“There’s still some good girls around here,” Dee shot back, glowing with a smile.

“Okay, Dense Terry, I stand to be corrected. But on another note, how is Mark doing?”.

“He’s fine—I thought I’d stop by to see if you have already done any Christmas shopping for him. If not, I’m on my way to the mall to buy a few gifts, and don’t mind picking up your gifts for him if it would save you some time, it is already the eve of.”

Danny is thinking, *“Come on, Dee, What’s up with this random act of kindness?*

So he got straight to the point: “Denise, I haven’t talked to you or Mark much since earlier this year! Mark is more on my slap list than my Christmas list.”

“Really?” She replied. “I’m sorry, I told Mark he’s got to do better about staying in touch with you. And for me, as usual, work has kept me busy and on the go. But, I promise to get together before you head back. I have a week or so off.”

“Dee, I need to know what’s going on with my son.”

“I promise to make it happen before you leave town, this time, cool?”

“Dee,” Danny replied.

“Scouts honor,” Denise replied back, holding up the scouts sign with her fingers.

Danny knew he couldn’t trust her but desperately wanted to believe her. However, he knew she was up to something but just couldn’t quite figure it out. So, he suddenly pulled out a handful of one hundred-dollar bills from his pocket, counted off one thousand and handed it to her and said, “Tell Mark I expect to see him at this house, with my family, on the 24th, 5th and 6th.”

“Of course,” she said, as she folded the bills and placed them in the front pocket of her jeans. “And before you leave town, *we will* have that chat,” Dee said.

“With Mark,” he said.

“With Mark,” she replied.

Shelly had been just a room away, far enough to afford them privacy, but close enough to have heard everything. She waited until Dee had made it to the front door before walking into her son’s room and asked, “What in the world is she up to, now?”

Danny pauses and takes a deep breath before saying, “I don’t know, but by Christmas Day, we’re about to find out.”

And as promised, I arrived at the Bradleys on Christmas Day, not knowing I was still a day late. My grandparents were so happy to see me. They shower me with hugs and kisses. But I could feel my emotions starting to build inside me as granddad Duke walked me back to my Dad's room as the nerves set in.

As soon as I stepped through the door, he says, "Mark Anthony Mayberry. Where in the world have you been, son? After talking about moving you to Texas, you just keep going Awol, what's up?" He asked as Duke fades from the scene.

And then I just broke down in tears.

"Talk to me, son.... I need to hear words, not see tears, Mark."

"I'm just tired, Daddy."

"Tell me something I don't know, son," he said sarcastically, as Danny gets up, closes the door and plants himself right in front me, and said, "Talk!"

"It's a lot of stuff Daddy. I don't even know where to start."

"Anywhere is fine with me," he replied.

"For one I'm tired of lying and hiding from you. My Mom is afraid that I'll eventually tell you the truth about everything that's been going on."

"The truth about what?"

"Everything," I said, as a tear started free flowing.

"Okay, well, amuse me, Mark!"

"Well, first off, they forced me to go to Alabama, again, this past summer, when they knew I was suppose to come see you. They say you been brainwashing me, trying to turn me against them and that's why they didn't want me around you much anymore."

"Who is they?" He asked.

"Mainly my Mom and grandparents," I answered. "They keep saying, *'Danny might be your father, but Mayberry is your Daddy, and don't ever forget it.'"* So, I'm not hiding from you, I'm just tired of fighting with them Daddy! That's why I told Mayberry the truth the last time I went to see him."

"Which was?" He asked.

"That my Mom has been lying to him about our relationship."

"And?"

"He asked me how long you've been involved, and I told him every since I was about seven or eight years old.... So, he just said he understood, my mom had not told him the truth and he didn't want me to be uncomfortable—so he sent me back home."

"How long were you there?"

"About two days. I was supposed to be there the whole summer. But what I think she's really upset about lately, is knowing that I want to move to Texas."

"And that surprises you?" He asked.

"Not really, but the way she reacted did surprise me. She fell out on the floor crying, saying you didn't even want me and now you're trying to take me away from her... And that she was tired of trying to please everybody."

"Really," Danny asked as his antennas shot higher. "What did you do?"

"I tried to help her off the floor but she said *'don't touch me, you're going to be the death of me.'*" So, I just grabbed the phone, went to my room to call you."

"Is that it?"

"No—after Mayberry sent me back home this past summer, they grounded me. They took away all privileges. I couldn't do anything or talk to anybody—including you."

Danny pauses before asking, "Is there anything else, I need to know, Mark?"

"Did you give her any money recently?"

"Why?" Danny asked, as his antennas are now touching the roof.

"Becuz—they gave me a lot of gifts for Christmas this morning, and they have never ever given me that many gifts at one time on any day.... So, when she said that you were in town, I just figured it had to be you that gave her that kind of money.

"Yeah, I did.... I gave her some money to pick up a few Christmas gifts for me."

"Well, none of them had your name on them, they were all from her and Braylon.

"Not one gift." He asked.

"Not one gift." I replied. "Then she said, *'Your dad wants to see you, maybe he has a few gifts for you.'*"

Danny takes a deep sigh, and asked, "Is there anything else?"

"I told you not to give her any money a long time ago, Dad."

"Is there anything else, Mark," he asked.

"No," I sadly replied.

"Mark, listen to me, at the end of the day did your mother bring back majority of the things you needed?"

"Yes," I replied.

"And most things you wanted you got, correct?

"So, the issue for me is not necessarily whose names were on the gifts, but rather this hide-and-seek game you seem to keep playing with me."

"But Dad," he cut me off, "Did I ask you any questions—no! So zip your lips and just listen, okay.... You have absolutely no excuse for not staying in touch with your father,

Mark.... This nonsense has gone on for damn near fifteen years now, and it's not going to change until you change, do you understand that?"

"Yes sir."

"So, I'm going to say this one more time, stop allowing anybody to dictate to you *if* and *when* you can talk to your father.... I don't give a rip who they are! Am I making myself clear?"

"Yes sir."

"And for the last time, Mark—it's not true.... I didn't run off to go play ball or anything else, knowing I had a son, Mark.... And you know that to be true.... But even if it were true, how do you explain my interest and involvement the past eight-nine years.... For four-five years, I really didn't know. You're only fifteen, son.

"But I'm not saying those things about you, Daddy—they are!" I replied.

"Maybe not, but your actions prove that you perhaps still believe them.... So quit with all the, *I want to move to Texas nonsense.* I can't even get you to call me in Texas, much less move to Texas."

"But Daddy," he cut me off again.... "What's our slogan?" He asked.

"That if we are going to ever have a strong relationship—we're going to have to build it ourselves, independent of anybody else's help," I replied.

I knew he was more than right about this complex situation. A part of me *knew* the truth, but another part of me was really struggling with *accepting* the truth about my Mom. It was still hard to imagine that most all these things she's been selling me on were motivated by her own personal and selfish ambitions. This man is my father, not some disgruntled neighbor that has severely mistreated me in someway. But there was just no love or forgiveness in my house for this guy, who, had shown nothing but love, patience and kindness towards them, with a lot of forgiveness thrown in.

And amazingly, the very next day he took me to the mall and spent *additional dollars* on Christmas gifts to make good on a few promises, made bad by my mom.

18

The Toleration

It was now late summer of '97, not much had changed between Mark and Danny. Dee arrives home and checks the mailbox. Waving at her neighbor, she reaches in and pulls out a handful of letters and circulars. On entering the house, she places the mail and her purse on the counter and starts to go through the stack: bills, bills, coupons, credit card offers to things she'll never accept or buy, but immediately, one letter catches her eye. It's for Mark—from Darren Woodson of the Dallas Cowboys. After thinking about it for a minute, curious as to what Danny might be up to now, she opens it and reads it.

The letter was reasonably short and very encouraging, but after carefully examining it, she puts it back in the envelope, reseals it, and places it on Mark's bed and decides to draft one of her own to rebut comments made about Mark moving to Texas. And after hours of typing, erasing, retyping and deliberating on the perfect words, she prints her final draft, grabs it from the printer and begins to read it under her breath.

Mark—I know things haven't been easy between us but I love you with all my heart as my first born and would never do anything to hurt you, son. All I ever wanted was the best for you. I didn't always go about it the best way, but I have always protected you and been honest with you. We all love you very much, and are proud of you. Daddy Odell treats you like his own son, mama Leola is crazy about you—and Mayberry has always been there for you. Your sister adores you, and your step-dad thinks the world of you. So with all that said, together we can get through all this confusion and make it work. I look forward to seeing you graduate from Pine Bluff High School and going on to college. You can be anything you want to be, and we are going to make sure that happens for you — Love Mom

After sealing her rebuttal, she apparently looked forward to placing her note on Mark's bed as well. Across the Arkansas state line, Danny is getting dressed and packed for a trip, when his phone rings—it's Mark. While he's happy to hear from his son, he's also upset, once again, to hear that he isn't coming to Texas to visit for the summer.

"What's up—where you've been this time, Mark?"

"I'm sorry I haven't called or been to visit yet," Mark responded dejectedly. "Believe it or not, they sent me to another AAU Camp this summer."

"For the fiftieth time, Mark, why didn't you call me?"

"Because I knew you'd be disappointed, Dad," I replied.

"Was this camp your idea, or their idea?"

"Mainly my Mom's, but she kind of tricked me into it," I replied.

"Really, that doesn't seem very hard to do Mark," he sarcastically replied.

"She said if I went on the AAU trip, she would let me come to Texas when I got back."

"And now?"

"And now—she said she changed her mind about it," I reluctantly answered.

"Why doesn't that surprise me—you know what's going on here, Mark, but you continue to allow yourself to get sucked into this craziness, calling me after the fact, blaming your Mom."

"What was I supposed to do?"

"Call your father! Let me know beforehand, Mark! Where is your mother?!"

"At the gym," I softly replied.

"Will you please tell her to call me the minute she walks through the door? And no is not an option.... Can you handle that?!"

"Yes sir."

"Thank you," he says, and hangs up.

Suddenly, Danny's phone rings again, and again it's Mark.

"Yes, Mark."

"I think I know why she won't let me come to Texas."

"Well enlighten me then, son, because this nonsense is so old."

"I think its the letter Woodson sent—she read it."

"Doesn't surprise me, Mark. She's your Mom, she thinks I'm unhealthy for her son."

"I know she read it, because I could tell it had been opened. Plus, she left me a sealed note today, in the exact same place she left his letter yesterday.... And my mother has never written me a letter before." I replied.

Danny pauses, takes a deep breath, and asked, "What did her letter say, Mark?"

"It's at home, but she basically said how they all loved me, and that she know things haven't been easy between us, but that we can work through it.... And that she is looking forward to seeing me graduate from Pine Bluff High School and going to college—somethin like that."

"Well, its obvious that your Mom and I are not even in the same book, much less the same chapter on these issues regarding you, me, us and *our* son together, Mark. But I have told you several times over the years that if we are going to ever have a strong relationship, we are going to have to do it *independent* of anyone else's help. And that couldn't be more clearer today, Mark."

"But I do wanna move to Texas and pursue football this fall, Daddy."

"Mark, how bout first pursuing a relationship with your father in Texas, and maybe, just maybe, the football thing in Texas might happen as a by product of that relationship, not a way to the relationship, cool-cool? He said. "I got a flight to catch," and hangs up on me again.

Unfortunately, I understood why he didn't trust me at this point. Deep down inside, despite not liking his response, I knew once again, he was right. I had not been as honest and forthright with him, nor had I been fair to him, either. I was still allowing my Mom and her family to control my every thought about this man.

And if I was going to make that move from Arkansas to Texas, I had about thirty days left to make it happen. But after struggling to find a way to approach my mother about the Texas thing again, September '97 had quickly come, which meant it would be Pine Bluff High and not Trinity High in Texas that I would be attending. And yeah, I had allowed them to keep me at home, locked up and on lock down, away from a man who was my own father.

As much as I wanted to get away from all of this confusion, deception and negativity, I just didn't have the strength or courage to stand up to her or them even though I knew my Dad would stand with me. So, I became even more discouraged with my family—and uncertain as to how I should proceed with my Dad Danny. As he said, a good place to start would be keeping in touch, returning his calls and focus on pursuing that much needed relationship with him as he was fighting to do with me. But as you could imagine, this was such an awkward and uncomfortable situation to be in. And every time I felt the courage to stand up to her, I would just fold under pressure. But whenever he would try cornering her about me, she would run from the pressure.

However, despite all the mistreatment, I could tell that my father was the bigger man among the men in my life, and I think they knew it too. But to get them to admit or acknowledge this reality meant they would have to explain the multitudes of *innuendoes* and *accusations* they constantly launched against him.

Nevertheless, he remained positive and hopeful of a better day, even though it appeared that he had lost this battle. That fall, he would attend a few of my football games and respectfully didn't try to force me to spend any additional time beyond my comfort. I had begun to regress, not progress in my relationship with him. I knew, at this point, that none of them had any validated reason to be so disrespectful and vindictive toward him—but they were. And to be honest, I wasn't much different. He was right, I could no longer blame them and my mother, it was now me too.

When he came to town, he would keep the conversations light. And I would talk sports because it was what I was most comfortable with. And he would coach me up about the game, the do's the don'ts; major programs versus small programs; the NCAA; the NFL; the collegiate draft etc. A lot of really interesting information I would gather from him, but whenever I would share some of this knowledge in conversation with my family, so that they could be educated too, they would still just shoot the information completely down with comments like, *'Boy, please—you gon be better than your dad; you don't need his advice; create your own footsteps; hell, he only wanted you to move to Texas because you're good in football.*

I would often just shake my head thinking, *I'm a skinny weak and frail kid with very little football skills, what are you guys talking about?! I was ten-years-old when this man first discussed the idea of moving me to Texas—Ten! I didn't even like football then, and not sure if I really do now,* I wanted to say.

Basketball was really the sport I enjoyed most, not football. They knew that! But it was the family's chosen sport for me. But even if all of the above was true, this man is my father for crying out loud! They had no idea how these comments were starting to affect me and my trust in them. Even at my age, I was aware of this man's accomplishments. So, why would anyone want to compare a kid, who hadn't done anything in football with my father's high profile resume?!

And my fathers response: "Its okay, son, just don't you live life always *comparing yourselves among yourselves, its unwise."*

"Then why do they keep doing it, Dad?" I finally asked.

"Because they don't know what they don't know.... *Fathers are not to provoke their children to wrath, discouraging them."* He said. "The very thing some folk often tear down is the very structure the good Lord put in place that our son's might grow into complete manhood, both emotionally and spiritually."

Now, I'm not confessing that I understood all these biblical principles then, but the leaders in my church-going-household, should have. He was right, this wasn't about encouragement—this was *slander, envy* and *jealousy.* And again, even if all of the above was true, this is not how family should deal with it. *If you have a problem with your brother, go to him, directly, not cut him down behind his back.* Now, I do recall that one being preached in church, sitting right in the middle of the entire Davis family.

But I don't recall, not one time, any of them taking the liberty to reach out to this *so-called-deadbeat-dad-of-a-father* of mine, to share the gospel truth about his disinterest in me. However, I have witnessed on several occasions, that same so-called *deadbeat father* try reaching out to them to share his position on these gospel truths regarding his interest in me.

But I think, at best, while under their control, my mother and perhaps the rest of the family were hoping I would turn out to be nearly as talented, athletically, as he was.

'And he didn't even want you,'" they would often remind me in the midst of the jokes, which only validated that forgiveness wasn't the issue here, it was resentment towards this man. And the pressure to cope with it all, for me, was enormous.

The emotional pain was so unbearable that at times I began to have *thoughts of suicide.* I wanted so bad to *trust* my father but I didn't want to *insult* my mother, which meant I would have to continue siding with the very people who stood so unjustly against him. Therefore, I would pray asking God to either please give me the strength to deal with this huge mountain of a problem, or just take me on up out of here. It was scary thinking about how I might go about killing myself.

At any rate, I thought I would make one more major push to get my Mom on board with the idea of me moving to Dallas-Fort Worth. And after an extensive discussion with my father, he agreed to re-visit this option legally once again, as I began to get seriously prepared for the transfer, though he warned me, this fight may get a little rougher. *But with God, all things are possible to them that believe."*

19

Finally Broken

The following weekend, I stopped by my grandma Shelly's to pick up some money my Dad had sent. He was on his way to town to help convince my mom that living with him would be the best thing for all of us. So while waiting for his arrival, I called a couple of my friends over to meet with me about my desire to relocate and finish my junior and senior year across the state-line. And perhaps get some advice as to how I might be able to persuade my Mom into letting go.

"Dude—ain't no way I'd let my Mom keep me from spending time with my Dad, especially one that can do the things your Pops can do for you," Carl said.

Mario then says, "I don't know nothin about my daddy, except wherever he laid his hat was his home," which prompted laughter from Carl and a smile from me.

Carl immediately shot back, "If your dad's head is as big as yours, his problem might be his hat to small, partna."

"What you tryin to say?" Mario asked, as he takes off his own hat, looking at the size.

"Yo head hurt, huh?" Carl asked, as we giggle a bit.

Mario takes offense to his comment, "So, that's funny—when the last time you checked yo own hairline, brah?"

I giggled again, as I then began to try putting a stop to this hilarious comical show before it even get's started.

"Come on guys, let's not get out of control here."

Mark was all business at this get-together, and his wheels were turning at 100 miles per hour with a few lug nuts slightly loose on all four tires.

"Anyway—what you gon do 12?" Carl asked.

For clarification, 12 was my sophomore football number.

"Well, it's not that I don't want to make the move," I replied. "My issue has more to do with my Mom and her acceptance of this move."

"Dude, yo dad got access to the who's who in Sports—he can help you—I don't give a rip who yo mama is—you know what I'm sayin," Carl replied.

Mario jumps in, too, with seriousness and said, "Mark, I know you love your mother, but you need your daddy, cuz. So, pack your bags and stop clowning."

"Clowning? 12 is drowning, if he keeps letting his mom keep him away from his dad," Carl added. "Especially, his kind of dad! He trippin!"

While I knew they meant well, they didn't understand the emotional stress or the number of family members opposing me on this issue. And my facial expression must have said as much.

"We're just tryin to help you make that executive decision, 12," Mario said.

"Well—it's not just my Mom, its my whole family," I replied.

"My Mama don't really like my daddy either, but trust me if he could do for me what yo dad could do for you, I'd break real wide," Carl said.

"What's her real problem with yo dad?" Mario asked.

"I'm not totally sure, but I think she still has a thing for him," I replied.

"Yo Mama is fine, though, 12," Mario said.

"Come on man—that's my Mom you talking about dude."

"Mario, you been checkin his mom out? Oh yeah, you ignant!" Carl chastised.

"I'm just sayin," Mario responded with a smirk. "She fine, dude."

"And I'm just sayin, don't be lookin at my Mom like that partna," I shot back.

Realizing he had crossed the line, Mario then said, "O-K, O-K, just playin ha ha."

Shelly then called out from the front of the house to tell Mario his mother had arrived to pick him up, and as if on cue, Carl reaches for his jacket as well, and said, "I gotta get goin too, playa. But tell yo mom she gotta let you go, 12."

They exit the house as I try getting prepared to approach her one last time. And later that night, I found the perfect time to lay it out again. She was in a good mood, and seemingly to be enjoying her day, but as soon as I said it, she blasted right back.

"Didn't I tell you I was done with this conversation?! Is there any part of NO you didn't quite understand?! Well let me make this clear once and for all—NO Mark Anthony—you are not moving to Texas, period! And don't approach me about this again! And if yo daddy want to move somethin, tell him to move some freakin money from one of his many bank accounts in Texas to yo broke account in Arkansas and help take care yo bills," as she tosses me a document and begins making her way out.

I, then, suddenly made a statement I'd wanted to make for a long-long time, "How is it you want me to ask the man for money all the time but I can't go live or even see the man, mama?"

"Excuse me! What did you just say?!" She asked, as she reenters the room.

"I just don't understand why you so against him, Mama? It don't make sense!"

"I said NO Mark!" She screamed, "And you too young to understand, son! Leave it alone! Let it go! Tell *your father* to write some damn checks, okay!"

So, that I did. I called grandma Shelly and asked if she could come get me, and minutes later, she was there and I was out the door. We make a few stops before making it back to the Bradleys house, it was 10 p.m. I had packed my bag for school for the next couple of days just in case I couldn't go home. And, yes, my Dad indeed had arrived and had made a few phone calls along the way, which had him a little ticked off, too.

Once he saw my demeanor, he asked, "So, what's going on, now; other than lying going on about your grades."

"I'm trying daddy but I'm just frustrated. She's always mad and yelling at me. It's just hard to focus around them," I replied in distress.

My Dad paused and remained silent, as tears start to fall from my eyes, once again, as I went on to explain. "After we talked, I know I was suppose to wait on you to chat with her about Texas move, but I decided to try talkin to her on my own, since she appeared to be in a good mood. But as usual, she went completely off."

"What did she say this time?" Danny asked, as he slowly takes a seat.

"The same, you are not moving to Texas, period! That she didn't want to have this discussion ever again!

Mark then reaches into his pocket and pulls out the document. And then she tossed this at me as she yellin and screamin, and said, *'And if yo daddy want to move somethin, tell him to move some freakin money from one of his many bank accounts in Texas to yo broke account in Arkansas to help take care of you.'"*

Danny takes the document, scans it and notices its a medical bill with a balance of $25.00 dollars. He shakes his head in disappointment, as Mark continued on. "So, then, I just asked her—how is it you want me to ask the man for money all the time but I can't live or even see the man, mama? And that made her even madder.... So, I give up."

After years of trying to reach out to this woman about his son, years of being denied access to this son, and years of being patient for his son, *Danny finally snaps!*

He looks at his watch—it's now 12:30 a.m. He calmly asks, "Where is your mother?"

"She's at my grandparents' house, we're living with them right now." I replied.

Danny gets up and closes the door, grabs the phone and dials a number. And as soon as she answers, he unloads in no particular order:

"For the past ten years, I have given you the benefit of the doubt Denise Davis Terry.... I've been patient, I've been kind, I've been respectful and forgiving towards you and your whole damn family.... I have stood by and watched you guys manipulate and play games with this kid's head since the day you decided to tell me about him....And this BS is going to stop tonight—do you understand me?! So, from this day forward, if you or anyone else in your adorable family got somethin to say to me, pick up the damn phone and call me yo damn self—don't ask my son, my neighbor or any of my damn friends, come to me! Furthermore, I do way more than my reasonable duty, financially, for this kid! And you know that! So stop trippin!"

And BANG! He hangs up the phone and looks at Mark, and says, "Now, take yo butt to bed! And if I catch you lying again about any damn thing, Mark, I'm kickin yo butt too—do you understand me?!"

"Yes sir," I replied quickly, as I made my way to the other guest bedroom.

Duke and Shelly having heard everything, waited until Mark had closed his bedroom door before entering Danny's room.

"You aright son?" Duke calmly asked.

"No, I'm not! I'm fed up with this nonsense! I've spent way too much and lost way too much for this woman to keep trippin with me like this."

Mark eases back into the room and decided to reenter the conversation, despite his Dad's orders. And Danny doesn't take any prisoners.

"What part of go to bed did you not understand, son?! He says with intense anger.

Mark tucks his head and heads back to his room. Danny's cell phone rings, interrupting him—it's Jackie, who was calling to update him on some urgent business matters. But instead, he asks her to do some urgent research for him, knowing it was time to force the custody of his fifteen-year-old son.

As soon as he hangs up, he gets up and walks out of the house. Hearing the sound of the front door opening and closing, Duke grabs his robe and heads outside as well to join his son, who is leaning against his car, gazing up at the moon—a full moon. The two of them remain silent for what seems like about five minutes or so. And it's Duke who breaks the silence and generally shared in no particular order, these words:

"When you were a lil boy, I was wild, crazy and stupid.... I drank, fought and chased women all over the streets of this lil town.... Hangin out in every night spot I could find.... And when the night came to a close, I would come in at three-four o'clock in the morning at times and just beat up on your mother for no reason at all.... And you and your two brothers would just cry, cry, and cry.... And at that time, the streets, chasing women and hustling up a dollar or two, meant more to me than my own family.... Truth is, I had no idea what a family was.... I never knew my father, even though he lived just miles of my front door.... And the first fifteen years of my life, the woman who I'd been told was my mother, was actually my oldest sister.... my mom had passed away when I was only five years old.... So, I never really knew my parents and often resented people in society that had parents that loved them cared about them.... I was so bothered by it, I would just feel agitated to see a family together.... And I guess a lot of that anger came from not ever having a family.... But no matter how bad of a person or father I was, for some reason, son, you always seemed to be happy to see me coming, and sad to see me go.... And at times, I would catch your brothers teasing you and giving you a hard time about me—but you just kept right on treating me the same; happy to see me come and sad to see me go.... But then one night, as you may recall, I came home and violently started in on your mother; I guess you guys were about twelve, thirteen, and sixteen years old then, and apparently y'all had-had enough…. JB, being the oldest, stepped between your mom and me, threatening to stand against me if I had intentions to physically abuse her that night…. and then Craig stood up with his head held high ready to defend his mother.... And that hurt me to the bone, to see two of my sons standing up against me, regardless of how wrong I was…. But when you stepped up, son, with your head held high and said, *'Not tonight Daddy, we can't let you beat her tonight,'"* that broke my heart," Duke said, as a tear fell from his eye…. I knew, at that point, God was speaking directly to me.... And I realized that moment, that the good Lord had managed to show, through you, son, His unconditional love for me.... And if I know my son," Duke continued, "He's already playing out in his head how he's going to apologize to his son and his son's mother.... And I want to say thank you, for being the father to my grandson, Mark, that I never was to you."

Duke then dropped his head, with his hands in the pockets of his robe and slowly walked away, as Danny continued staring straight ahead with his face now, flooded with tears. What an incredible and surreal moment for this father and son.

As my grandad Duke made his way back into the house, I was standing in the window, while grandma Shelly stood in the front doorway. I heard her ask, "Is he okay?"

"He'll be fine.... He's just having a lil talk with the Lord," Duke replied, as he gently made his way back to his bedroom as we, too, let go of our own tears after hearing my Dad Danny quietly release his pain.

20

The Humility

Around 7:15 the very next morning, Duke is dressed for work. He kisses Shelly, and says his good-byes to his grandson before heading out the door. Mark is getting ready for school and Danny was already dressed, red eyes and all, after being up the rest of the night. He already apologized to his parents for his actions and tried to reason with these lingering consequences that still seem to haunt him behind Denise's late announcement that *her son was his son.*

He enters the kitchen about the time Mark was on the tail end of his breakfast, a bowl of cereal. He takes a seat next to him at the table and Danny jumps right into it with a face of regretfulness as Shelly leaves them alone.

"One of the things I always try to do, son, is admit when I've failed.... Its not always an easy thing to do, but is certainly a necessary thing to do.... I want to apologize for my actions last night."

"But, Dad," I quickly replied, before he cuts me off.

"It was inconsiderate of me to go off on your mother like that even if I did have a valid and just cause."

"But what's she's doing is wrong."

"It is, but it still doesn't give me the right to cuss her out, son, especially in front of you.... That's not how we love those who wrong us.... *We are to bless those who despitefully use us...* I can't force your mother to be fair to me, anymore than she can force you to admit something that didn't happen."

"I understand that but Dad...."

"Right always becomes wrong when it's forced, son.... So, forgive my behavior, charge this mistake to my head and not my heart, cool?" He said, as he reaches over and pats me on the shoulder, getting up to take me to school.

I'm thinking, *you gotta be kidding me! Going off is exactly what you should've done, and you're apologizing?! No one in my household would have ever apologized for their unjustified actions towards him!*

But I guess my family and I are just playing church, we haven't quite arrived at that level of biblical understanding just yet. But I continued to make small talk out of it as we made our way, as he continued to share God's position of love on the matter.

As they approached PBHS, Danny's silver drop top Mercedes is drawing major attention. He stops in front of the athletic field house, where the football players are generally dropped off, as a few of Mark's teammates and other classmates start to gather near the curb. Danny notices his son's attitude is a bit more confident as he prepares to exit the vehicle, especially knowing those same teammates that once gave him a hard time about the identity of his father, was in the crowd.

"Dang, Mark Mayberry, whose car is that?"

Smiling broadly, Mark says proudly, "My Pops."

Danny sat silently, as he watched his son intentionally taking his time to exit the car.

Another one of the growing number of students asked, "That's your Pops?"

Grabbing his book bag from the floor behind the passenger seat, Mark looked up and said, "Yeah—why, what's up?"

Another nameless classmate, trying to get his cool on, tip-toed around the front of the car like a Kool Moe Dee wannabe and said, "That's a sweet ride, Mister Mayberry."

Suddenly, Mark turned and said, "Bradley—not Mayberry—it's Bradley!" He said as he looks in the direction of those once-upon-a-time harassing teammates.

A wave of recognition swept over the throng of Pine Bluff students, as they went from typical teen obnoxiousness to near reverential silence. It was as if the teacher had just walked into class, and all the clowning abruptly stops.

Danny had experienced being in the fishbowl, and had learned how to acknowledge and sometimes ignore the attention. But now, he was observing how his son dealt with his first exposure to being in that fishbowl.

"Okay, Mark Mayberry, it's about time to drop that last name, don't you think?"

Mark smiled, "I'm ready! I been waitin on you! But I like D. Bradley Jr. better."

Sliding his sunglasses on, Danny put the Benz in gear, shakes his head in doubt and said, "Mark, in a small town like this *solidification fuels expectation*—once they know *who you are,* they expect you to be *what you are,"* as he drove off leaving Mark wondering what it all meant.

Reaching for his cell phone, Danny called one of the local florist. Yes, he was not only going to apologize to me but he was ready to reach out to my mother. After he had placed an order of a dozen red roses to be delivered before noon, with a card attached that just said, "ME," his business partner called with that information he requested regarding the custody laws in Arkansas and their requirements.

He then contacts a local attorney to discuss the name change and the possibility of gaining custody. The attorney promises to get back to him later in the day with more information regarding both. But for now, he was focused on making peace with Denise.

"Dee Terry—Danny, you have a minute?" He asked with humility.

"Not really, but what's up," she replies, her tone a bit lighter.

"First of all, let me apologize for my behavior last night.... The way the medical bill was presented to me fueled a fire that has apparently been burning for a while, and I lost it. It was wrong and definitely not the way to handle our differences."

Denise paused, and then said, "Okay—that's cool," she said, as if in deep thought.

"I really am sorry, Dee. And to express my sincerity, I sent you a gift just in case you struggled with accepting my apology. Did you get it."

"Oh—so that was you that sent the roses.... I've been tryin to figure out all morning who I might have had in the dog house."

"Well, I guess that would be me," Danny lightheartedly replied.

"Okay.... Thanks, that was very thoughtful. Now I might believe you're sincere."

"I appreciate that and I know you're busy, just wanted to apologize to you. Take care and I'll be in touch."

Dee, knowing how Danny usually wanted to extend the conversations, was caught off-guard by his sudden move to exit so quickly. She scrambles for words for a second before just saying, "Thanks for calling, apology accepted."

That evening, Danny and Mark are at the Bradleys eating their favorite fast-food dinner, Rich's hamburgers and watching Monday Night Football, Redskins versus Cowboys. Danny was about to make another character move, unbeknownst to his son, that would send shock waves throughout the Davis's entire family.

"Its my understanding, your step-dad works at Dominoes Pizza, what time does he get home from work?" Danny asks.

"I think about 11 p.m."

"Is he working tonight? Danny asks, as he looks at his watch.

Pausing for a second, Mark replies, "Yeah, I think so."

Danny grabs the phone and dials 411 as Mark goes to the kitchen to get a beverage. After getting the number for Dominoes, he pushes his plate aside and places the call. Mark re-enters the room, as his eyes grow big while being fixated on Danny. He suddenly ignores his burger and the game. A moment later, his step-dad is on the line.

"Braylon—Danny, did I catch you at a bad time?"

"Yeah—what's up," he replies, after a pause with a slight attitude in his voice.

"I wanted to apologize to you for my behavior last night, man.... I kind of lost it for a minute and I wanted to call you man-to-man, brotha-to-brotha and apologize for my actions." Danny politely said.

Unfortunately, the call didn't go as well as Danny had hoped—and his apology wasn't received as well as that of his wife. So after the step-dad spoke his *complete* mind, making known several things he was displeased with, including the idea of Mark moving to Texas, he requested a meeting within an hour at a local hotel and wanted him to bring Mark along with him. He agrees as Braylon then abruptly hung up, leaving Danny shocked and a bit concerned with his request.

After pausing with the phone still in his hand, Danny, knowing Mark was watching his every move, asks "Has Braylon ever threatened you?"

"No, did he just hang up on you?!" I asked.

"Yeah, he did.... And he wants to meet."

"Meet?! About what?!" I surprisingly asked.

"I don't know but he wants me to bring you along, too," Danny suspiciously replied.

"You serious?!"

"Yep.... Grab my keys, I think we need to hear what he has to say."

We walk into the hotel and take a seat in the lobby facing the entrance, waiting for Braylon to show. Danny asked, "Is there anything I need to know before he gets here.

"No. Nothin I can think of, but it looks like he just walked in." I replied.

Braylon makes his way over to the table. My Dad gets up to greet him by extending his hand, but Braylon ignores the greet and takes a seat and looks across the table at me and says, "So Mark, what's up? I thought we had this conversation already."

"What conversation, Braylon," I asked.

"About this move to Texas," he says. "Why are you doing this to your mother?" He asked, as Danny slowly took his seat.

"Doing what?" I replied.

"All that you and your mother has been through with this guy, you don't know?"

"No Braylon, I don't," I replied.

"Well Mark, for starters, why would you expect yo daddy to take care of you in Texas if he won't do it here in Arkansas?"

"You serious?! I surprisingly asked.

"Do I look like I'm joking! He sarcastically replied.

Danny is sitting back, arms folded, listening intently, his eyes going back and forth between the two, awaiting his son's answer as Mark looks at his Dad with a *"Can you believe this guy,"* look, before turning back to Braylon and saying, "Unfortunately, you been listenin to my Mom way too much, my Dad do stuff for me all the time."

"Since when, Mark?!

"You really are serious!"

"Since when?" Braylon asked.

"My Mom got all y'all fooled, Braylon."

"Answer my question, Mark? When has Danny done much of anything for you?!

"Braylon, I really can't think of any time my Dad hasn't done for me."

When?! Give me a time?"

"I just did! I said he does for me all the time. In fact, I can't recall a time I asked him for anything that he didn't do, Braylon, including tons of Christmas gifts."

"Really? What Christmas gifts, Mark?! What about that play station you wanted that he refused to buy you a few years ago?!

"You serious?!" I asked. "A Play Station!" Thinking, *the Christmas thing just flew right over his head, not knowing that-that was my Daddy's money?*

"Where is it, Mark?" He barked.

"Braylon, if I had asked my dad for a "play station", I am certain I would have one."

"So you lied to us, then," Braylon said

"Well, yeah, if you're sayin I told you I asked my dad for a play station!"

"Okay, now you're admitting you've been lying to us? Braylon shot back.

"Braylon, you can't believe everything my Mom is saying."

"So she lying too?!" Braylon asked.

"If she's tellin you he does practically nothin for me, she's not shooting straight with you! Where do you think a lot of these expensive clothes come from, my Mom, Mayberry, my granparents?!"

Danny politely lifts his hand and said, "Mark, I think you've said enough, son."

But Braylon interrupts this fathers parenting suggestion made to his son, as Danny retreats and listens.

"Furthermore," Braylon says, "Don't ever call my wife trippin with her like that again, I don't care what time of the day it is! Mark don't need to move to Texas to be successful in football, you made it from Pine Bluff he can make it from Pine Bluff. Again, you might be able to fool a few folks around this lil town, but you can't fool me.... I'm not from Pine Bluff.... And if you really cared anything at all about yo son, you'll help take care of him!"

I then sat back up in my chair and said, "I just told you, Braylon, you don't know what my Dad does for me...all you know is what you're being told!"

"I know everything he don't do know, Mark!" Braylon shouts back.

"Apparently, you don't!"

"Mark, I said that's enough, son!"

"Please, they trippin," I said, as I lean back into my chair, hot and agitated.

Danny repositions himself at the table and said, "Braylon, I heard you out, brah. And unfortunately, you are not in the know with what's going on with my relationship with my son. All I was trying to do was apologize. That's it. And you've taken this thing to a whole new level."

"You heard what I said," Braylon shot back.

"Yeah, I did. And I must admit, you gotta a lot a nerve callin me out here to front me about what I do or don't do for my son," my Dad said, as I sensed the temperature starting to rise between them.

Braylon then abruptly jumps up and stands over Danny and throws his hand up and repeated, "You heard what I said?!"

Danny calmly stands up and says, "And I said you don't know what I do for my son, partna!"

I then quickly reached over and grab my Dad's arm and said, "Don't do it, Daddy!"

After a brief stare down, Braylon looks over at Mark and says, "If you want to move yo butt to Texas, then get gone!"

Braylon heads for the exits as Danny watches him closely. He then looks at me and asked with that *don't lie to me,* look, "What's with all the football talk, Mark?

"I don't know daddy. I think a lot of it started when my mom overheard me tellin one of my friends that you might be takin me and Mario to the Texas and OU spring games and maybe their game at Cotton Bowl.

Danny drops his head, leaning on the table with both hands and ask, "Do you really-really wanna get out?"

"Yeah!"

"Don't lie to me, do you really wanna get out?!" He asked sternly.

"Yes sir."

"You sure?!" He asked, as he looks at me directly in the eyes.

"Yes—I do."

"Then bow yo neck, son, its time to go—do you understand me? It's time to go!"

The next morning, Danny was on the phone with his attorney, whom he had already apprised of his situation with Mark, regarding name changing and custody. She tells him that generally he could file a petition, and the judge could rule on both, instead of filing petitions on each matter separately. But if he chose to file them independently, the name change would be simple, but the custody petition—if Denise is going to fight it, might take some time and is often a little more challenging to overcome. However, she went on to inform him that the two things a judge will strongly consider, is Mark's age, and his level of maturity. Then it would simply boil down to the judge's opinion as to whether he would be in better hands with his father or his mother.

Regarding the name change, she told him, a petition would be filed with the Circuit Court Civil Division with a proposed order for the judge to sign—and if there has not been a parental petition or child support order filed beforehand, then it's a quick in and out. But, if there has been such an order filed, then it would certainly block the name change, which would require both Denise's and Mayberry's signature to make it happen.

About three days later, I'm at home house packing a few things to take back to Grandma Shelly's in an effort to spend more time with my Dad, who decided to stay in town a lil longer. As I'm talking to him on the phone, my Mom walks through the door yelling my name, "Mark!"

"He's on the phone!" Cassie yells back.

Obviously agitated, she suddenly appears at my bedroom door and says, "Get off, I need to talk to you, now," and then walks away.

As soon as she does, I tell my Dad I'll call him back. As soon as I hang up, she steps into my room and asked, "Why didn't you call me back yesterday?!"

"I just figured I would talk to you once I got home, mom."

"You are at it again!" She said. "Every time you and yo Daddy get together, you always doing and saying stuff you have no business saying!"

I dared not ask what she was talking about, because I already knew exactly what she was referring too.

"What did you say to your step-dad the other night?"

"Nothin Mama...I told him the truth."

"The truth about what?!" She asked.

"He fronted me about what my dad do and don't do and I set him straight about it. He then got upset and said if I wanted to move to Texas, then go!"

"Well, let me set you straight about it, once again, Mark," she shouted. "You are not moving to go live with Danny—so you can get that out of your head! I told that lying deadbeat dad of yours a long time ago, I'm not giving him my son!"

Once again, she was shutting the door on my chance at perhaps a better life."

But I had to ask, "What is he lying about, mama?"

"Everything Mark! You'll understand later. Right now, you just way too young to comprehend what went on and what's really going on between Danny and I.... All

Danny is doing, son, is messing with your head, Mark! It's as simple as that! Now unpack that bag, you're not going back over to the Bradleys for a while, even if your dad is in town."

At this point, I knew the truth; she knew I knew the truth; but she was unwilling to acknowledge the truth—except when being confronted by my Dad. And while my mom nearly always expressed her negativity toward him, he nearly always responded with positivity toward her. He just refused to fight her fight, and I wanted him to swing at everybody that help her set up and promote this fight.

But as the old saying goes, *we are truly a product of our environment with a tendency to be like the people we hang around.* Unfortunately, I didn't realize how much of me had become just like them.

I was starting to act like them, talk like them and even think like them. I was suddenly becoming that same selfish, envious and jealous person toward others as they were towards him. And I could clearly see it happening but I didn't know how to stop it. And my mom, knowing that I had kind of figured this thing out, begins changing her strategy a bit. Instead of trying to continue selling me on this old worn out idea that my father didn't want me, she began pushing this subliminal message that *I was just simply way too young to understand what was really going or had gone on between them.* And that begins to bother me even more—still.

But by early October of '97, Danny had failed to get Denise to sit down and discuss the name change issue, but he didn't fail to make good on another promise, the Texas / OU game, in Dallas, the Cotton Bowl, located on the grounds of the State Fair. Jackie, his business associate, joined us too, along with one of my teammates, Mario Nix. I didn't know the complete plans for the day but Jackie did, she asks, "Do you still plan to take Mark to the field to meet Coach Brown and Coach Blake, during pre-game?"

We had arrived late, due to traffic and parking, so he took us directly to our seats, which were great seats, by the way. But it would be after the game that he would take us to meet both coaches. But for a lack of a better description of the *State Fair Grounds*, this place was off the hook. The bands of both schools were marching through the Fair playing their respective fight songs, people were cheering so loud, you could hardly hear the person next to you. Everybody appeared to be dressed in either burnt orange or crimson and cream. I remember thinking, *Wow—this is unreal.*

As we made our way into the stadium, our seats were lower level, 50 yard line, 20 rows up. Mario excitedly remarked, "Dude, we're at the Texas / OU game, baby!"

And all around us were the sights and sounds of OU / Texas mania. Fans from each school were mouthing off to one another, telling jokes, most laced with profanity and obscenities. I noticed my Dad observing my reaction to it all, as I speechlessly took in this amazing event. Mario and I had seen this Red River Shoot-out on television, but seeing it live was very-very different. This environment was beyond imagination, I don't care where you might have grown up. And the size and speed of these guys, on both teams, were incredibly amazing.

Suddenly, Mario turned and asked my Dad, "You played quarterback in this game?!"

He just smiled and winked, as the Oklahoma fans broke out a loud Sooner chant, while rival Texas fans shouted the Longhorns chant even louder. While Mario, though in awe, jammed to the Sooners fight song, I felt scared, nervous and withdrawn. I kept a straight-face the whole time not knowing what to think or how I should even act. I guess being here really exposed where I was mentally, emotionally, and spiritually. And the more this great contest played out, the more I imagined my father taking the snap, completing the pass, or running for a score in front nearly a hundred-thousand screaming fans with television cameras everywhere. I'd watched these quarterbacks manage this extremely difficult situation as I tried imagining him at the helm, too.

Somewhere in the midst of these thoughts, I begin hearing a multitude of comments made by my family, *'you gon be better than your daddy.'" 'Your daddy can't wear your shoes.'" 'Did you forget, he didn't even want you; don't try following in his foot-steps, create your own footprint.'"*

And suddenly, right there on the spot, in Dallas, Texas, at the Cotton Bowl, even though I knew those comments were unhealthy, unfair and untrue, I too, began to feel resentment towards this man, which only validated the jealousy and envy of my family.

Therefore, as Mario was having the time of his life, I sat quietly, reserved, wanting to go home, back to Arkansas. Finally, the game ended with Texas winning 27-24, and the four of us began making our way to the exit, en route to the Longhorns and Sooners locker room area. As the rowdy shoulder-to-shoulder crowd inched forward, an ugly-ugly fight broke out, right there in front of us. The chaos visibly shook me and Mario up a bit, which prompted my Dad to make an executive decision, forego any attempt to make it to the post-game locker rooms and head to the house instead.

On the way home, we stopped at a restaurant to eat. Mario, who is still excited by what he'd experienced, asked my Dad, "What was it really like to play quarterback in that kind of game, at 5'10 180 pounds, Mister Bradley? Those guys are huge!"

Danny said with assurance, conviction and coolness, “Mario, its hard to explain the rush, the thrill, the intensity, of what its like to be a part of a special-special event like that, But always remember, its not the size of the player, young-fella, but rather the size of the heart of the player.” My Dad said. “But the reason I brought you guys out, is to broaden your vision.”

“It definitely broaden my vision,” Mister Bradley.

“Mine too for that matter,” Jackie added, as she chuckled. “That game is serious.”

But he went on to share how critical exposure was to a person’s overall perception of reality. He would often say we live in a world of images and perceptions, *that knowledge is the principle thing; and in all thy getting, get understanding. We are destroyed from a lack of knowledge, where there is no vision the people will indeed perish.*

“I day dreamed about playing for Oklahoma, the Orange Bowl, a shot at the National Championship—at quarterback,” he said, as the waitress brought out our food.

Somehow I knew at this point he was talking directly to me.

“And I confessed that dream at the tender age of fourteen, cast up from the hip down, while watching the ‘78 Orange Bowl game, Arkansas versus Oklahoma.”

“Cast up from the hip down,” Jackie frantically asked. “What happened?!”

“I dislocated my knee in the last football game of the season, my 8th grade year,” my father replied, as I continued listening intently. “But that didn’t discourage me.”

“But why Oklahoma and not Arkansas?” Mario asked. “Arkansas was a really good program back then, too, right?”

“Arkansas has always been a good program,” he answered. “But unfortunately for Arkansas, I wanted to play quarterback and Coach Holtz recruited me to play defensive back and receiver. And I considered it, especially with all the pressure the state placed on me to stay. And I really liked Lou Holtz alot, but I was divinely destined for OU.”

As I listen to him share his story, I kept hearing those voices from home, which none stood out more than *‘Danny didn’t even want you; don’t follow in his foot-steps, create your own footprint.’*”

As I fade back into the conversation I hear Jackie ask, “So you knew at fourteen that football and OU was what you wanted to do, cast up from the hip down?

“Jack, I knew that day, despite being told I will probably never be able to play football again, I began confessing that night, January 1, 1978, to attend OU. And from that point forward, I’d watch Oklahoma football, the Barry Switzer Show each week to see how Thomas Lott and JC Watts, two great option quarterbacks, who looked a lot like me, handled themselves on that national stage. I would listen closely to what

Switzer had to say about them and then meditate on his comments as if he was saying those things about me.... Then I began writing OU on school tablets; school books; school annuals, it didn't matter, I'd confess it daily to myself and anyone else that would challenge me on it," he said. "And after OU beat Nebraska for the Big-Eight Championship in '80, sending the winner to the '81 FedEx Orange Bowl, I convinced one of my high school coaches, Jimmy Sanders, to drive me all the way from Pine Bluff to Miami, Florida, to the Oklahoma / Florida State game, in hopes of encouraging Coach Switzer to seriously take a look at a kid who was destined to be the Sooners next Championship quarterback."

"Wow," Jackie said. "I didn't know that—you never told me that.'

"So afterwards, as I was making the list of the six schools I would visit, I got a call from coach Switzer.... And the selection process for me was over.... I still took the visits but my mind was already made up before the process even began."

"Who won the game?" Mario asked, as he looks over at me, knowing I was a Florida State fan to the max.

"JC Watts and Sooners 18-17 in the final seconds," my Dad replied.

Now, mind you, I haven't said a word the entire time, and right when I was about to make a comment he shares that bit of information, which deflated me. Just another reason why this was not a good trip for me.

However, I knew I needed to get my act together if I was ever going to establish the kind of relationship with this man the good Lord wanted us to have, but personally at that very moment, I suddenly just didn't see it happening. I could officially say, at that moment, I had become **jealous** of my own father, who had done nothing but love me. The question for me was, where in the world do we go from here? And how could he continue to try fathering a kid that has also turned his back?

The Exposure

21

A few months later, it's now my sixteenth birthday, and I'm surrounded by family, the Terrys and Davises, who were all singing happy birthday as I made my wish and blew out the 16 candles on my birthday cake.

My Dad Danny had just left town from an extended Christmas stay in an effort to help me stay strong through it all. He saw many of the character flaws that were beginning to change my attitude, and he was concerned about the direction I was now heading. He was committed to convincing me, too, at this stage, that I didn't know what I didn't know. But what he didn't know, I had begin to tune him out.

He spent a little more time, this time around, sharing and discussing the do's and don'ts that any teenager would need to hear, spiritually. Though I appreciated him sharing the multitude of mistakes he made along the way, I didn't quite see how he could really tell me what not to do, if he failed at it, too. But he never felt that his failures disqualified him but rather made him more qualified to share what not to do when faced with life's many challenges. And again, though I had been more open in the past, now, I was just ready for him to close his trap and just let me be.

But thank God for my father's *wisdom* and *patience,* he was always *instant in season and out of season.* He was going to share the good news of Christ with me, whether I wanted to hear it or not, even though he was always *gentle* and *considerate*, *never forceful or insisting*. Again, right became wrong when its forced, he believed.

Anyway, as I had made my wish, blew out the candles as the phone rang. And I see my grandma Leola whispering to my Mom, which almost always meant that it was my Dad Danny on the line. My Mom motions to me, and silently says, "It's Danny."

I take the cordless from her and immediately head to one of the bedrooms to freely chat. He gave me a 'Happy Birthday' shout out and a few other encouraging words, before I update him as to how things were going and he updates me as to how the name change and the custody process would work if I was to ever really opt out.

Knowing that moving to Texas was out of the question at this point, I asked, "But we are doing the name change, regardless, though, right?"

"The papers are drawn up, and I've told her not to send them until I have at least had a chance to talk to your mother," my dad replied. "And if there are no legal obstacles that we are unaware of, and I don't think there is, the name change could happen within a month or so. So, I hope you're ready to take on this new identity."

"Past ready. But yeah, you would need to talk to her before she receives them in the mail. For now, I still live here."

"Is she there?" He asked. "I can do it right now."

Mark peeps around the corner, scopes out the situation and says, "Now might not be a good time, they all pretty much know it's you on the phone, including Braylon."

"Okay, I'll reach out to her before they deliver the papers, cool?"

"Cool." I replied with mixed feelings still.

"Got to get going, by the way, go by your grandmother's and pick up your gift."

"Thanks."

"And if you're still interested, the spring games at OU and UT is coming up, if you still wanna tag along, it would be great exposure to see these programs from behind the scenes," he said in closing.

"Dad, come on, man—you know I'm with that!" I replied.

"Okay, don't stand me up for the twentieth time, Mark."

"I'm not going to stand you up, that's a promise."

He wished me happy birthday again, told me he loved me as we hung up. I wasn't quite comfortable saying I love you's back to anyone, especially my father. So I would just quickly shoot it back because it was seemingly the right thing to say.

Forty-eight hours later, Danny was at dinner with Salena, he noticed his cell phone message light blinking. While Salena had stepped away to the ladies room, Danny checks his voice-mail, its his Mom, telling him to call Denise, urgent. He decides to make the call to be certain all was well with Mark as he enjoyed the sounds of jazz.

"Dee—this is Danny. I got a message from my Mom—what's up?"

"When are you coming back to town?" She asked.

"Not sure, why?" Danny suspiciously replied, as Salena makes it back to the table.

"I wanted to talk to you about a car for Mark?"

"What about it?"

"Well, since he's now sixteen, I was wondering, if I get Mayberry to provide the insurance, would you buy him the car?"

Danny paused, looked at Salena, and says, "If you can get Mayberry to provide the insurance, would I buy the car?"

Dee replied matter of factly, "Yeah."

Danny dropped his head and rubbed his eyes with his free hand as Salena shakes her head in disbelief also. Though she appeared to be on the verge of saying something, she remained silent, but her expression spoke loud and clear.

"Denise—no, the answer is no," he said gently. "I am not about to participate in a *car deal* that you've brokered with Mayberry."

She pauses and said, "Oh—okay, just thought I'd ask," then hangs up as Danny shuts off the phone and places his cell back on the table.

Salena breaks her silence, "You gotta give it to her, Denise got courage.... Out of all the things Denise needs to be discussing with you, regarding Mark, she calls wanting to discuss the most insignificant of them all," Salena sarcastically said. "This women is a trip-trip.... I use to give her the benefit of the doubt, but its obvious that Denise doesn't give a care about your relationship with your son.... I've told you once, and I'll say it again, what Denise is doing should be against the law."

Danny takes a deep breath, and says, "Unfortunately, she just won't quit."

"The question is, when are you going to quit letting this woman push you around like this, Mister Bradley? How much more are you willing to put up with? You've lost one wife, your football career, changed careers to be more available for Mark—and about to lose me," Salena said firmly, "if you don't get this girl in check!"

"Babe, come on sweetie."

"Denise Terry appears to not only have Mark's life on lock-down, but she got your life on lock-down, too."

Danny then leans back in his chair in deep thought with no response, disappointed in her assessment about him and the situation, before saying, "Salena—Denise doesn't have my life on lock down. But I am trying to be patient, I'm all this kid really got."

"I understand that, and I'm with that, but what about us, Danny? I've been patient for the past four years. When I came into this picture, you were just getting over your divorce from Pam because of this girl! Denise don't want Mark, she wants you! And if she can't have you, she's committed to making life miserable for you, which may cost you another divorce before you even get married!" Salena says with frustration, as she reaches for her purse.

"Denise is a married woman with a family, Salena."

"Really! Well, hell, why don't you try telling her that!" Salena replied, as she gets up from the table and abruptly walks out the restaurant.

In addition to this new piece of drama, with all the sacrifices he's had to make to be a responsible father to me, a promissory note from the sale of his health club had gone sour months earlier with the tenant failing to pay. Such fallout ended up in litigation, costing him over $450,000.00 in savings, proceeds, and legal fees, forcing him to downsize sizably and even file for bankruptcy, a decision that was extremely difficult for him to make. But fortunately, he recovered in just months after losing almost everything and was back on his feet by way of a network marketing opportunity he joined, just prior to his resignation from the Cowboys. And by the first quarter of '98, Danny had become one of the top 25 money earners with Excel Communications, a company that had become a $1.2 Billion publicly traded conglomerate in the efforts of a host of independent reps, which later caused him to regret having to seek protection.

And Salena, who had just finished training to be a Flight Attendant, appeared to have had enough. Unbeknownst to Danny, on her graduation day, she chose to relocate to Los Angeles as opposed to perhaps remaining in Dallas/Fort Worth as her base. And Danny began to feel the reality of another relationship gone south when he attempted to kiss her at the conclusion of her commencement exercises, as she simply turned away. Consequently, at this point, this relationship was all but over as far as Salena was concerned. She was moving to Los Angeles with no intentions of returning.

However, by the spring of '98, Danny fulfills another promise, as he continued working on the name change, despite his turbulent feeling towards Denise. He and Mark walk into Head Coach Mack Brown's office at the University of Texas in Austin, with OU scheduled as their next stop. Danny was committed to exposing his son to a different environment outside of small town Pine Bluff. And while doing so, he, too, became enamored with the facilities at UT. Coach Brown hugs him while he gave Mark a firm handshake. They took a seat in the guest chairs in his office to chat.

My Dad remarked, "Coach—this makes no sense! This is not a facility to be used—this is a show-room floor for some sort of bid project!"

Not having anything to compare this complex too, except the Cowboys facility, I was likewise awestruck by this place. It was plush-plush. And I knew my Dad have seen a few facilities, so this place had to be *impressive.*

"That's probably very difficult to say as a Sooner, huh?" Mack asked jokingly with a smile while Danny giggles and says, "Diplomatically—yes, personally—no. I'm still a huge Mack Brown fan coach—you know that."

While they chatted and got caught up, I faded from the conversation from time to time, trying to imagine what it would be like to be a part of a program of this magnitude, wondering if I had what it took to make it at a place like this. We had already driven around the campus so I got a chance to see the size of this landscape, and it was huge.

After regaining consciousness, Coach Brown was sharing the tremendous support the program receives from the community, the alumni, and the fifty-plus-thousand students on campus. At that, I paused on the inside and thought, *that's more than the population in the whole town of Pine Bluff.*

He goes on to mention the advantages regarding recruiting in the state of Texas, which had, he thought, the best High School talent, athletically, in the country. This echoed many of the same things I'd already heard from my Dad and his support group, when I seriously considered moving to Texas.

Coach Brown then looks over at me and said, "Mark, your Dad was a great player—if he had played any other skill position other than Wishbone Quarterback, he could have probably played ten years in the NFL."

Not knowing how to respond, I just smiled at his comment, despite having heard the total opposite from my family over the years.

"You mind giving us a tour?" Danny asked. "We were just in town for a few days and thought we'd stop by and watch a practice or two."

"Sure," Mack said. "Come on."

Along the way we run into some of the assistant coaches, each of them complimenting my father as they introduce themselves, again, not knowing how despised he was in my small little world.

Once inside the locker room, with coach Brown as the tour guide, my Dad would occasionally observe my face as Coach humbly showed off the luxuries of The Longhorns Football Complex. *Now I hadn't been to OU yet, but this was going to be hard to compete with,* I thought to myself.

"What do you think son?" He asked.

"Man, this is crazy," I humbly and nervously replied.

We followed Coach Brown through two large doors that led to a tunnel, which lead us into the Darryl Royal Memorial Stadium, an entrance I had only seen externally on television. Coach then points out the indoor practice facility as we made our way over to their outdoor practice fields, which was just about in session.

As we got closer, a comment Mario made previously, during the Texas / OU game, began to resonate with me. The size and speed of these players were stupidly amazing. If I wasn't already terrified—I was now. So while my Dad was out roaming practice with Coach Brown, I watched from afar, thinking, *There's no way these guys used to be my size—and I'm like Mario, how did my Dad accomplish so much among these giants at his size—I don't see many 5'10 players on this field, much less at quarterback regardless of the style of offense.*

For me, fear had completely set in. I wanted to come see this but now wasn't sure if I really could do this—at this level. Therefore, all this comparing my family kept reminding me of, suddenly became that much more ridiculous, while at the same time, my envy of him grew even more.

So as practice came to a close, Coach called up his team near the spectator's area on the boundary and did something I'd never seen or wished my whole family could be there to witness, I think.

Coach Brown says: "I want to introduce you to the only player in the history of this great Conference to be selected as the MVP and Offensive Player of the Year, unanimously, in the same year.... He led us to the National Title game that same year, and he's one of the most talented players I've ever coached, and more importantly he's one of the best people I've ever coached.... Former quarterback, University of Oklahoma—Danny Bradley."

Not having seen any of my Dad's college career (games) in person, made me suddenly feel as if I had. I'd only read about his accomplishments and Coach's comments, unbeknownst to him, was like throwing a lil salt on an already open wound. But speaking of modesty—my father never even talked about it. With him, it was always about *Faith, Family and Fatherhood.*

So being the considerate man he was, knowing what it was like to be one of those players, who just needed to go shower, eat, and lay it down, he decided not to give a speech. He stepped right into the middle of his universities great nemesis, raised his hand, as they huddled around him and suddenly I heard a voice yell, "Stay Focused on three; one, two, three—STAY FOCUSED!" The whole team yelled.

Before we said our good-byes, my father asked Coach Brown about UT's up and coming summer football camps. Coach gave him the run down and thought, too, I would enjoy the camps and encouraged him to enroll me.

I nodded in agreement, thinking that I would at least attend the camp, perhaps. Mind you, I haven't really done anything in football at this point. And barely played at PB for the Zebras. Then coach went on to say that these camps would be a great way for me to discover whether football is a sport I'd like to really pursue or not. I accepted the advice as he and my father hugs again, as Coach then heads back toward his office, while we made our way back to our car. During the journey, my Dad says, "What an amazing job they've done with their athletic facility.... It's off to OU in the morning, to see how the family is doing—hopefully the Switzer complex rivals this monster."

He notices my demeanor and asked, trying to cheer me up a bit, "So what do you think, big-timer? Can you envision getting an education from a major program like this and perhaps making that *big catch* on national television with a hundred thousand rooting in the stands?"

Dejectedly, I replied, "I don't think I can make it at a school like this."

By this point, we had reached the car, with his head down I went on to say, "It's just more than I imagined. Its just seems to big."

"Mark Bradley, there is nothing—and I mean nothing—too big for you to accomplish if you have the skills and the confidence. You can graduate from any university in this world, son, if you apply yourself, and be just as accomplished as any of those guys you saw on the field today, if this is your gift and apply yourself."

"But you can handle this kind of stuff at this level, Dad.... For me, after seeing it close up, I don't see how I could make it at a place like this," I replied with concern.

He concedes for now as we get back on the road on I-35 headed back to Dallas. After complete silence for the first twenty-minutes of the trip, my father asked, "What do you see yourself doing in life, son?"

"I don't know. I thought I did until today," I replied with a high level of uncertainty.

"Well, we got a lil time, let's think about it," he said.

"I can always do network marketing," I quickly replied.

"Network Marketing?" Danny asked, being a bit surprised by my answer.

"Yeah, it's working for you," I replied, being dead serious.

"Great, then, do network marketing. But it would be wiser to own the network marketing business, not work for one. And that would require you get educated, son.

"I understand, but a place like UT and OU, just seems like its to much to deal with; the stadium is too big, the campus is too big, the players are too big—it all appears to be just too big for me, Daddy," I fearfully replied. "You can do this, and I thought maybe I could do this too—until today."

He pauses for a second to gather his thoughts, to ensure his every word counted. After all, I understood he had a responsibility to me as my father, to see that I get a chance at life. And he took that very seriously, but I didn't think he truly understood how hard life was for me. But he then makes a few statements that caused me to regress just a little with the *'Woe is me,'* mind set.

"Sometimes in life, son, a person has to be *terrified* before they can be *edified.* I knew this would be a struggle for you.... Young men with little to no exposure, no hope, no dreams, usually lack confidence in themselves," he said. "They often see life through the eyes of fear—not faith.... *And God has not given his children a spirit of fear, son, but of power, love and a sound mind.... All things are possible with God; You can do all things through Christ, which strengthens you,* even when it feels like He's abandoned you.... So where is your faith."

"Its just hard living with people that don't seem to really care about you."

"Trust me, I get that," my dad replied. "They don't trust you, believe you, or support you, unless it perhaps in someway benefit them, too?"

"Yeah," I replied.

"They won't listen to you or talk to you, they talk at you and down to you."

"Pretty much," I replied as a matter of fact.

"And you're wondering where is God, how could he possibly allow your family to be so inconsiderate and disinterested in you and the things you really wanna do?"

"Yeah!

"Mark, things are not always what they appear to be.... God has not abandoned you. He's a good God, son, and *promises to never leave you or forsake you.* But cannot and will not stop what we allow.... Or else He'd be breaking His own covenant with man."

"But you didn't have to deal with this kind of stuff with your family, Daddy."

"Son, every family has issues. Maybe I didn't have the exact same issue with my mom that you have with yours, but I did encounter a ton of obstacles growing up, too, which lead me to many of those same questions: does God really care? If so, where is He? Why would He allow these things to happen to me? But when we see evil or something unfortunate happen to someone we don't like, we, then, magically thank God for bringing His justice against that person.... So, yes, I been there... Its called the spirit of confusion.... And God *is not the author of confusion, but of peace,* son."

I'm thinking, *man, that's exactly how I feel.*

"We all deserve hell, but God gave us heaven.... Not because of our goodness, by any means, but because of His unconditional love for us," he shared. "And despite how dismal your situation may look, son, *there is nothing too hard for God.*

"But Dad, we go to church every Sunday," I sadly replied, trying to understand.

"I understand," my father quickly replied. "But we can also go to class five days a week and still fail the course," he said, certain he was referencing my situation academically. "*But its not just you, son.* I came from a family of violence, envy, strife, drug use, drugs sold, robbery, adultery, fornication, abandonment; you name it, somebody in my family was doing it, all the while attending church I might add. So, church attendance don't make us holy or righteous, son, its the blood of the cross and the grace of God that makes it possible for us to live right."

Now, I know my situation is bad, but I didn't see it being that bad. I hadn't seen or knew of any of these things going on within my family.

"I guess I need to just accept the fact that my family is not perfect.... I thought going to church was living right, I know that's what they believe." I replied, confused.

"Son, we don't go to church because we're Christians, we go to church because that's what Christian people do.... And no, living right and being perfect are not exactly the same.... *The heart is willing but the flesh is weak. And God judges the heart."*

"Well, we all must be confused about church and living right."

"Understood, but a man who's living right always recognizes and admits his imperfections, but the perfect man has no imperfections.... And if a man has no imperfections, son, he doesn't need God, he is God.... And since we know the only man that walked the face of the earth with perfection was Christ, then we know *there is no one man perfect, no not one, but Him.* Hang in there, your mother will change her position about this situation once *"the word"* that's being preached in church gets down inside of her."

"Well, I don't quite see it happening," I replied.

"Mark, we all must grow from faith-to-faith, son.... I, too, am not completely what I ought to be, but I am nowhere near of what I used to be," he said with conviction.

A million things were going on in my mind at this point as he shared, as my emotions just suddenly overtook me. In my head, the biggest problem I had was the lack of support and encouragement from my mother, but he obviously believed that one of the biggest problems I had at this stage—was me.

"Even if I believed this was possible, Dad, she's not gonna let me go.... All they gon do is give me a hard time, and I'm tired of fighting with them," as tears just rushed out.

But Danny paused, recognizing that the battles his son has going with his family had simply worn him down. His mind just wasn't strong enough to deal with the pressure his family had placed on him. Touching him on the leg, he said, "It's going to be alright, son.... I'll cancel the trip to OU and get you back home."

This concerned father thought to himself, *Yeah—I might be wrong, but it's time I force a sit down with somebody in the Davises' family—this has now become an absolute travesty.*

22

The Forewarning

The next day, Shelly and Danny's seven-year old nephew are waiting at the gate for Mark and Danny to deplane at Little Rock Airport. As soon as they do, Shelly can see two things immediately: Mark has been crying, and Danny is a little agitated. Apparently something went wrong with this visit, including the plane ride home. And Shelly wants to know what happened, to which Danny tersely replies, "We'll talk about it later, mother."

By the time they pull up to the Bradley house, it's about 1 p.m., Danny requests to speak with Mark alone, in the car. As Shelly and his nephew exit, Danny reaches for his cell phone, dials the Davis home and hit speaker. Odell answers.

"Mister Davis, this is Danny—I'm back in town with Mark.... If you have a moment, I'd like to sit down and chat with you regarding a few issues going on with Mark."

Odell pauses and says, "Oh, okay.... what's going on with him?" He asked.

Danny could hear the wheels spinning in his head over the phone line, and frankly replied, "Not sure, Mister Davis.... I've tried getting Denise to sit down and discuss these concerns on several occasions, but unfortunately, it hasn't happened yet. But it's my understanding that Mark lives with you the majority of the time, so I'm sure we can shed some light on what might be going on."

"Well, okay—sure," Odell replies hesitantly, "What time?" He asks.

Danny looks at his watch and says, "Can you do 1:30?"

"Yeah, I guess I can make that.... Where would you like to meet?"

"You tell me," Danny replies, as I begin to ponder if my grandad would really come.

Odell gives him a location; a local restaurant on Olive Street. Danny accepts and heads that way. On arrival, I look over at my dad and said, "He's not gonna show."

"Why?" Danny asked.

"Becuz, he's probably called my mom and she probably told him not to come."

Danny didn't respond, he just sat and waited. The parking lot was full, and it's now 1:40 p.m. He sends me inside to search for him just in case we missed him, which was difficult to do, based on where we parked, near the entrance and the time we arrived.

I come back a few minutes later and say, "Nope—I didn't see him."

One thirty comes and goes and still no Odell Davis. Frustrated over being stood up, Danny gets on his cell and calls Odell again, and this time Leola answers and says, "No—he's not here."

Danny then calls Denise and gets her voice-mail, for which he leaves a message asking her to call him back immediately, urgent, with the quick. And by 2:00 p.m., we had made our way back to the Bradleys, with Odell as a no show.

And over two hours later, it's Denise that dials him up—not Odell.

"Ms. Terry—it's time we get together," Danny said politely.

"What's going on—what's wrong?" Denise asked.

"The usual, everything, Dee—what time can we meet?"

"Where is Mark," she then asked?

"With me, where else would he be, Dee? What time can we get-together?"

"I can meet you in about thirty minutes at the Admiral Benbow Inn on East Harding."

Danny hangs up, grabs me and headed that way, a three-block drive. As we sat in the parking lot of the hotel awaiting my mom's arrival, I then said, "And she's not gonna come alone, she'll bring somebody.... She's not gonna meet with you by her self."

Danny, again, chose not to comment while in deep thought. And, as predicted, Denise pulls up in her SUV, with Odell

"I knew she wouldn't come alone, if she came at all.... And I think my granddad has to know that a lot of what my mom is doing is wrong, daddy."

"Well, son, I'm not convinced of that—your granddad's position seems to be the same as his daughter.... But today, he'll get a chance to prove us both wrong.... And if you have anything to say during this discussion—say it; and don't you hesitate—do you understand me?" He asked.

"Yes sir," I replied.

Until this moment, I was convinced that there wasn't going to be a meeting. So I didn't have any fears as to what the outcome might be. But, after they drove up together, I became extremely concerned. I knew my Dad was *for real* and I guess I was about to find out just *how real* the two most dominant people in my life really were. And finally, doggone it, if my Mom had any trump card to play to validate her animosity towards this man, this was definitely her time to play it.

So as my leading parents enter the hotel, my Dad and I wait till the door closes before we exited the car. I tried to get a glimpse of my Dad's real demeanor, but I couldn't really read him. As we entered, we noticed the two of them had taken seats on opposite sides of a rectangular table in the lobby. So we took the chairs at opposite ends of it. Not one greeting was exchanged and they didn't say "one word" to me or even look my way, which wasn't too alarming under the circumstances.

My Dad opens the discussion.

"First of all, I'm very disappointed in how you have handled this entire situation over the years, Denise."

"What's the problem?" My Mom asked, as if she didn't see any reason to be alarmed.

"The problem is this kid has no confidence; his self esteem and attitude about life is negative and hopeless; he says you guys don't really care about what he thinks or how he feels.... And quite frankly, I'm a lil agitated by the fact that all of us at this table are born-again believers, yet there seems to be an alliance—a calculated effort to keep my son and me separated."

My Mom interrupts with a comment that was obviously directed to Odell, not me.

"But Danny, don't you think if you and I communicated more, we wouldn't be having these *so called* differences about Mark?"

"Denise, yes, perhaps so if *you* were willing to communicate more. I've tried reaching out to you, but you obviously haven't seen a need to talk," he replied. "Even Mark has witnessed the number of attempts I've made to reach out to you."

"Danny,' she replied, with a solemn look as if to rebut his ridiculous response to her question, which my Dad senses and decides to further validate his statement.

"Well, Dee—there he sits…. Why don't you ask him?"

My Mom doesn't even look my direction, nor had my grandfather at this point. So, he does it for her, and said, "Mark, son, sorry to put you on the spot, but for clarification, how many times you recall that you seen me make attempts to sit down with your Mom about these issues?"

"Several times," I replied nervously.

"How many voice mail messages of mine have you retrieved?" He asked calmly.

"A lot," I replied, not knowing how my honesty would affect this tense get-together,

"So, there it is, Dee. He didn't say every now and then or on a few occasions, but several times and a lot," my dad shoots back.

"Well, why did you bring him back so quickly," she asked.

"Because he wanted to come home, Denise.... And when given an opportunity to talk about his life, his future and what he wants to do with it, he simply falls a part?" He said.

"What happened?" My Mom suspiciously asked.

"Well, for one, he says he's not interested in getting an education.... And two, this kid chose to walk away from an opportunity of a lifetime at two of the best academic and athletic institutions in America, simply because he doesn't think he's smart enough. And when I asked why, he says *'because the freaking campuses are too big and stadiums are way too big; and that his mom and family will not allow him to pursue it even if he believed he could make it happen—they won't support me, he says,'"* as my Dad makes eye contact with both of the primary leaders in my life.

At that comment, Odell decided to speak, by first attacking, "Don't you think you're pushing this football thing a lil too much on Mark? How do you know he even wants to play football?"

Now knowing that my family were huge-huge football fans, especially Odell, often talking about me going to all these same major colleges, comparing me to this same man over and over again, is now asking, if *'my dad'* might be pushing me too much towards football? I thought, *you have got to be kidding me!*

Danny paused in disappointment, and then looks Odell right straight in the eye and politely said, "Why don't you ask him, Odell? He's still in the room—he hasn't left yet."

For real, I thought.

And shockingly, my granddad likewise didn't even look my way. So, my Dad, once again, turns to me and asks, "Mark, son, if you don't mind, can you please tell us whose idea it was to visit these campuses?"

"Mainly mine," I replied, again, not knowing how honesty might affect us all.

"You sure," he asked, again.

"Yeah," I replied. "You've encouraged me but it was mainly somethin I wanted to do.

However, I could tell that ruffled my grandfather's feathers a bit, as my Dad continued on, "Football is my least concern, sir. But even if it was my focus, I'm his father, Odell. Who is perhaps more qualified to help this kid than anybody you might know.... As his grandfather, the question you should be asking is why Mark doesn't think getting an education is important?"

"Oh, yeah," Odell immediately replied. "He's goin to college...yes sa he is! Even if I got to pay for it myself...he's goin to college—I guarantee you that!"

My Dad's expression preceded his words.

"Well Mister Davis, if you guys deny this kid an opportunity to get an education for free, through relationships I've fostered for years, then trust me, you will have to pay for him to get one because I'm not givin him a quarter."

A quarter, I thought to myself. Now, mind you, this was a very serious discussion and I was excited we finally got a chance to sit down and talk, mainly to discover more about why my mom despised this guy, but when he made that comment, I wanted to laugh. My Dad is fairly articulate, and just the way he closed that statement was classic and kind of funny.

Odell's comeback with, "Well, Mark is already gettin scholarship offers from major colleges all across the country, Danny.... So he is goin to college and might not have to pay for it," he shot back, as my mom looked on with this *what do you have to say to that,* look. And I was too, for that matter.

My Dad just smiled and shook his head in disbelief as he gathered his thoughts, before saying, "Have you read them? Do they say, this is a scholarship offer please sign right here on this dotted line, or are they just simply questionnaires?"

Now I knew I hadn't really did anything in football, just yet, but it was kind of cool to get letters from all the schools, appearing to be offering me a scholarship.

Odell nods his head, signaling, "Yes—these are scholarship offers!"

Danny bowed his head as if to say, *these folk really are clueless.*

"Odell—let me help you. Most every kid in America that plays high school football often gets these form letters—not scholarship offers, but form letters from colleges and universities who think a kid "might" someday be a player.... So, you might want to go home and re-read them.... I'm not telling you what I think, I'm telling what I know."

"Well Danny, here's what I know, don't concern yourself with Mark.... Mark be just fine.... Yes he will!" Odell shot back, as he pushes away from the table, signalling that he was about ready to go, as my mom reaches for her purse.

Danny takes a deep breath in frustration as he gradually stood up, gathered his keys and said, "Son, I'll be in touch," and walks out.

At this point, I knew without question my Mom had no validated reason as to why she was so against this man accept the obvious. Instead of her setting the record straight, in front of me and her father, he simply cleared his name from all the criminal charges brought against him by the two leading detectives in my household. He had shined an even brighter light on this senseless game being played by my family, which left me really concerned about exiting this building with them, even though I was unsure if I wanted to leave with him, either.

There was complete silence in the car on the way home, which was a short drive, as Odell breaks the dead air, "Oh yeah, you goin to college. If I got to pay for it myself—you hear me? You will get an education, Mark!"

Now I didn't know all of my grandfather's finances, but what I did know, he didn't have tens of thousands of dollars in reserve to pay for my education. And if such was the case, it was obvious that he was just boasting a bit in front of someone he knew could perhaps afford to do so. Nonetheless, this was the first time I got the chance to see the two sides debate face-to-face. And unfortunately, for me, they appeared to be intimidated by this man. His success, wisdom and knowledge seemed to agitate them both. They were not as nearly as talkative and direct with him as they are behind his back. My mom I believe chose not to say much out of fear of what my granddad might discover. But after seeing how he dealt with it all, perhaps my father might be right. Maybe he knew more than I thought he did and was in cahoots with helping her stay in control. They knew he was in a much better position to help me, but they didn't want to admit or accept the help, if they couldn't control the help.

In the meantime, Mayberry had all but faded from the scene. He wasn't talking much at this stage, at least not to me, although he did stay in contact with my mom and the family. They seemed to be indebted to him regarding the whole thing. In their eyes, Daddy Mayberry could do *no wrong,* while my father Danny couldn't do *no right.*

And I just didn't know how to break away, especially with some of the ill-feelings I, too, had towards the man, which kind-of-sorta tied his hands. And he certainly didn't want to force me to break away and make this situation that much more challenging for me to deal with. Again, he was a firm believer that *right becomes wrong, when it's forced.* So, in a nutshell, it appeared as if he was stuck like a duck in this thing called life. And over the next couple of months, I was under the highest level of maximum security I'd been since my mom's announcement.

My sixteenth birthday had now come and gone, and yet there was no change in my name. Apparently, he had not made contact with my mom to have that chat, and the last session ended before he could get around to it. So he decided to have the attorney go ahead and send the petition by mail, as he began making plans for me to attend UT's and OU's summer football camps. I re-thought my position on it, contacted him and decided to go. Coach Brown seemed like a great guy and I still wanted to visit OU.

And by mid-June '98, true to his word, I had prepared to spend the entire summer in Dallas, Norman, and Austin. And this time, I was pretty excited about it, and even approached him again about the idea of moving, believe it or not. He was graciously pleasant about it. I knew that this was what I needed to do, despite how attached I was to my family. And He, too, had the papers for the name change in hand, and made it clear that at the conclusion of the summer camps, I should officially have a new name and perhaps a new address. We even discussed college entrance exams, and tutors to help me prepare. But I think he only chatted about it to pacify me, not that he believed that I would really do it, because he would often challenge me on it by conference.

"I know I keep allowing her to change my mind—but I want to get out," I replied.

"Yes, we know you need too, but will you are two different things.... So why don't you go ahead and, at least, tell your mother about the name change. Its been over a year, it appears that getting another opportunity to talk with her might be slim to none."

"Dad, I'm changing my name, regardless," I replied with conviction.

They say their good-byes and Danny hangs up and calls his mother, Shelly, to share what he had not yet shared with Mark.

"Mother, the name change just got a bit more complicated."

"How so? She asked.

"Apparently, Denise filed for child support against this dude back in '84, according to the Attorney working the job," Danny said.

"You're kidding," Shelly surprisingly said. "Government assistance I can see, but not down right child support, knowing the man is not the child's father, Danny."

"That's what I'm being told.... But either way, government assistance or child support, a petition in court has been filed against Reginald Mayberry as father of Mark Anthony Mayberry, which will now require signatures from both him and Denise to change his name," Danny replied.

Meanwhile, at the Davis house, Denise and Mark had finished dinner and was now watching TV with the grandparents. Cassie was out with her dad. *What a great time to chat about the name change,* I thought. So, being confident that this was absolutely the right thing to do, I asked to speak with her in our old bedroom. Once inside, I took a deep breath and just laid it out.

"Mom, I understand that movin to Texas is out of the question, I've decided to not bring that up again, I think.... But I do want to change my name."

"To what?" She frantically asked.

"From Mayberry to Bradley."

"Mark!" She said, seeming to be surprised. "Why would you want to do that?!"

"Mayberry is not my name, mama!"

"Mayberry is your Daddy, Mark!"

"Mama, Mayberry is not my daddy!"

"Mayberry has taken care of you from the day you was born up to this point, why would you want to hurt him like that?!"

I pause, thinking, *Mom, come on, you can't really-really believe I'm still that clueless about all this.... This man may have taken care of you all this time, but not really me,* which I then replied, "Mom, I appreciate all Mayberry has done, but I don't want to carry the man's name any longer. He is not my father—plus I don't even hear from Mayberry much anymore."

Suddenly, she stormed out the room and soon thereafter my granddad, Odell, and this time even grandma Leola was standing at the bedroom door.

"Mark," Odell says, "Your mother told me you want to change your name?"

I paused with no response.

"The only reason Danny wants to change your name is cause you're good at sports, Mark. That's all this is about, son. We've had this discussion before," he said.

Again, I'm thinking, *no, maybe it's because he's my Dad. And if I'm not mistaken, your kids carry your name, Odell, why can't I carry my father's name?* But, again, I chilled. I chose not to say what I thought.

Seeing my Mom reenter the scene, made me regret even broaching the subject, knowing they had a history of teaming up against me, for which I, then, say, "But I haven't even done anything in football, granddad."

Hoping I could get some kind of support from grandma Leola, she then surprisingly says, "Mark, I think you're making a mistake changing your name, son."

And I'm thinking, *They had finally managed to convert her. She was no longer neutral regarding this situation.*

Noticing the anguish on my face, my Mom says angrily, "If I let you do it, you will have to keep the name Mayberry, and just add Bradley!"

"I don't want to do that, mama."

"Everybody already know you as Mark Mayberry, son!" My mom replied.

"I understand, but I should be known as Mark Bradley, mama—not Mark Mayberry."

"Mark, I think you're making a mistake, son," Leola said again. "It appears that this guy is indeed brainwashing you."

My mom then bolts from the scene and says, "I don't have the patience for this right now. I'll call y'all later," as she rushed out the house.

About a week later, my grandma Shelly called on behalf of my Dad to inform me that it was time for my summer trip to begin. I assured her with a bit of uncertainty that I would be ready. But as soon as I hung up the phone, grandma Leola, who had overheard my conversation says, "You know your mother is not going to allow you to go to Texas to attend these summer camps, Mark. So, if I were you, I wouldn't make too many plans with Danny.... You know how crazy she can get."

At such point, another relative walks in while Leola was red flagging me, "The hell with Danny Bradley! Why you trippin, Mark!"

Which always validated just how uninformed they were about my relationship with this man. But saved by the bell—the doorbell rings. It was my friend Tanisha, who couldn't have come at a better time. So I went outside to fill her in on the latest regarding the name change, and just as I was about to share the situation dealing with the summer football camps, my grandma Leola called me back inside—my mom was on the phone. So I told Tee to hold on, I'll be right back.

And as usual, she jumps right into it strong, "Mark, you are not going to Texas to visit your Dad this summer until he and I have a better understanding! And I don't know what's up with this football camp stuff, but you can forget it! It ain't happening!" She said, "Plus, I've already asked your Daddy Mayberry and your granddad Odell to see about paying for you to go on another AAU basketball trip this summer, since you had such a good time at the last one.... But the problem is, this particular AAU camp is in Dallas—and if I can't trust that you **will not** call Danny, then you're not going anywhere this summer." And bang, she hangs up.

Unbelievable, I thought to myself. *I give up—I'm done with even trying to fight any part of this nonsense anymore. This junk has been going on since I been a kid-kid! I'm not going on no doggone AAU trip to Dallas!*

Thankfully I had asked Tanisha to wait because I definitely needed someone to vent my frustration too, as I started immediately having thoughts of suicide, again.

However, with just weeks removed from that conversation, and as embarrassing as it is to admit this, here I was again headed to do the unthinkable. While my mom and granddad, Odell drove me to meet up with my AAU basketball team, I felt like a prisoner being transported to a jail cell. As we rolled up to school, I saw a few vans parked in front with my AAU teammates piling into them, as my mom began reiterating how I **was not** to call my Daddy Danny while in Dallas, under no circumstances.

"As I told you before, son, some of this might not make any sense to you right now, Mark, but later on we'll help you understand why we've been so protective of you where Danny is concerned…. I've already given all the coaches instructions not to let you leave with anyone, and I mean no one," including Danny," she said sternly.

I recall thinking, *Lord, when does this stupid senseless war come to an end? And why doesn't this man deserve a break? After all, none of them has been able to prove any of their frivolous charges against him—so what's the freaking point!* But an even better question is: *why am I continuing to allow them to manipulate me into thinking that there is more to this story?! Just tell me what the hell the man did and let's get on with it already, please!* I thought out loud in my spirit.

In their eyes, this man was just flat out not worthy enough to be my father. But yet, I'm living with and around several fathers, who were about as *unqualified* as they claimed he was, making them just as guilty of not having any love, respect, or character. And had raised me to be the same, or else I wouldn't be agreeing to such a ridiculous idea of being just miles away or even blocks from my father's front door and not call him. And I'm sure they were proud of the young man I was becoming.

So while we were traveling back and forth to the Grapevine Mills Mall, after and in between games, I would point out to my teammates streets and places my Dad had taken me. But one of my teammates that didn't quite believe these stories, suddenly asked why hasn't your dad been to any of your games, if he lives right across the way? And having been through this before, I withdrew and just said, "He's out of town."

My coach, after overhearing our conversation, pulled me aside and says, "Not trying to get in your business, but what's going on with you and your Pops?"

I didn't know exactly what he knew, and I didn't want to expose anything new, so I politely replied, "Nothin really," as I tried to look surprised that he would even ask.

My coach then pauses, looks at me in thought as if he knew I was not shooting straight, and says, "Your dad seems to be a nice guy, Mark. I don't really know him, but from what I hear about him around town from reliable sources say that he's a good guy.... And if that's true, don't let nobody keep you from your father, Mark.... I don't care who it is, especially one that can help you get out of that small town and make somethin of yourself. "

At that moment, I realized that this coach was making known that he wasn't down with disrespecting my Dad like this. I knew then that if I wanted to call him, I could. But, at this point, I was just too embarrassed to make the call. I had disappointed him on so many occasions with so many broken promises, I began to think maybe that he should just give up and just let me be and let us go ahead and just do what ever we were going do and be. I mean, really, come on, what's the point?! Why keep trying to father a son that my entire family has made it perfectly clear that they **do not** want him in my life.

However, even though I was way too afraid to challenge my beloved mother and family regarding the move to Texas, I was definitely unwilling to stand by at let them rob me of my true identity. So the name change without doubt was going to happen. This man was more than worthy of having his son to, at least, carry his name—don't you think?

23

The Accountability

It had now been three days since I'd returned from AAU basketball camp in Dallas. I was already feeling bad about being blocks away from my Dad but wasn't allowed to contact him or better yet chose not too. And as I played video games in my bedroom, I could hear my mom enter the house from a trip she had to take with her job. She wanted to know off top, did I call my Daddy Danny? I informed her, unfortunately, that I didn't.

"And when he start asking questions, what do you say?

I knew what I should say, but I also knew what she wanted to hear. So, I just tell him I chose to go with the AAU team instead of coming to Texas and attend the camps.

While she appeared to be pleased with that answer, I knew she would have a problem with my next statement. "I did talk to Grandma Shelly, she said an attorney would be sending you the name change document for you and Mayberry to sign."

"So, you're going to do it regardless of how I feel about it? She asked.

I stop playing my video game for a second, and answered, "Mom, I don't wanna continue carrying Mayberry's name.... He's not my father."

"Mark, don't hurt your daddy like this?" She pleaded.

"Mom, I'm not a Mayberry."

She paused while reaching for her purse. She then pulls out a document, places it on the coffee table and begins to write her name on it, and said, "I've already gotten the papers Mark Anthony, but you will be the one to tell your Daddy Mayberry and get his signature—not me.... And he just happens to be in town, so, let's go!"

"Why do I have to be the one to talk to him, Mama?!" I asked.

"Because it's not me that's requesting the name change—you are! So, lets go!" She says, as she gets up and starts towards the door.

I, then, reluctantly got up from the sofa, put on my baseball cap, and followed her out the door. And as we pulled up in front of Mayberry's parents home, instead of parking, she just stopped the car, wished me luck, and pulled off.

I stood there thinking, *She's really going to make me do this all by myself!* So, I think about it for a minute and decided I can't back out now. I then step up and rang the doorbell—Mayberry answers.

"What's up, Mark? How are you? Where you been? Its good to see you?"

I told him I was fine and then got straight to the point.

"I stopped by to talk to you about the changing of my last name," I replied with concern, not knowing how he might respond, as I reached into my pocket and pulled out the tri-folded petition and handed it to him. "My mom has already signed them, she brought me by to get your signature."

He took the document and didn't even look at it. He just placed it on the nearby table and said, "Oh, okay—I'll sign them before I head back to Alabama. But how have you been otherwise?" He asked, as he gets up and exits the room obviously a bit stunned.

"Fine," I replied, again.

I didn't know if he was angry or what—nor did I know where he was headed. So, I grabbed the house phone and called my friend, Carl, who lived near by, and asked him if he would come scoop me up. I told him where I was and needed him to come, now!

I hung up just as Mayberry reenters the room with a soda in hand. He picks up where he left off. "And your grandparents, how are they doing?"

I politely told him that they're fine; Cassie is fine; the family is fine; school was fine; grades are up and down, but I'll be fine.

"And football? How is that working out?" He asked.

"Hanging in there," I replied as I glance through the window, looking for my ride, which had just arrived.

"You expecting someone?"

Carl, then, honks the horn on que. "Yeah, my ride is here.... So, just let me know when I can get those papers back," I said, with hand on the door knob and turning.

"You bet, I'll sign them before I head back," he responded, with a tone of certainty.

"Thanks," I replied as I exited and made a beeline for the car. As soon as I was in the car and strapped down, Carl was full of questions.

"Dude, what's going on?"

"Take me to my grandma Shelly's house," I replied frantically.

"What's up, what happened?" He asked again.

"Man—my mom made me be the one to approach Mayberry about the name change!"

"Are you serious?!" He asked.

"Can you believe that?!" I asked, as I try to gather my wits.

"Man, this situation with your Pops and folks is jacked-up."

"Who you tellin…. And I'm tired of dealing with it!"

"Tired, you should be fed up, 12," Carl said.

"I just don't get it, Carl.... I just don't get why she would chance taking this thing this far, knowing I know what's up?"

"What the heck did your dad do to your mom? She treats this man like he killed somebody in her family," Carl shot out.

"I don't know—I've been trying to get answers to that same question for the past five plus years, and from what I can see, he ain't done nothing to her or them," I replied.

"You should have just left and moved on to Texas, dude."

"Yeah, I know.... She got my whole family trippin about this craziness."

I could feel myself beginning to get emotional for the two-hundred and fiftieth time, as my eyes started to well with tears but held them. "I didn't do it because I just didn't want to fight with my mom about this every single day."

"Come on, man.... Where have you been? You're fightin them now every single day."

"But one day," I said, as a tear finally fell. "If I ever get out, I will never come back and deal with all of this strife, CB."

"Never?!" Carl asked.

"Ever!" I replied with conviction. "Unless my mom changes her ways, I **will never** come back to this nonsense."

"Wow, that's pretty strong, but I understand," Carl replied. "She got this thing against your Dad that just won't quit," as they pull up to Shelly's.

"Yep! And it appears that she's willing to fight him for the rest of her life on this." I sadly replied, as I exited to car.

About a week later, Danny's 500SL is flirting with the speed limit on I-30 east, en route to Pine Bluff, after discovering Mark's whereabouts the previous week. He makes a cell phone call to his Mom's house. When he gets the answering machine, he leaves a message instructing his mother to locate Mark and bring him to the house.

However, his cell phone rings shortly thereafter.... It's his attorney, who informs him that she hasn't heard from Denise or Mayberry regarding the change of name petition. And that we will need the signatures of both to overturn the current petition filed by Denise several years ago. He tells her he'll get back, after he brings closure to it.

It was now 7 p.m. when Danny pulls up to his parent's house. Mark and Carl Booty, were standing outside chatting, as Mark's body language expresses his nervousness.

"How you Mister Bradley?" Carl asked.

"Good young fella—and you?" Danny asked in return.

"Good—just trying to keep up with your son."

"You and me both," Danny replies, while looking directly at Mark.

As he turned to enter the house, Carl turns to me and says, "Your Pops is bout the coolest dude I know, but he appears to be a lil hot."

"Well, if I was him, I'd be too," as I extended my fist to say my good-byes.

"Didn't you just see him while you were in Texas, how did that go?"

"Unfortunately, it didn't, but I'll explain later," I replied.

We brake as I paused to think about my answers before heading into the house. But for privacy, he took me out to a local eatery located in the Pines Mall called *Garfield's*. And on the way, I made known that Mayberry had been in town and had not signed the name change petition, he had left them behind in Pine Bluff.

We sat at a corner booth, and all seemed to be surprisingly fine. The waitress took our drink orders and handed us menus, but once he informed her that he would not be eating, that took my already nervous mind-set to stage-fright. And as soon as the waitress gathered the menus, he looks me in the eye and said, "Talk—I'm listening."

And I immediately thought, *Awe-man, he must know!*

To make sure of what he knew, I asked, "About what?"

He drops his head, and then said, "Would you like to tell me what happened to you this time over the past few weeks, Mark?"

Since he didn't seem too-too upset, I figured I had a better chance by just telling him the truth, uncut. So I told him exactly what happened, that once I started making plans to come to Texas, my mom, appearing to still be bothered by that meeting at the Admiral Benbow Inn, decided that she was not going to allow me to go visit him until he and her had could come to a better understanding.

"They sent me on another AAU basketball trip, a tournament."

"And just for the record, again, who is they, son?"

"My mom and grandparents." I replied, jittery.

Then he asked the one question I did not want to have to answer.

"Where was this tournament Mark?"

But before I could get it out, tears began to well up and fall from my eyes, so much so, I now couldn't talk. I just couldn't find the words or the guts to answer the one question to which he appeared to already know the answer.

"Where was this tournament, Mark?" He asked again.

"In Texas," I muttered, as tears now raced even more down my face.

He pauses, takes a deep breath, and leans back and said, "Texas—where in Texas was this tournament held, Mark?"

All of a sudden, I felt as if I couldn't breathe. And again, I just couldn't get it out.

"Where in Texas was this tournament held, son?!" He asked, as his voice rises.

"Dallas," I responded solemnly, as I cut my eyes up at him.

He takes another deep sigh, pauses in deep thought with disappointment imprinted on his face, and asked, “So, you went all the way to Dallas, Texas, with your AAU team, during the same time you were scheduled to be in Texas to attend a football camp that you requested I make arrangements for—is that what you’re telling me?!”

I had no response. I knew it was an ugly thing to do, but hearing it and now seeing the effects of it face-to-face validated the level of garbage this man had to deal with from both me and my family. He was about as disappointed as I had ever seen him—and I was probably about as broken as he had ever seen me.

“Is that what you’re telling me?!” He asked again.

I just didn’t know how to respond. So, I just shook my head, “yes.”

“Why didn’t you call me, son?! And please don’t blame your mother!”

I was numb—I didn’t know what to say when having to face the reality of my actions. He was right, I shouldn’t be allowing my mother or anybody to keep coercing me into these displeasing positions with my father, and I certainly can’t blame them anymore, this was now all on me.

“Let me ask you again, “Is there any reason as to why you chose not to call your father again and inform him that you guys have made other plans?!”

“She made me promise not to call, Daddy!” I finally cried out. “Or else I would have been grounded for the whole summer again with nothin to do, and I didn’t want to go through that again.”

The waitress was coming to re-fill their drinks but Danny waves her off.

“Didn’t I just ask you not to blame this all on your mother?!

But it was all I had folks—it was the truth. I guess in hindsight, I should have been willing to suffer, as he had done for me than to go on another trip and further suffer him.

“Let’s get real here, Mark—what kind of relationship do we really have—one minute you cool and then you’re not; another moment you with me and then you seem to be against me; one day you’re in, the next you’re out.... What’s up—I’m confused?”

I paused for a second, then said, “I think you’re a good guy, successful, made a name for yourself; know a lot of people; done a lot of positive things; been a lot of places.”

“Is that it?” He asked.

“Yeah—pretty much,” I replied quietly, as I tried to regroup.

“So, after all we’ve been through together, the past ten-twelve years; all the sacrifices you’ve seen me make; the money, the time; all the phone calls that didn’t get returned; all the praying we’ve done together; crying we’ve done together and all you think of me is that I’m a successful guy, who knows a few people and been a few places?

Man, when he said it back, it sounded very artificial and disconnected. It was clear I had no real concept or understanding of responsibility and accountability. So I began trying to apologize, once again, for frustrating the one person I truly believe loved me, despite some of the mixed feelings I had about him and them.

"Dad, I know you care about me, and I appreciate you pushing me to be better, but as you well know, they don't really want you in my life. I'm not totally sure why Mom even told you about me.... But I do believe my Mom's main problem is more than just her once-upon-a-time personal interest in you. At this point, she's just flat out jealous of you and what you've become.... And to be honest, at times, I have those same feelings of jealous towards you, especially with all the playa hating going on inside my house."

Danny pauses, knowing that was a pivotal point in his relationship with his son. So, he relents, as Mark continues: "It doesn't feel good to admit to my father that I have negative thoughts toward him, but when you live with people who's always comparing you up against your own father, it's hard.... Its hard to even like you after being around them everyday.... So the reason the move to Texas was so impossible for me is because every time I got closer to doing it, it felt like I was losing my Mom."

Danny, though furious on the inside, tries to regroup and come back with a more calmer demeanor, "Son, your relationship with your father shouldn't ever jeopardize your relationship with your mother—if anything it should strengthen it."

"I understand that-that's the way it should be, but that's not the way it is with her. She makes me feel like its over if I decide to team up with you in any way.... It just all looks like one big competition thing with them when it comes to you.... My Mom knows *they* can't really help me do the things I really want to do—but she doesn't really want *you* to help me do those things, either, if it doesn't benefit her in some way."

At this point, Danny had to try to find a way to manage his feelings in an effort to somehow think clearly enough to better help advise his confused and now abused son. It was obvious to him that Mark believed he was already defeated. So, he tries to comfort him as the loving father he's always tried to be, but this time he finds it difficult to find the words to calm this out of control situation.

"Mark, as crazy as this sounds, your mother cares about you. In fact," he says, "I truly believe she really loves you. But unfortunately, son, her love for you has been contaminated by perhaps years of fear and selfishness, which is causing this unhealthy perspective she has on love; causing her to make some really bad decisions, son. Love **is not** the face of these things she's been displaying. So hang on in there, and let me figure out how to help change the direction this thing has been going for the past sixteen plus years, cool?"

"But as I told you a while back, Daddy, they **are not** trying to change."

"Maybe not, son, but do you want her to change?" He asked.

"Yeah, but she seems to have her mind made up about you, and me for that matter," I replied, wiping away more tears.

"Perhaps, but I believe prayer can change anything, son..... And just because she or they seems to be unwilling to change, doesn't mean you can't change, Mark.... In fact, you must change, if you want to experience a better life."

"But what she is doing to me is wrong!"

"It is," he replied with concern. "But we've known that for a while now, son; but you will continue to be just as wrong and self-centered, too, if you don't let this go and forgive her, Mark.... You **do not** want to likewise live life bitter, angry and resentful, son.... Selfishness builds up walls and declares war, son; but love will build bridges and promote peace.... One day you'll be a father, and everything you do and say will either bless your children or curse them," my father said compassionately. "So you want to start now by getting your thoughts right, words rights, and your attitude right about this thing call *Love, Life* and *Relationship,"* he said.

"You would think my grandparents would know better, but they don't have no problem with any of this, with them too, its all about how imperfect you are."

"Well, I'm not perfect, Mark. And neither is any other father on this earth. But I don't have to be perfect, to share the good Lord's perfect message with you, son. Knowing God and having a relationship with Him, allows an imperfect guy like me the opportunity to still be a good father to you.... You feel me?" He asked.

Yes, I nod, hoping that I really was grasping this imperfection thing from a spiritual perspective, because they were definitely using it to cut him almost daily. But then, he suddenly reverses course on me.

"However, the next time you make a commitment, at my expense, that you don't keep—it might look like I don't know anything about church or God, Mark Anthony Bradley—or else there will be some doors snatched off the hinges if you stand me up one more time—do you understand me?!"

"Yes sir," I said, leaning back in my seat hoping that he would not try making good on this threat, at *Garfield's.*

"From this day forward, be accountable, Mark! Now, let's go check on the status of this name change," he said, as he gets up and places a tip on the table to head out.

Delighted that this situation didn't get out of hand, we were headed to deal with another hot topic that just might. As I played with the dashboard gadgets in his car, I suddenly realized that this confrontation was about to take place at my Mom's place of business, of all places.

Once outside her building, he calls her and makes known that he was outside her office. Surprisingly she comes out and appeared to be in a good mood until she realized I was with him, which slightly changed her demeanor a bit. She approaches the car on the driver's side, the top was down, which allows her get a full view the man and his vehicle, to which both were often topics of conversation in our house.

"What's up?" She asked.

"It's my understanding that Mayberry hasn't signed the name change petition yet," my Dad said. "How can I reach him?"

She looks at him a little puzzled and replied, "I think he's back in Alabama. But he told me that he would sign and send them from there."

"Really?" Dad suspiciously replied, knowing where she was headed.

"That's my understanding as of yesterday," my Mom replied.

"Well unfortunately, Dee, Mayberry doesn't have the papers, Mark does. He left them at his mother's house," Danny shot back.

"That's not what he told me," she responded.

"I understand. What's his cell number?" My father bluntly asked.

My Mom paused, as if she was trying to recall the number, which prompted me to say, "I think I have his cell number and his address."

"You do?" He asked.

"Yeah. I got his cell number." I replied.

He turns back, looks up at my Mom, and said, "Never mind.... Sorry to disturb you," as he put the car in reverse and begins to make way.

My mother then politely asked, "What time will you be home, Mark?"

"Not sure, I'm with my Dad," I replied with confidence for the first time ever.

He then put the SL in drive and was ready to pull off, but braked long enough for her to walk up again, "If you're available, can I stop by about eight tonight so we can all three talk?"

As he eased off the brake and moved forward he replied, "I'll believe it when I see it, Dee. But call before you come," as he pulled off.

Later that night Danny and Mark were asleep in the den up front near the driveway, at the Bradleys. It was about midnight when Danny's cell phone rings—it was Denise!

Maybe this time she is *for real-for real* about sitting down with the two of them, but unfortunately, it's way pass 8 p.m.

"Hey, I'm sorry I missed the deadline," she said. "But I am now outside your office—can you come out? I'd like to chat."

"Mark is asleep, Dee," Danny said.

"I figured that, but we can still talk, can't we? I don't bite," she said.

"Hold on," he says. Danny gets up, looks out the window and sure enough, he see's Denise sitting in her SUV, the dashboard light illuminating her face. He thinks about it for a second or two, and said, "I'll be in out in a minute."

Danny, who had already showered and dressed in normal warm-up sleep gear, pauses and then quietly eases out of the house through the den so as not to wake up Mark.

Before he closes the passenger side door of the SUV, the dome light reveals that Dee had also showered and was now wearing *a robe* with her hair slicked back, gelled up and wet as if she was ready for a Playboy interview.

Knowing he was now in danger zone, he says, "You look like you're ready for bed?"

"I am," she said cozily with a smile. "The drive is short, so I figured I'd be aright.

Danny pauses and then says, "I'm just curious, how are you able to just leave the house at this time of night, robed up, oiled up—looking like you're ready for a Victoria Secret photo shoot?"

Laced with seduction and innuendo, Dee replied, "Because I got it like that."

"Oh, I see," Danny responded with a smile shadowed by his concern.

"No," she softly said, "my husband is out of town and my daughter is at my parent's."

"Okay—so that explains it.... So, what's up?" He asked, now curious as to what Dee might really have on her mind.

Dee then shifted in the driver's seat so that she was facing him with her back up against her door, asks, "Could you have ever really dated me, like seriously dated me?"

Danny knew where this was now headed but was rapidly losing strength to get out of it, asked in return, "What do you mean?"

"You know, could I have ever been like your women-women?"

Danny pauses, not knowing how to really answer the question under the circumstances. After all he wasn't having much success fostering a relationship with his son while in her care, so he knew he had to be very careful with his answer. Plus, the robe, the slick-backed hair, the bedroom eyes—she was working it and it was starting to work him. He finally says, "I guess it depends, Dee."

"On what?" She asked, as Danny thinks about his answer, he suddenly hears the voice of JB, who often tried to play counselor during their occasional workout sessions, *You know what Denise wants, just hit it—and she'll deliver your son to your doorstep.*

Danny snaps out of it, "Dee, what relevance is this?" He asked.

"I'm just curious," she pressed on. "Could I have ever been your woman-woman?"

He hears his brother JB's voice again, *All your problems with Mark will go away if you'll just go ahead and just sex her.*

And Dee wasn't ready to let it go, and went on, "Before I got married—was it possible for you and I to be an item—could I have ever been your girl?"

Danny paused again before answering, "Perhaps—maybe—possibly, if I had not gone off to college—we certainly had a cause," he replied cautiously. "But...."

Dee then suddenly leaned forward and interrupted Danny with a French kiss that lasted about ten seconds but seemed like ten minutes to him. And Danny, who has been the constant professional, like most men trapped in a lustful situation, actually began to kiss back, as they both suddenly thought better of it and pulled back.

They, then, sat in silence for about another fifteen-seconds, which probably seemed like fifteen-minutes, during which Danny could now hear the voice of JB screaming even louder, *Just do it, DB...and get control of this situation with your son!*

Danny finally finds his voice.

"Dee." He says.

"I'm sorry.... I don't know what I was thinking.... For some reason, I just felt the need to do that.... So, let's get refocused here and talk about Mark," she said.

Danny takes a deep breath, knowing that both of them were now way too aroused to continue on with this conversation, to which he suddenly says, "I think it might be best we discuss Mark at another time."

"I think that's a good idea," she replied, as Danny slowly gets out of the car.

He quietly reenters the house and notices that Mark has been up and now seemed to be pretending to be asleep. Wondering if he saw what just went down, he thinks about waking him, but decides to go on back to bed himself.

The next morning, at the breakfast table, my Dad kept looking at me before finally asking, "Did you get up last night?"

"No, why?" I asked in return.

"Just wondering.... Your mother stopped by late, but you were already sleep.... I went outside to chat for a minute, but when I came back inside you were laying on the opposite end of the sofa."

And right when I was about to answer, the phone rings, grandma Shelly answers it. It's my mom, wanting to talk to me.

"Have you talked to Mayberry?" She asked.

"No," I replied.

"Well, have your Dad call him, I'm sure he's got his cell."

"Mom, you talk to the man all the time, just call him and tell him to sign them."

"Mark, this is between you, yo Daddy Danny and yo Daddy Mayberry.... And since he's changing your name, he ought to be willing to buy you that car he refused to buy a while back, don't ya think?" She replied and hung up.

Moments later, the doorbell rings. It's the FedEx guy coming to pick up the name change documents, it was now being over-nighted to Mayberry, by my father. He assures him that the package will be delivered by 10 a.m. the next morning. They agree, shake hands and the FedEx courier exits.

As the delivery truck drives off, Danny decides to give Mayberry a call before I could inform him of what my Mom just said. But being interested as to how Mayberry might handle this call, I backed off and listened in, intently.

He places the phone on speaker as Mayberry answers and appears to be surprised to hear from my Dad Danny. They make small talk for a minute or two, before the conversation turns to their common issue.

"I'm just trying to recover from the many years I've lost with my son, Mayberry."

"I understand," Mayberry said. "I don't know what Denise could've been thinking, DB. She apparently been lying to me about this situation from day one.... I didn't know you were involved in Mark's life until Mark informed me a couple of summers ago when he came to visit me here in Alabama."

"He told me as much." Danny replied.

"Dee has been tellin me that you didn't want to have anything to do with this kid."

"Mayberry, it's obvious that Denise had an agenda, but it would have been nice for you to have just called me.... You could have discovered this truth a long time ago."

For real, I thought to myself, as my Dad shared that insight.

"I know that now," Mayberry replied. "But I should have reached out to you the first time I started hearing the rumor that Mark was your son.... Mark had to be about two-and-a-half, going on three years old at the time," Mayberry said.

"That was indeed the time to reach out," my Dad replied.

"After I heard the rumor, I could tell he was your son by his body structure.... He had your features, including the wide-shoulders and all. He was built like you," he said.

"Well, I'm sorry it's come down like this, but I don't want you to feel like you're losing him, Mayberry.... You're welcome to keep in touch with Mark as long as he's open to it," my Dad says, as he looks over at me.

"Thanks—I appreciate that. Mark's a good kid, Danny," he replied. "But just know, I really didn't know what the real deal was until Mark told me."

Danny told him he understood, and informed him that he should be receiving the name change petition via overnight mail to his home address. And asked if he could sign them and get them back to us, likewise, via overnight mail by way of the pre-paid return envelope placed inside the package; making known to him, that we would like to finalize this before the start of school in the fall, which was just around the corner. And Mayberry agreed to be prompt and courteous, as they said their good-byes and hung up.

Turning to me, he asked, "Tell me again, how often does this guy reach out to you?"

"Not often at all," I replied. "Mayberry really stopped reaching out to me nearly five years ago; and really backed off after I told him the real deal about three years ago."

Danny pondered that for a few seconds before asking, "Do you trust him?"

Then I pondered the question, before saying, "I've never had any problems with Mayberry. But, no, I can't honestly say that I trust him-trust him. He talks to my family way too much for me to truly trust him like that."

"Do you trust me?" My father asked, with a smile.

"Yeah, why you ask? I replied likewise, with a smile.

"Well, hey, I have to ask these things when dealing with you and your folks."

"I do—I trust you," I replied, waiting to hear his reasons for asking.

"Well, I got a feeling this situation with Denise and Mayberry is about to get a little stickier, which will probably force you to choose sides again, son. So, my suggestion to you—choose wisely this time, Mark."

As we exit the house en route to the Mall to shop for school clothes. I couldn't help but be mindful of the fact that this man started this trip being highly disrespected and insulted by all of us, and nonetheless, he still seems to be in control; refusing to allow all the negatives regarding our bizzare circumstance, outweigh his hope in the positives. But unfortunately, this father's love for his son was to be challenged to the max once again, when Mayberry decides to do the unthinkable.

24

Envisage

It had only been two weeks since Danny had what he thought was a very civil conversation with Mayberry, followed by his receipt of the name change petition. And according to his attorney, there was yet no signed document in sight! So, Danny dials Mark up in Pine Bluff to gather some additional information on Mayberry.

"Mark, have you heard any feedback around your house about Mayberry and the petition document?"

"No, sir.... What's going on?" I asked, as I could tell he is a lil disappointed.

"It's been two weeks, and I haven't heard or received anything back just yet."

"I think they might be stalling, Daddy, if you ask me?"

"In hopes of accomplishing what, son?"

"I don't know, maybe hoping I would change my mind."

"Well, yeah, I can see how they could think that—you have changed your mind quite a bit over the years, Mark."

"Well, I'm not changing my mind on this one," I replied with absolute certainty.

"You sure?"

"Positive!"

"Okay—give me this man's home number, and work if you have it."

Mark gives him the home number as Danny abruptly hangs up.

He then immediately decides to call Mayberry at home, but gets an answering machine. He leaves a general but polite message.

A couple of evenings later, Danny, and yeah his girlfriend Salena, who was visiting from LA, are pulling up to a movie theatre. Before going in, Danny decides to reach out to Mayberry one more time. It had become clear that maybe Mark's observation was perhaps right. He got the answering machine and again leaves a message, but this time, this message was anything—but general.

"Mayberry, this is my third and final message regarding this issue. I have no idea why you're not returning my call, but it's imperative that you get back to me promptly, or else I will have to take this issue to a whole new level, legally, my brother. That's not a threat—that's a fact!" And BAM, he hung up!

Three hours later, as Danny and Salena are exiting the theatre, he turns his cell phone back on and checks his messages. This time there's one from Mayberry. He hits the speaker button so Salena can listen in.

And Mayberry goes off, saying not to ever call his house again leaving threatening messages about an issue he knew nothing about. "And tell Mark not to call me for anything ever again!" And BAM, he hangs up.

Danny looks at Salena and says, "This dude just tripped out!"

And Salena, who was already, unbeknownst to Danny, done with it all, including him, simply said, "This would be a really good made-for-TV soap opera—but unfortunately it's not.... And it now sounds like somebody extremely important to him must have gotten your message and is now in search of a few answers—themselves."

Her comment brings silence for a minute as Danny cranks up the car and dials Mark and plays Mayberry's voice-mail message for him.

"Wow—I'm surprised, especially after the conversation he had with you!"

"Well—I'm not. But listen to me very carefully, Mark. Stay away from Mayberry and his family from this point forward—do you understand me?"

"Daddy, Mayberry ain't even an issue with me," I replied.

"Let me make myself clear again, stay away from Mayberry and his *entire* family—or we're going to have a major problem, Mark.... Do you understand me?"

"I understand," I replied.

After we hung up, I sat up that night thinking about the message that Mayberry left, which also sent a direct message to me too. And with him being the one person I thought operated halfway respectable regarding this ordeal, his response perhaps exposed that he just might have an agenda also. It was disappointing, but it wasn't like we had this great relationship anyway. But I was still surprised by his response, even if he didn't want to sign the papers.

Nonetheless, at this point, everybody in my family seemed to be circling their own wagon while they sat back and watched the wheels fall off my Dad's wagon. But this revelation didn't make me happier and more hopeful, it made me more resentful and that much more insecure about everything. And instead of running to my father, I started slipping away from him again. I just didn't want to be in the middle of another ugly battle over the changing of my name. They didn't accept him, and deep down inside, I guess I really didn't either. And in a weird kind of way, I was apparently okay with that, even though this man had proven to me time after time that he was an *entirely different* guy than the picture they had painted of him.

So after deciding to concede, again, I surprised my mom one afternoon at her office with one thing on my mind—a car. I had finally found the solution to this problem. But unexpectedly, despite how doable this plan was, she shot me and it completely down.

"Mark, daddy O is not going to let you drive his truck.... If your father wants to change your name, he should buy you the freakin car!"

I'm thinking, *Mom, come on. The name change has nothing to do with this?*

And the thought of asking my father to provide me with a car, at this point, wasn't even remotely an option for me. *Haven't we been disrespectful enough to this man?* I wanted to say, but I'd learned to keep my thoughts and feelings to myself with her.

"Maybe if you talk to granddaddy, O, he'll do it! It's just sitting collecting dust!"

"He's not going to do it, Mark!" She replied, agitatedly.

"But he doesn't even drive it, mama!" I pleaded, as I begin to get a lil teed-off.

"Mark! I said, no! Now, I'm done with it! I got work to do, son!"

"Unbelievable," I thought, as I leaned forward in my chair, before saying, "I can't change my name—can't move to Texas—can't drive anybody's car."

"Mark!" She says, raising her voice even louder.

"I'm just saying mom, I can't do nothin, be nothin or have nothin.... But everybody claims to love me so much," I said with frustration.

Now my mom was teed-off.

"Have you lost your damn mind? You better call your damn Daddy and stop trippin!"

I started to shoot back with, "*Which one mama, Mayberry, Braylon or Danny?!*

"In fact, let's do that right now!" She said.

She picks up the phone and dials, who else, my Dad Danny, and hands it to me. And I just shook my head in disbelief that she could be so cruel and insensitive, as I tangled with another bizzare thought, *Here we are arguing about a vehicle she wants my father to provide that he wouldn't even be able to ride in, while in the meantime, they have a vehicle, just sittin in the driveway, which I can't even ride in...what's wrong with this picture—family?!*

Just as I was about to hang up, my Dad picks up. He was leaving a jewelry store looking at wedding rings for Salena. They had finally reconciled and getting married.

"Dad—this is Mark."

"What's up?" He asked.

Not wanting to start off by asking about a car or anything else of value, I first asked about the name change petition, and he informed me the attorney had finally gotten the papers, and by August 20, 1998, I would officially be a Bradley.

"Cool," I told him. And I was genuinely happy about that, even though I didn't quite sound like it at that moment. I knew it was the right thing to do. But I pressed on as my mother observed my every word.

"On another topic, I need to talk to you about this car thing."

"Okay, talk—what about it?" He asked.

"I'm having a tough time getting around, starting to need one pretty bad. I might be walking place to place around here for the next couple of years. Its just tough with trying to go to school and play ball."

"I understand," my Dad replied. "But since I only support student athletes, then I suggest that you improve your grades—then I'll consider it."

"What's wrong with my grades?" I asked, disappointedly.

"If you don't know, son, that further tells me how disconnected you are with your academics. They gotten worse than they've ever been, Mark. But if you are serious about this car business, then show me you can maintain a respectable grade point average (GPA) for one semester, and I'll do it. If not, I guess you're gonna to have to find another way to style and profile, young fella."

"Dad, you know why my grades have been down," I said.

"Of course I do—but its you that chose not to follow through, son.... I've been working my butt off to place you in an environment where you can focus and excel, but you keep choosing to stay put and perhaps even fail."

"Dad."

"Mark."

I then paused, not knowing how to end this call and yet looking for a way to convince him to help me with this car thing, which was certain to get my mom's vote.

He then said, "Look, here's the deal—improve your grades to a 3.0 in any one semester, you get the car. If not—I guess you'll walk.... Unless of course, you are willing to reconsider the move to Texas."

"And why would you be so willing to do it then," I asked.

"Simple, because then you'd be making a 4.0 decision to free yourself from a 1.0 environment—and according to my calculations, that equates out to be about a 3.0 GPA, cool—cool—have a nice day Mister Bradley," and then he hangs up on me.

As I sat there holding the receiver, my Mom could tell by my expression that the answer was perhaps "no," as she said mockingly, "And you wanna go live with him, boy please—you better go ask somebody."

Even though I didn't like his answer, under the circumstances, I understood his answer. But I had no idea why my mom, under these circumstances, wouldn't help me persuade my grandfather O, to let me drive his truck. After all, this was about the spirit of competition with them, right. *Well, give me the truck, claim you bought it and rub it in his face, Mom,* is what I wanted to say.

However, knowing he still needed that car, from the start of school, Mark really began committing himself to his studies. And from time-to-time Danny, while in town, would catch him literally asleep with a book on his chest after a late night study effort. He passed most exams while he struggled to make good on others—it was frustrating.

But Danny, with the help of Mark's guidance counselor, made it possible for him to clearly see that Mark was making a serious effort to improve his GPA, despite his disruptive home life. And to keep from totally disappointing him, by Christmas, even though he didn't meet the academic requirement they discussed the previous summer, Danny decides to purchase the car anyway—a brand new 1998 Jeep Wrangler.

As Danny and JB were prepping for the ride to Pine Bluff. Danny had planned on surprising Mark with the Jeep, but discovers when talking to his mother, Shelly, Mark and his family were headed out of town this Christmas.

"I saw Denise in the grocery store, yesterday," Shelly said. "And she said they were headed to Mississippi to her in-law's house for Christmas—they may be already gone."

Danny asks her to call the Davis's on three-way to make sure that such wasn't the case. And she did, which is where the Bradley's had a history of tracking Mark down. Odell answers, as they exchange seasons greetings, before Shelly asked for Mark.

"Well, I think he's outside helping his mom pack the car. They about to head out of town.... But hold on, let me check," Odell replied hesitantly.

Less than a minute later, Mark was on the line expecting to talk to grandma Shelly, knowing that it could be his Dad Danny, and it was.

"Mark, what's up? I hear you guys are headed out of town," he said.

"Yeah," I replied. "We leaving in about an hour."

"Well, do you have to go?" Danny asked.

"Not really," Mark replied halfheartedly.

Danny senses Mark's shortness but didn't pry knowing the circumstances.

"Well—I'm about to leave headed that way, and I have a few gifts for you—why don't you ask your mom if you can stay."

"I'll ask her, but she's probably gonna say no," I replied disinterestedly.

"Even if you tell her I may be delivering you a car," Danny replied! "A Jeep Wrangler.... Perfect for a sixteen-seventeen year old kid in Southeast Arkansas."

Suddenly, I froze, not knowing how to respond to that.

"Hello," Danny said into the phone, puzzled by his son's silence, Shelly listened in.

"Yeah, I'm here," I finally responded.

"What's up? I thought you would be excited about this, Mark.... I know you didn't make the grade but I decided to come through anyway.... So, what's going on?"

"I'm good—I'm aright," I replied.

"You good.... You're aright," Danny repeated back, a bit confused.

"Yeah, I'm good, don't worry about it," I replied with an obvious stance that said, yep, he's jumped ship again.

"Would you like to tell me what the hell is going on Mark?"

"I'm just saying, I'm aright—I don't need a car after all—I'm good."

Danny pauses and pulls the phone away from his ear while Shelly remained silent but befuddled by Mark's response. He can't believe what he just heard. Over the past year an a half, he was his son's *only hope* for a car, and now he was—*aright?!*

Not knowing what brought about this latest dramatic turn of event, Danny knew whatever it was, it wasn't good. This is that *stickier* situation he had previously warned Mark about, which would cause him to, again, choose sides.

Suddenly Shelly asked, "Mark, baby, what's the problem, son?"

"Nothin, I was just saying, I'm good,"

Danny immediately cuts in and says, "Mother, thanks for connecting me; Mark, sorry to disturb you, son—enjoy your Christmas, sir, and Happy New Year."

Then he hangs up on both Mark and his mother, Shelly.

Reluctant to tell JB what had gone down, Danny just shares that a business related matter has come up and he won't be caravanning with him to PB. They hug and exchange season greetings as JB suspiciously drives off, knowing something went wrong.

And on the heels of that disappointment, Danny gets another bit of unfortunate news; His grandmother, Shelly's mom, was slowly passing away, and Salena, his fiancé, had mysteriously gotten married on him—in LA.

Devastated and broken, Danny slowly begins to unload the gifts from Mark's Jeep and began to take them into the house, piece by piece under great duress. As he tried to make sense of it all, his body language and despair resembled that of the one in LA some years ago, which led him to a hospital bed in Pine Bluff.

He sat around the house stressed and depressed with very little rest, while he reminisced about his time with all of them. He had lost love relationship number two while trying to build a meaningful love relationship with his son. And with his beloved grandmother, all but gone—he was back in another bad place. He read scriptures, walked and paced to comfort his pain, trying to enjoy 'This Christmas' at home—alone.

Meanwhile, at the Davises, my Mom was trying to get me to hurry up so they could get on the road. But before we did, there was one more thing she wanted me to do.

"Mark, take your Daddy Mayberry his gift, and I'll wrap your step-dad and Grandpa's while you're gone."

"What car am I taking?" I asked, not feeling no ways bad for my real father.

"Take mine," she replied. "And hurry up, we gotta get going."

My gift to Mayberry was a 30"x 20" game size high school football poster of me in action. And I didn't quite know how Mayberry was going to respond since he threw me under the bus, too, behind the name change. But once I got to his mom's house, you would have never pegged this guy to be the same dude who had left that harsh message a few months ago.

"Merry Christmas!" He said.

"Merry Christmas," I replied shyly.

"What ya got there?" He asked cheerfully as if he knew I was coming.

"Just wanted to drop off your gift before we left town."

"That's a nice picture Mark—thanks son. This is so cool." Mayberrye replied, as he looked admiringly at the poster-size photo.

As I started for the door, it dawned on me once again, how my mom would make sure that *every daddy* in my life received a gift from me on father's day, birthdays, and Christmas, except my Daddy Danny.

Mayberry trailed me to the car and said, "Take care Mark and Merry Christmas, again—I'll be in touch about the time you guys make it back to drop off—your car."

"Okay—thanks," I said, as I made my way back home. And as you may have figured, I'm a *very confused and twisted* young man at this juncture. Even though he had warned me to stay away from this man and his *entire* family, here I was once again doing the very opposite with people who had shunned him, lied to him and disrespected him. The question is, is there any real hope for me?

A week later, Mayberry was headed from Alabama to deliver this car and I wasn't in that festive of a mood about it anymore, as we all sat around trying to anticipate his arrival. They were all excited that I was finally getting a car, despite having one sitting in the driveway, unused, and in great condition. And what made matters worse, I discovered that many of the outfits my Mom modeled for the department stores, she purchased them also for personal use, too, making her argument of not being able to afford many of the things I needed—embarrassingly bogus. And she had a nice wardrobe of clothes. However, they went on and on about how Mayberry cared about me and loved me and that I needed him in my life; and that he's doing what my Dad Danny wouldn't do etc. etc. And the more they talked and boasted about Mayberry, the more they're motives seemed to exposed them. You see, they didn't know about the Jeep, that this, *alledgedly,* sorry-no-good-deadbeat-of-a-dad of mine had bought for me this past Christmas. But when you're just as guilty as they are, what can you really say folks—nothing. You just roll with the flow.

In response, I just said, "Hey, I appreciate Mayberry making the sacrifices, spending the money and for making the drive from Alabama to bring me a car," hoping my mom and granddad would have a *epiphany* about the car sitting in our driveway, collecting dust. But that flew right over their head.

My friend Carl stopped by wanting to go hangout at the Mall. And I jump at the opportunity to break free for a minute. But before we get out the door my mom asks again, that 64 dollar question, "Have you heard from your Daddy Danny?"

I told her no, as I continued to ease out the house.

"Well, it's about time you call him," she said. "You need some more winter clothes, Mark," She said, as she tosses me a new cell phone she'd purchased for me.

I'm thinking again, *Mom, thanks for the cell, but let it go—I'm with you, I'm on your team.... Let's not keep abusing this man!*

I didn't even respond to her remark, but I'm certain she could see the deflation written all over my face. Nevertheless, Carl, who was familiar with almost all my issues, took notice as soon as I stepped into his car.

"Let me guess, your mom still pushin you to ask your dad for a dime despite the limited time, huh?"

"All she wants is money, CB," I replied, with this car thing heavy on my mind.

"But if that was true though Mark, why didn't she just file for child support against him?" He asked. "Isn't that what they all do?"

"Well, child support would have probably been cheaper, as much as he does. But as crazy as this may sound, my mom couldn't file because she had *already* filed child support against Mayberry."

"Come on man.... You serious?!" He asked.

"Yeah—so filing twice against two different guys at the same time is probably against the law.... But now that the name change has taken place, yeah, he too better expect some child support papers to come in the mail," I replied.

"Yeah, dude, it's very *personal* with your mom.

"You think!"

"You livin a soap opera dude!"

"Yeah—tell me about it," I replied.

"You need a sitcom, Mark—and call it, *'My Four Daddies.'*"

I smiled at his comment but deep down inside, I'm disgusted, as he continued on.

"Think about it, a lot of black kids don't have a relationship of no kind with any father, right?

"Right?

"And many of the white ones we know, are afraid to admit that they don't have much of a relationship with their fathers, right?"

"Right," I replied.

"And the media is always writing articles about how irresponsible and absentee-like we are, knowing that there is a lil bit of irresponsibility going on in their households, too, correct?"

"Correct," I replied. "Many of their Dad's aren't there because they work too much.

"Which means that most kids our age don't have **a** father inside or outside the home."

"True, but what's the point?" I asked.

"Dude, you got four! That's a winner on any network in the country!" Carl shouts.

I must admit, all of my friends could be funny sometimes and that comment made me laugh a little, but at the moment I wasn't in the joking mood. In fact, I didn't need a comedian—I needed counsel. And the only person *I knew* that was capable of helping me process, who knew the story-line—was my father.

But how could I call him when my issues directly involve him, I thought. *Haven't I done enough to disappoint this man—why would he even answer my call at this point?*

But I couldn't resist. I decided to reach out to that one person in my life who wasn't a *soap opera character*—and amazingly, he answers. I could immediately hear what sounded like someone announcing a flight, so I knew I needed to make it quick. And unbeknownst to me, he was en route to Los Angeles to repossess *another vehicle* he had purchased for Salena, after she had suddenly married someone else.

Therefore, without knowing these things, you can only imagine what my call might have sounded like to him. And I could tell that he was stressed and apparently very disappointed in a few people he held in high regard, including me.

"What's up, Mark?" He asked. "What gives me the great privilege?"

"I was just checking in an wanted to apologize about the incident at Christmas."

He said he understood but wanted to know what was the real motive behind this call.

At that, I took a deep breath and just jump right into it, hoping to get him to talk and truly share his opinion and/or his intuition about this whole car ordeal.

"Well, you probably won't be surprised by the latest. My mom and granddad, Odell, apparently have talked Mayberry into getting me a car, and I'm starting to feel a lil uncomfortable about it.... So, I thought I'd call and get your thoughts on it."

"Come on, son, when has my opinion really mattered with you?"

"Well—despite what it looks like, Dad, your opinion matters a lot to me. You are the only one that seems to ever make any sense about all this junk," I replied.

"Well, unfortunately," he said, "we will just have to agree to disagree about that but since you had the guts to call and ask, here's my short essay on it, Mark.... This is not about a car, son. This is about control and manipulation.... If this was indeed about a car, you would have accepted the car offered by your father, whom you claim is the only ***one*** somebody that ever makes any sense out of all of this."

"So what do you think I should do? He's on his way from Alabama to bring the car down now," I asked, hoping he would give me a yea or nay.

"That's on you, son. However, if you do decide to take this car, you won't just be slipping back into the hands of the enemy—you'd be the enemy, as far as I'm concerned. Now, that's a spiritualistic take on it—not a humanistic take on it," he said frankly.

"I understand," I replied, as Carl pulls into the parking lot of the Mall.

"But this is your life, Mark Bradley, not mine. You're the one that has to start taking responsibility for the choices you make.... But as I tried to inform you a while back, this is that *stickier situation* I warned you about.... And told you to choose wisely."

"I understand—I won't take the car," I replied.

"Again, that's your choice, son—not mine."

"But I agree—I just didn't know what to do. But you helped me make a decision."

"Have I? Or are you just checking my pulse, trying to figure out when I might really start snatching some doors off the damn hinges around there?!"

My first thought was, *this man knows me extremely well. A part of me was doing just that, especially since he had gone silent on me the past five weeks, knowing he was definitely due to make good on his threat at this point.*

"But just know, if you do decide to accept, I have a strong inkling this situation will get more complicated, more confusing and perhaps even more dangerous.... So take care and I'll be in touch." He says, as I began to ponder his comment.

25

Love Unconditional

The next day, for the fiftieth time, here I was, again, doing totally opposite of what I'd swore I wouldn't do—accepting the keys to a late model BMW—from Mayberry. And suddenly I heard my Dad's voice, *if you do decide to accept, just know, I have a strong inkling that this will get more complicated, confusing, and perhaps even more dangerous.* Then I began to reason it, again, thinking, *It's already complicated, daddy, I can't get any more confused.... How more dangerous can it get?*

Mayberry begins to inform me that it's a five-speed as he explains the gears. I then recognized that this was not a new vehicle, but rather one of the "older model cars" I saw just sitting in his driveway too, collecting dust.

Now imagine that, I thought. Odell has a newer model Nissan truck just sitting in his driveway, which **I can't drive,** but it was okay for Mayberry to drive a vehicle, all the way from Alabama from his driveway, that **I can drive.** Come on man—how do you justify this kind of behavior folks? It was cool for someone else to make the sacrifice, except anyone from my *so-called* beloved family. But why am I complaining, I chose to let them continue manipulating me and stay in this mess. So I said the heck with it—I need a car—I'm doing it!

The next day, I decided I would get more familiar with the mechanics of the car and take it out for a spin. I had driven a standard before, so I wasn't to-to concerned about getting settled in. However, as fate would have it, while I was out styling and profiling around town, I decided to head over to my friend's houses to show off my ride. As I pulled up to a stop sign, I looked left and apparently too long to the right, and then slowly proceeded into the intersection. I reach over to play with the air conditioner controls, and suddenly I see a motorcyclist approaching rapidly out the corner of my eye. I immediately stop and tried to put the car in reverse, but the engine stalls right there in the middle of the intersection. And the cyclist slams into the front driver's side quarter panel, as I ducked for cover, while hearing my Dad's voice echoing in my head, again, *and even more dangerous; more dangerous; more dangerous!*

When I opened my eyes, I could see the motorcyclist bounce off the pavement about 30 feet from the point of contact! I jumped out of the car and ran across the street to this beauty salon yelling for somebody to call an ambulance, as they too saw the accident and was already scrambling. I heard one of the ladies say, as they ran out of the salon screaming, "Oh my God! Oh, my God! He might be dead y'all!"

Already terrified, I exploded in tears as my body begins to tremble uncontrollably. The scene was chaos as I zoned out, almost as if I wasn't coherent. Police, fire and paramedics arrive and amidst all the chaos, the officers finds me, as the paramedics tried to stabilize the cyclist. One officer starts questioning me, while he tells another check my car for alcohol and drugs. With tears streaming down my face, I give them my account of what I recall, stumbling through it as if I was on drugs. But told the officer, when asked, "No, sir, I didn't do drugs or use alcohol."

At about this same time, my Mom and Grandma Leola showed up, frantic, asking everybody what happened! I could barely answer any more questions about the accident, so a few of the ladies from the salon helped me share with the officers, what they saw

One said, "I think he simply just ran the stop sign."

Another says, "Yeah but the kid on the bike was going way to fast."

As he started writing me up a ticket, the assisting officer approaches and said that he found no drugs or signs of alcohol use inside the vehicle, and that the car was "totaled."

The attending officer tore the ticket from his pad, handed it to my mom and looked me straight in the eye and said, "Son, I'm giving you a ticket for running a stop sign, the directions and information are on the back.... But if I were you, I'd pray that young man you hit—lives.... Or else, you could be charged with vehicular homicide."

If I wasn't already spent before, that comment certainly did it. I was done. I started doing just that, praying, as my tears begin to flow heavier.

The following day, my grandma Shelly gets a call from her sister Jo, asking had she seen the newspaper? Shelly rushes out, grabs the paper from her front yard and began to read. As she does so, she hangs up on Jo and immediately called Danny and began reading him the article regarding Mark's accident, which said in various words, *"Mark Bradley.... the son of former Sooners quarterback, Danny Bradley.... as the driver of a BMW.... caused a near fatal crash.... and the motorcyclist was taken to Jefferson Regional Hospital, in critical condition."*

There's this long-long pause from Danny, before saying, "Damn it.... I warned Mark, mother, that taking that car was not a good idea."

"What car?" Shelly asked.

"It appears that Mark may have taken a car from Mayberry that his folks was pressuring him to take." Danny replied, agitatedly.

"Well, I'll be," Shelly replied. "So apparently your offer wasn't good enough, huh?"

"Apparently not."

"And I take it that you haven't heard from Denise or Mark about this accident, either?"

"No—I haven't. But I'm sure she wasn't expecting this to be a top story in newspapers either," Danny responded with frustration.

"This doesn't make any damn sense, Danny! My grandson has nearly killed somebody in a car accident and we got to find out about it in the newspaper?! This is just unacceptable!"

Jo had arrived at the house and was making her way down the hallway shouting, "It sure is unacceptable! Dee has gone way too far with this trifling mess!"

"It's time I reach out and have a lil talk with Denise Davis," Shelly added.

"Mother—no! Let's wait and see how they deal with the situation.... At this point, they know we know, so let's just wait and see.... This is not all on Denise—Mark has to take some responsibility, too."

Though still angry, Shelly said, "Danny, look, that's my grandchild, too! Now I've tried to stay out of this mess as much as I could with you and Denise, but this craziness is starting to really tick-me-off!"

"Mother, I understand," Danny replied. "Let me handle this—I got this!"

"I can't tell!" She shot back.

"Mother—I got this!"

"Well, by the end of this week, you better tell me somethin worth hearing or I got this!" Shelly said, then hung up on him.

Unfortunately, by the end of the week, my father had nothing to report to grandma Shelly. None of us had reached out to him and we monitored any call that look like it could be from the Bradleys', thus said my Mom.

But my father remained completely silent and invisible on the matter. But couldn't control grandma Shelly. I went to school with another one of her grand kids, Tamira Bradley, my cousin, who had heard of a few negative things I'd said about my father Danny, her uncle, to a few of our classmates in passing, who said, "Tell Mark, I need to holla at him—soon," one classmate tells it.

I had heard through a mutual associate that *she,* this cousin, had planned to call me out. So I avoided her on notice and started retracking my comments, *denying* having ever said anything negative about my father, in an attempt to shut down this unnecessary confrontation with members of his family that I barely even knew.

A few months later, as he remained silent, I fought hard to overcome all of these emotional feelings that had so easily beset me. And in doing so, I focused on sports, which at the time was track and field. And at one point, I thought about quitting. But decided that it would be the thing I would eat, live and breathe. And on this day, at the

Arkansas State Track Meet, I high jumped 7' 2" and long jumped 22'1", which qualified me for the National Indoor Track Meet in Bloomington, Indiana. But will I get a chance to go compete, or will I be going to jail?

Well, the motorcyclist I hit, thank God, lived, which meant I would get, yet, another chance to make something of this life of mine, which is currently just full of all kinds of family strife, selfishness and chaos.

Later that evening, I rushed home to tell my mom the exciting news since we seem to be bonding a bit better after the accident. She had been shopping, the living room sofa and coffee table were covered with shopping bags. They were clothes for an upcoming modeling gig she had the following week.

"Mom, I've been invited to the National Indoor Meet in Indiana."

"Really—congratulations," she said kind of nonchalantly.

"Yeah, the hotel and flight is covered, all I need is some spending money for food."

"I thought the school pay for y'all track trips," she disinterestedly replied.

"No, Mom, not this meet. This is a National Invitation for all top performers."

"Baby, Mama don't have it, son."

"Mom, it's only for three days. I'll eat at McDonald's. I can make it on forty dollars!"

"Mark, I understand, but Mama don't have forty dollars."

"Thirty will do, Mama—I just want to go and participate."

"Why don't you call your Daddy Danny," she said, without even blinking.

"Twenty-five will do, Mom!" I pleaded.

"I don't have it son," she said flatly. "Call your Daddy Danny."

I had already planned on hanging out with my friend, Carl, so when I grabbed my invite letter for the track meet and stormed out of the house, he was already parked in front of my mom's house waiting. And the minute I slammed the door to his ride, I began to vent. But Carl was done listening to me whine and complain.

"Dude, you sound like an old broken record—call your Dad, make up with him and get yo butt out of Pine Bluff," Carl said. "I agree with yo Dad, the problem ain't yo mom, the problem is you partna."

"Its too late for all that, man.... He's done and I don't blame him."

"Done! Boy please! Yo daddy loves you Mark! Just apologize dude and transfer out of this place—stop trippin."

"Why would he listen to anything I gotta say?"

"Because he loves you, 12," Carl replied.

"I don't know, CB.... What if he asked me about the comments I made?"

"Tell him you're sorry and make up, that's how you answer it! This man truly cares about you 12! I can see that and I'm not even the one being chased!"

A couple of weeks later, determined to make this trip to Indiana, I decided to go ahead and take that step by reaching out to grandma Shelly for help, even though I'm certain they've all heard some of the derogatory comments I made about my Dad in the streets, which I sincerely regret. This man has been nothing but good to me, but somehow I just got caught up into trying help my Mom explain to everybody, who now knew this man was indeed my father, why our relationship was so estranged.

Nevertheless, it's the day before I'm to travel to Bloomington—I'm standing at the Bradley's front door, ringing the doorbell.

My grandma answers the door. She's surprised to see me but more than reasonably disappointed in my behavior. She had indeed heard the rumors and was sad to think I could have done such a thing. But thank God for her gentleness, she was graceful. She finally asked what brought me by, knowing I haven't talked to my father in a few months. And, yes, as selfish as my answer was going to sound, I had no place else to go.

"Well—I've been invited to participate in the National Indoor Track Meet in Indiana, but I need about thirty dollars to go and my Mom says she doesn't have it, and says I should call my father but I don't know what to say to him," I said, as my eyes well up.

"Try telling him the truth; your father loves you, Mark."

"But I've disappointed him so many times, grandma Shelly, I doubt if he would even believe anything I have to say anymore," I replied with concern.

She picks up the phone and dials his number.

"Your son is here and wants to talk to you," she says, and hands me the phone.

I then paused and wiped my eyes and just went for it.

"Dad, this Mark."

"How you doing, son." He said, so lovingly.

And the moment I heard his voice, his tone, and just the way he said my name, I just lost it. My emotions just took completely over. The tears rushed out of me like a dam. I knew this man cared about me, yet I couldn't seem to appreciate the love he had for me. It was smothering. I felt so uncomfortable and yet so protected in this man's presence, even over the phone.

"Talk to me, son," he said warmly, as grandma Shelly started to cry.

"First, I wanna say I'm sorry for not staying in touch. I know I keep saying the same things over and over, but I really do apologize for putting you through this Dad."

"Mark, its okay, son.... All is well.... What can I do for you?"

"Why you say it like that?" I asked.

"Well, its gotta be something or else you wouldn't be calling—so what's up, its okay, son.... Love doesn't keep a record of the wrongs, son.... What's going on?"

Again, this man knew me *way* too well.

"Well—I've been invited to this National Indoor Track Meet in Indiana. I'm supposed to leave early in the morning, and as usual, no one in my family is willing to help me. The flight and room is covered but I don't have any money for food."

"How long are you required to be there?" He asked.

"About three days.... All I need is about thirty dollars, Dad.... I know it's last minute, but I didn't have anywhere else to go."

"Does your flight come through Dallas?"

I pulled out my flight ticket from my gym bag and looked at the information.

"Yeah—it does—I arrive in Dallas tomorrow morning at 9:30 am."

"You going alone?" He asked.

"Yeah—my coach can't go—it's just me."

"Cool—I'll connect up with you in Dallas and make the trip with you."

I then paused, not really knowing if I should just say okay or try to explain more as to why I've been so irresponsible. So, I asked, "Your sure?"

"Absolutely, of course, I'm your father, why not? I'll see you in the morning."

As we hung up, the tears continued to roll and I felt this great deal of pressure seemingly being released. I didn't quite know what stress really felt like until that very moment. Which made me wonder, how have I even been able to function all this time.

My grandmother hugs me and says, "See what happens when you run *to love* instead of *away* from it.... I know you love your mom, Mark, it's time you wake up and start respecting your father, son," She said, which only made me appreciatively sadder.

However, despite these roller-coaster of emotions I've experienced throughout this entire ordeal thus far, I left the Bradley's house that night feeling more hopeful but yet concerned. I was still a little nervous and unsure as to what his attitude might be once I'm face-to-face with him.

And I went to bed that night wondering, *is he a ticking time bomb waiting to explode or still this loving father who is being forced into watching me—implode?*

So, off to Indiana I go, relieved, but again concerned as to what mind-set my father might be in on arrival. At any rate, this to me sure felt like Love Unconditional.

26

Divine Forgiveness

We arrive in Bloomington, Indiana safely, and just in time for a wintery blast of heavy snow. As we entered our hotel room, my Dad tossed his cell phone and told me to call my mother and let her know I made it. During the call, I also gave her the name and phone number to the hotel, just in case she needed to reach me.

After I hung up, I sat and chatted with my Dad for a while, watching the snow drop from the sky like a good southern rainstorm. I made reference to how cool it was for the track meet officials to allow me to stay with my father rather than at the participants' dorm room. My Dad then suggests we change into something dressier, he was taking me to dinner at a nice steak house which was just about a block away from their hotel.

While my father was in the shower, the room phone rings. I decided to answer it. Once he's out, he asked who called? I told him it was one of my mom's relatives, who lived locally, who wants to come see the events. And, that I had given her the room number and made known that I was staying with my Dad.

He immediately pauses, and asked, "Who exactly is this relative again?"

"A distant cousin," I replied. "I don't really know her that well," I added.

"Understood, but listen up," he said. "I know this is all new to you, son, but in the future don't ever give out your dad's room number to anyone without my consent."

I apologized, after which we finish getting dressed and went to dinner.

Minutes after the waitress takes our order, a white gentlemen approaches the table and taps my father on the shoulder. He introduces himself as a former NFL scout, who scouted talent in the Texas and Oklahoma area, who remembered him from his college days. They make small talk and he introduces him to me and our reasons for being in town. And this guy congratulates me as he made his way to his own dinner party.

As he walked away, I looked at my Dad a lil wide-eyed and remarked, "How do people know you all the way up here in Bloomington, Indiana?!"

Just then, the waitress brought out our food. I looked at the baseball-sized piece of steak, the dollop of mashed potatoes and three small carrot sticks in the center of my plate and said, "Dad, this ain't what I ordered."

Danny smiles and said, "It's not?"

"No, this is not my order."

"Son—I think it is."

I shook my head again, "No, its not—look at this plate—where's the food?"

Danny grins and winks at the waitress and asked, "Would you like another plate?"

"No, but is this it?! I asked shockingly.

"I'm afraid so, son," Danny said with a smile. "But we can order an additional plate."

I paused with this serious look of concern and said, "Nah, that's okay—I saw a McDonald's on the way over—we can stop right there on our way back—and I can finish grubbing, cuz this ain't gon get it!"

Danny giggles, tells the waitress all is well and she politely smiles and walks away.

Later that evening, about 11 p.m., we're back in our hotel room laughing about my restaurant experience as I indeed dip into that McDonald's bag. My Dad decides to get an update on the snow conditions for tomorrow, so he grabs the TV remote and scans for the Weather Channel. While we're watching the weather guy talk about more snow for the Bloomington area, suddenly there's a knock at the door.

I looked at him puzzled as we both notice the time on the Weather Channel, which now says 11:30 p.m. The knock comes again, and my father suddenly shows by his facial expression, who he thinks it might be. He then said, "Mark, this is why you don't give out room numbers—get the door."

I get up, disappointed that I had made such a mistake and answered as the third knock is made. But to my surprise it's not only the relative—it's also my Mom, Denise, wearing a Vogue like smile.

"Surprise!" She said, as she entered the room. "I came to support my baby! What's up Mister Bradley, what y'all doing?" She asked, as they stepped on past me.

My father politely speaks as my Mom introduces him to her relative.

Meanwhile, I stood stunned while glancing at my Dad to try to read his mood as my mom takes a seat. After a short chat, my father grabs his room key card and heads towards the door, and says, "I got to make a call, I'll let you guys visit."

About thirty minutes later he returned, just as they are saying their good-byes. Not long after they've left, my mom calls the room to talk, not to me but to him. I couldn't remotely begin to express how disappointed I was in my mother flying all the way from Little Rock to Indiana after admitting that she didn't even have 'any' money to help me make this trip. But he graciously takes her call, and here's how that conversation goes down.

"What's up?" Dee asks.

"You tell me, Dee? I'm cool, but I'm wondering what's up with you," Danny replied.

"What do you mean?" She asked.

"You don't show up in a snowstorm 450 miles from home, after claiming you don't have 'any' money to help this kid make this trip," He said.

"My relative here in Indiana paid for my trip," Dee responded.

Danny pauses, knowing Denise's game and just said, "Okay."

"What time does the meet start in the morning?" She immediately asked.

"Don't know, perhaps you should ask Mark," he replied, as he hands me the phone.

I took the phone and after giving her the information, her next question was, "Who else staying in the room with you guys?" She asked.

"Just us—why?" I asked, even though I kind of know at this point why she's asking.

"I thought about coming back, but I guess I'll see you tomorrow."

Bingo, I thought as we hang up.

And then I look over at my father who was reading a work manual, and said, "You know the only reason she came, right?

"No, what's that?" He asked without looking up, knowing what I was about to say.

"She only came up here to see you, Dad—not me."

"Yeah, okay," he disinterestedly replied.

"I told you she still got a thing for you."

"She a married woman, son," he said, while appearing to be uninterested in this conversation. But I pressed on.

"Dad, my Mom only came to a couple of my track meets in Arkansas when the sun was out—why else would she come all the way to Indiana, in the snow?"

"Apparently, to be close to her son," he replied, still with his head in his document.

"Close to me?! She came to be close to you!" I replied, knowing that he had to know this to be an absolute true. "If my mom really wanted to get money to me, she could've just had the relative to do it on this end, but once she found out that you were here, suddenly she finds the cash to not only feed me but to make the trip herself."

He then looks up at me and said, "I appreciate that insight, but its time to go to bed, Dr. Ruth. You have a long day tomorrow young-fella."

"Who is doctor Ruth?"

"Go to sleep," he said, as I got him to smile.

The track meet, over the next few days, went well, and after this memorable event, my dad and I were on good speaking terms again, thanks to his *forgiving* spirit. But before long, I had fallen back into my old ways even though I made an oath to never disappear again. The National Indoor Track Meet kind of placed me on the map. You could say the buzz around town was starting to get to my head. I begin to get a little conceited. My family saw it as confidence, but my Dad thought of it as down right cockiness. I had become a top prospect in track and field, and even began to turn a few heads in football. The local media had begun to write articles about me and often referenced my Dad's success in comparison. My family didn't like the fact that he would often get the nod in these editorial conversations, which always led to somebody saying something disparaging about him and whoever wrote such an article.

I had come to accept the fact that my mom was competing with my father. Again, he wanted me to have his kind of success but she didn't want him to help me achieve it, despite his resume. And as the spirit of confusion would have its way, validating that words do have power, I, too, at this point, wanted to prove that I could make it without his help, which only threw even more fuel on this already out of control barn fire.

So, as my senior football season was under way, my Mom and family would be in the stands cheering on this soon to be top prospect with tons of letters from colleges and universities rolling in. But this time around, my Dad was not in his usual incognito spot for which he had occupied the past couple of years.

Apparently, he had decided to withdraw from attending any of my games, after I went Awol on him, again. He had often made it known that he was going to be my father—not my friend, buddy or fan.

But nevertheless, despite the position we had taken with my father, my mom, after all the pain we had caused this man, decides to add insult to injury one more time, by calling him directly pressing him about school clothes. And it gets ugly, again.

Chicago

My father had just checked into his hotel in downtown Chicago to meet with a well-known NBA player, an All-Star, about a business opportunity, when the call came in.

"Why haven't you contacted Mark about his school clothes?"

"Pardon me," Danny replied.

"Mark needs some school clothes!" She repeated. "Why haven't you contacted him about his schools clothes this year?! School started over a month ago," she said with a sultry tone.

Danny pauses and said, "Dee, you can't be serious."

"I'm gonna ask you one more time, why haven't you contacted my son about school clothes, Danny?!"

Danny pulls the cell away from his ear, trying to remain calm, takes a deep breath, but struggled this time to maintain his composure, "Ms. Terry, for the past thirteen plus years of this boy's life, whenever he wanted or needed anything, particularly, school clothes, you forced him to call—why are you now making this call?"

Ignoring Danny's question, Denise simply replied, "Mark needs some school clothes, Danny—it's as simple as that."

"Well—I suggest you have Mark call me himself, til then, the answer is—no."

"Well—I guess I'll have to contact an attorney and see if we can force you to take some responsibility," Dee shot back sarcastically.

Danny thought to himself, *Responsibility!*

Then asked, "Did you use the word attorney and responsibility in the same sentence?!"

"I didn't stutter," she replied. "Get my son some school clothes or else!"

"Or else what, Dee?! Or else what?! Here's the deal, tell your attorney, once you find one stupid enough to take on many of your unprofound beliefs, to bill me damn it!

"Fine, I'll see you in court," she replied, and hung up on him.

Pine Bluff

A week later, the Davis house was full after another Friday night victory with the Pine Bluff Zebras. At first, all was well until the jokes started, or should I say the jealousy turned toward my father.

"Boy, I told you—you going places! Your daddy can't wear your shoes," one said.

"Shoes—Mark 6'1 and Danny is all of what—5'10 with heels," another one said.

"Feet too small," someone else shouts out as they're all erupting in laughter.

They were obviously feeling pretty good about themselves, since they figured my Dad wasn't showing up anymore. In their mind, they had run him off just in time—as it was about to get really good for them, they thought. And with recruiting season just around the corner, it was their turn to wear the Superman "S" on their chest around town even though my father was perhaps *the only* Superman they knew, not to speak of being *the only* father in my life that had bona fide rights.

It wasn't enough that they had managed to prevent me from establishing a meaningful relationship with him, but they had jokes to go along with it. But the sad thing about this situation, I had *allowed* them to disrespect him at will. So to keep from hearing any more of it, on this night, I called my hang out buddy, Carl, and rushed out as my mom yelled, "Be in the house by 12 midnight!"

A few high school friends were throwing a house party, and as usual, we swung by. And while trying to enjoy myself, we ran into a new friend of mine. We struck up a conversation with him and before I knew it, I'm venting about all my family problems to this guy. And he listens and then manages to persuade me to follow him out to his car, where he and some of his boys were hanging out.

Once we're in the car, one of his guys fires up a joint, hits it and passes the joint back to him. He takes a hit and prepares to pass it to me, saying, "Hit this-this is what you need, 12—it's a helluva stress reliever, playa."

"Nah, I'm good," I replied immediately.

"You sure?" He asked. "We all got family issues, Mark—but this eases the pain," as he takes another hit. "It's easy on the body, easy on the mind, and will make all your problems disappear," as he coughs a few times from the smoke.

Then I began to rationalize why I shouldn't try this—I do need some relief. But as I pondered, interestingly, I didn't think about what my mother would say, I thought about what my father might do, then said, "Nah, I think I'll pass.... My Dad would kill me if he knew I was smoking weed."

He took another big hit and said, "Mark," as he coughed again, "let me ask you a question, where's your dad at the moment—*Dallas; New York; Chicago;* you said he travels a lot—right?"

"He does," I replied.

"Well, hell, if your Daddy can reach out and touch you right now, a thousand miles away—we need some that breeze he's smokin, playa!" He said, as his boyz burst out in laughter giving him dap.

He had a point, but as much as I thought about taking a puff, I quickly thought better, held up my hands and said, "Nah brah—I'm good.... I don't get high," as I opened the door of his vehicle to exit.

"We understand, 12. We don't really have a dad, so we get high," he added, as another one of his boys shot out, "Hell—I get high with my dad, dog, we smoke weed together," he said, which caused a huge outburst.

As I began to get out, my new friend grabs my arm and says, "Just remember that smell my brotha—it solves all problems in the natural."

I nodded and vacated the car and rushed back into the party to find my boy, Carl, to break wide from this scene. "I just nearly smoked a joint," I told him. So, as we made our way out the door and on towards my house, I began debating if I should go to my granddad, Odell's, or my Mom's. It was 2 a.m., I'm not only late but I'm also smelling like weed. My grandparent's was the safest way to go but decided to go on home to my mom's. And as expected, she was still up, waiting. And as soon as I walked through door, she storms out of her room and followed me to mine, and asked, "Do you know what time it is?!"

I apologized for being late, but then she gets a whiff of the marijuana scent, and suddenly said, "What da hell! So, you gettin high, now?!"

"Nah Mama, I'm not gettin high," I replied.

"If not, Mark, why are you smellin like weed?!

"I haven't been gettin high, mama,"

"The fact that you're saying that you're not high, tells me that you are just that, Mark—high!" She shouts.

At that, I had to laugh which probably made me look even more, guilty.

"So you think this is funny?!" She asked sarcastically.

"No, it's not, mom—I'm not gettin high," I replied with a smile.

"Son, you headed in the wrong direction. You gon be just like some of these sorry lazy dope heads around here, who was once talented but now just thugs!"

I dropped my head now wishing I had gotten high—that comment hurt me to the core. I mean, that comment hurt. She then says, "I'm callin your dad tomorrow and we'll see what he has to say about his son using marijuana."

Again, I wanted to ask, *Which one, mama.... Mayberry, Braylon and Danny?*

But she continued, "And I'm gonna test you're lying butt first thing in the morning to see what else you might be puttin in your body!"

Before I could say another word, she walked out and slammed my door.

The very next morning, a Saturday, my mom calls Shelly and asked if she could get Danny to call her soon—it's urgent. And while she awaits his call, she had me pee in a cup. If you recall, my mom is a probation officer, so testing urine is all in a days work for her. And minutes later my Dad Danny called.

Right out the gate, she went for the jugular, "Your son came home smellin like weed last night, I just had him pee in a cup to be tested—what you gon do?!"

Suddenly, I said to myself, *there it is—that validates it. Now that she thinks I'm getting high—I'm Danny's son.... He's the one that gets tagged as the father of the dope-smoking son.... But as long as things are well, I'm her son, Mayberry is my daddy.*

So in response, he asked to speak to me and likewise gets straight to the point, "You been using drugs, Mark?"

"No, I haven't," I replied, exasperated. "I tried to tell her—but she trippin."

"Excuse me?" Dee abruptly asked.

"Mark—have you been using drugs?" He asked again.

"Answer me?!" Denise demanded.

"Mom, I can't talk to both of y'all at the same time."

"Mark," my Dad says, "Listen to me and focus for a minute, okay?"

"I'm here," I replied, as my Mom continued mumbling and sputtering.

"Have you been using drugs?" He asked a third time.

"Dad, I was in a car with some guys smoking a joint, but I didn't touch it!"

"Well, she's not totally trippin, if you came home smellin like marijuana, son."

"Dad, I assure you I did not smoke any marijuana."

"Okay, let me talk to your mom," he said.

I handed her back the phone.

And again, she jumped right at him, "I said yo son is gettin high—what you gon do?"

My Dad paused and said, "Dee, I believe him, but test him and call me with the results.... I'll be in town by sundown."

They hang up, but later that evening, about 7:30 p.m., my Dad Danny was indeed in town. And since no one had seen me since the a.m. hour, he puts out a personal *all-points-bulletin*—to find me. He drives all over town, writing down addresses and taking down phone numbers. Finally, after three hours, he spots me coming out of a convenience store with three guys carrying cases of beer and bags of chips.

He sees us loading the brew and snacks into a Red Cutlass with expensive rims, as he pulls up behind the car and calls out my name. After recognizing who it is, I motioned my friends to go ahead as I get in the car with him, a lil terrified I might add.

"Looks like you guys had enough beer to host a fraternity party—are these the same guys your mom believes you got high with last night?"

"Dad, I didn't get high last night?" I responded defensively.

"You didn't answer my question, son."

"Yeah—one of the guys is a user—but I'm not."

"From the looks of it, son, you might as well gotten high, and drunk for that matter."

"I don't drink nor am I doin drugs, Dad," I replied a lil frustrated.

"Oh, really?"

"Yes, really."

"Well, let me ask you a question, son; if the cops pull that car over right now and find beer and just the scent of marijuana with three minors in the back seat, what do you think they will say.... *'oh, Mark B, we understand that this is not your alcohol, or the weed—so why don't you just call someone to come take you home, but the rest of you jokesters are going to jail. Is that what you think?'*"

I had no response to that. So he continued, "No—they're gonna take you to jail along with the rest of them—guilty by association."

Not knowing how to reply, I just stared at the dashboard and out the car window.

"Hey, I understand you got some issues," he said, "and I realize that I'm not necessarily in your top ten most favorite people right now, but I love you independent of what you think of me, Mark—and I didn't fly down to play games with you, son, I came to save you from many of the same traps that a lot of young men turn to when the pressures of life seems to be too overwhelming for them to deal with."

"I wasn't gettin high though, Dad," I replied.

"You missed the point, Mark...you're guilty by association, son," he said. *"Bad company will always corrupt good moral character*—so you might wanna check your hangout list extremely careful."

"All I'm saying is I wasn't getting high."

"I get that, but what I'm saying is you can always judge the character of a person by the company he keeps—am I being understood?"

"Yes," I responded soberly.

"And as long as I have breath in me, regardless if you ever like me or not—I'm gonna do everything I can to steer you in the right direction.... Just remember, *there's a way that seems right to a man, son, but its end leads to destruction."*

"It's not me that doesn't accept you, Dad," I replied, looking him directly in the eye.

"Maybe not, son, but your actions clearly say, that you clearly approve of those that don't, making you again a guilty party by association."

"All they care about is themselves, Daddy," I said as my voice trembles. "I know I keep blaming her but she never gave me the opportunity to choose what I wanted to do.... It was always **no, no** and **no** for **no** reason at all.... So, yeah, I thought about gettin high if it would ease the pain, but I didn't.... And I knew I was smellin like marijuana when I walked through the door, but it was my way of saying this is how I feel, this is what you and this whole family has done to me," as the tears rushed out of me again.

It was both heartbreaking and infuriating for Danny to see Mark in this state. As he placed his hand on his son's back to console him, he said, "Despite the unnecessary weight your family has placed upon you, you've got to find a way to forgive them, son. Hurting people hurt people, Mark.... So, you got to forgive them.... I'm not saying condone their behavior, but I am saying that forgiveness will free you from having to live with the anger, resentment and bitterness the rest of your life."

"But what she's doing is just down right selfish, Daddy," as the tears flowed.

"Yes—she's been very selfish; and unfair; and manipulative; and controlling; all of the above—but we've all done some pretty stupid selfish things, son.... But we live and we learn, and if we're smart we'll take a lil advice alone the way and repent—confess, and ask God to *forgive* us too, so that we can move on with life—guilt free."

As he talked about God's *faithfulness* and His *willingness to forgive* us of our shortcomings, and how *we must walk by faith not by sight,* he began convincing me that living in this *angry state of mind-set* will only lead to more rebellion.

"And once a young man with great potential feels cheated and trapped beyond his control, if he's not anchored in something deeper than his own strength, he will make decisions that will not only cause damage to himself but also to those around him."

My father always seemed to know the right things to say—and prayer was often how he would nearly always close these sessions with me. So as he prayed, I would pray asking God for help. And I always feel better afterward, which always eased my mind.

However, this whole idea of praying for people who didn't seem to have my best interest at heart was still very difficult for me. This man had enemies in my family for no just cause at all, as far as I've been able to discover, but he always found the strength to ask God to *bless them and forgive them.*

Again, all of us should have had great respect for this man, yet we slandered and mocked him, despite all the patience and kindness he showed toward us. We were always in church listening to sermons about *love*, *life* and *relationships,* but it was this *unaccepted* father that seemed to be the one who was teaching us about this thing called *love, life* and *relationships.*

And wouldn't you know it, by the end of recruiting season, out of all the letters I received from major college programs, not one of them, *not a one,* offered me a football scholarship, or even invited me to come visit their campus. Even I was taken aback by this reality, despite being warned of that possibility a few years earlier, by my father. But now that the 'whole truth' was out and on the table, as *National Signing Day* had practically come and gone, suddenly *no one* in my family was talking—at all.

And the promise my granddad Odell made about paying for my education, *regardless,* had dissipated entirely. He and my mom avoided any and all conversations about the subject. So in my household, I went from *Mark Bradley,* the possible future NFL star, to *mark bradley* its time you get out, get a job, and while you're at it find yourself a car.

And suddenly, my beloved family, who claimed to love me so-so much, now treated me as if I didn't even exist.

27
Divine Wisdom

All of the valuable advice my father had attempted to give us had become a reality. He would often remind me of a truth that began to show itself mightily at this point, *"Son, you don't know what you don't know."* And to save face, as the media made a slight mockery of the matter, I searched out my *feel-good friend* with the *Cutlass* to provide me with the other matter—the drug they said would bring relief.

But, in the meantime, after going hiatus on my father, yet, again, I decided to at least return one of his many calls, and amazingly, again, he answers.

"You were right, I didn't get not one single scholarship offer from anybody."

"Well, Mark, it's not just about talent, sometimes it's about location. But there's more to life than just football.... What else is going on with you?"

I noticed quickly that he didn't have much to say about it. Apparently, he felt that he has said all there was to say on this subject. He appeared to be done. But I wanted to talk about it, so I went on.

"I also saw an interview with Coach Houston Nutt, who said the exact same thing you've been trying to tell us."

"Which is?" He asked.

"That they recruit much heavier in the state of Texas than they ever do here in Arkansas.... The talent pool in Texas, he said, is just much better—and I feel so stupid for not listening."

"Well, again, I'm sorry it didn't quite work out, but there are a ton of other things you can still do other than play football, son. I tried to have this very conversation with you some time ago.... But you were not trying to hear it. So let me say it again, whatever you choose to do, you'll need an education to pursue it."

He didn't want to have any part of all this football talk again, especially after being stood up and disregarded and shut out time after time after time. But I continued on.

"But I still wanna pursue football though, Daddy," I said solemnly.

"Football is not everything, son.... At this point, I suggest you start thinking about the next thing you might want to do—you knew you had to make some drastic decisions to possibly extend your football opportunities—but you were unwilling to make those changes," my dad said. "And I am not going to be played like a puppet on a string of circumstances anymore."

I paused before answering, knowing he was right. But not willing to take no for an answer, I asked, "So what do you think I should do—because right now I'm embarrassed and the media is kind of having a field day with this 'no interest-no scholarship' thing."

"Come on, son—you don't really want my input, you guys just wanted my output."

"I know I look just as guilty as them, but I do appreciate everything you've done, Dad.... But I really do need to get out of here."

"There's no need to patronize me, son.... I've given you the benefit of the doubt for years and gone beyond the call of duty for you, but you keep changing your mind—leaving your Dad hanging.... But I gotta finish up a business meeting. I'll check on you later," and bang, he just hangs up on me.

Consequently, as I sat and reflected on it all, I realized how disappointed and discouraged I was with myself, my family and sadly with him, too. I had gotten so use to him bailing me out of so many situations, I guess I had grown accustomed to expecting him to do it in every situation, regardless of the position it might put him in. And since it was obvious that our plan, *the family plan,* had officially failed, I wanted him to make it right again—for the sixtieth time.

So as I lashed out at him on the inside, I began to do, again, what my family had always done, compare myself to him. I wondered even more, with more resentment, *how did he manage to make it and become this big-time major college quarterback, during a time when black quarterbacks were scarce.... he ain't half the talent I am.... For crying out loud, I just wanted to get out playing any position—he managed to get out playing the position.*

But then, again, I would think, *don't do this Mark—this man loves you.... He's your father.... Get rid of this deep imbedded envy toward this man—you need him.... You can't learn from someone that you're competing with—any more than one can follow a leader they aren't willing to root for.... Let these feelings go!* I would counter with.

The very next day, Danny, unbeknownst to Mark, places a call to the University of Oklahoma in an attempt to help him get in as a walk on. After making a convincing pitch, the team representative says, "Yeah, of course, send me some game tape on him and I'll see what I can do—by the way, how do we reach Mark, I'd like to chat with him about 5 p.m., today?"

He gives him Mark's number and says he'll make sure Mark was available to chat at such time, and that he would overnight the game tape in a couple of days.

They hang up, and Danny immediately calls Mark, but Denise answers.

"Dee—Danny—is Mark around?"

"No, he just left," she replied. "What's up?"

"Can you get him to my mother's house by 5 p.m. on the dot?"

"Yeah—why—what's up?" She asked again.

"Can you do it?" Danny asked insistently.

"Yeah—what's going on?" She asked a third time.

"He's got a phone call he can't miss, Dee—straight up 5, can you get him there?"

"Yeah sure—from who?" Dee asked.

"From the University of Oklahoma," Danny replied.

This time Dee replied, "Oh, Okay," with a little bit of reluctance in her voice. "But hold on, Mark just walked in the door.... Here—it's your Dad Danny."

I could tell something was wrong because she slightly shoved the phone in my hand, which prompted me to ask, "What happened," before saying hello.

"Mark, you say you're serious about getting out, right?" He asked.

"Yeah, what's up?"

"Well, I need you to be at grandma Shelly's by 5 p.m.?"

"Okay," my eyes opened wide, excited he was giving me another chance.

"Mark, don't play with me—are you serious?"

"Daddy, I'm serious!"

"Be at mother's house by 5 p.m., OU will be calling at straight up 5 p.m.... Not 5:01, Mark, but 5 p.m., do you understand?"

"Yes—I'll be there."

"Don't be late, son.... Call my Mom if Denise can't get you there on time."

"Okay," I replied with a bit of uncertainty and yet excitement.

"Mark," Danny said sternly. "Don't be late and just be yourself, cool?"

"Cool," I replied.

"And by the way, do you have any high school game tape?" He asked.

"Yeah, I have some game tapes," I replied.

"Take them with you and leave them with my mom.... I'll be in touch." He said.

As we hung up, I was excited with fear. I was both hot and cold, not knowing what to think or how to react to this possibility. And about 5:20 p.m., Danny, leaving his meeting, curious about Mark's conversation with OU, he calls his Mom to get the 411.

"Mark's not here," she says. "And OU has called twice, now," Shelly said.

"Unbelievable!" Danny said. "What did you tell them, mother?"

"I told the guy that I was expecting Mark at any time, so he said he would call back again about 5:30," she replied.

"I told Dee to get him there by 5 p.m. She knew this was important."

"When is that girl gonna stop this foolishness—here comes Mark through the door now.... Here—it's your father," Shelly says, as she, too, shoved the phone into his hands, as Danny digs in out the gate.

"I said 5 p.m., not 5:27, Mark Bradley!"

"Dad, I told her I had to be here by 5 o'clock, but she just kept running errands."

"Errands?!" Danny shouted into the phone.

"Yeah—did she know OU was calling?" I asked.

"Yes son, I told her," he replied.

"Well it appears that she was stalling on purpose then."

The phone beeps, I put my Dad on hold and answered it. And after about a five-minute hold, I click back, "You there?" I asked.

"Yes—I'm here, what's up?"

"That was the guy from OU, he said he thinks they may have given all their scholarships out, but since you are one of their favorites, he would personally do everything in his power to help me get in as a walk on, if he could.... He also said once he gets the game tape from you, he will sit down with Coach Stoops.... And I'll leave the game tapes here with mama Shelly."

"Cool, but if you are serious, Mark, I'd stay available and ready to make a trip and keep all the details about this between us, please, sir," he said.

"I will, but I now know why my mom was stalling with the errands; she was trying to buy time to sell me on the idea of enrolling to Arkansas Pine Bluff (UAPB)."

Danny pauses as he takes the phone away from his ear, takes a deep breath, and then asked, "Is this the first time she's said anything about UAPB?"

"Actually, yes. None of them has had much to say after no one offered me that scholarship that they were so convinced I'd get." I replied disappointedly.

"What did she say?"

"That if I was going to continue to play ball, why don't I stay home and enroll at UAPB—that their program is as good as OU's.... and that she was going to call Coach Hardman and talk to him about me being apart of their program."

"Not surprised," my Dad replied. "But hang in there, son.... In due time your mom will be fine, the question is—will you."

He warns me not to allow anyone to keep me from my dreams. But as he talked, I felt resentment and agitation beginning to rise up in me all over again. I thought, *this is my father, who has shown me nothing but love—beyond reason. Why am I still so caught up into this competition thing my family has going on with this guy?*

As I fade back into the conversation I hear him asking, "Mark, are you there?"

"Yes sir, I'm listening—go ahead."

"You gotta look at this from a pure business perspective, son. A Junior college might even be an option if you want to still get into a major program. Otherwise, doing Arkansas Pine Bluff will not allow you to make such a move, its a four year program."

"That's my mom pushing that, Dad—not me."

"But that's okay, if you want to stay at home and be a part of the black college experience, which is uniquely different than the major college experience. You can still get a good education, but unfortunately, the football program at PB lacks the resources, son.... Academically, you'll be fine, but athletically, you must stay healthy.... Any major injuries at a program that lacks resources often means—career over," he says. "That's unfortunate, but that's just the way it is."

I told him I understood, and it made a lot of sense. I didn't know much about small college programs like UAPB, even though I had been to many of their games. But I had seen up close what a major program like OU would look like, when visiting UT, which was indeed more terrifying than edifying.

It's now about 7 p.m. by the time I walked back into my mom's house. She was on the phone with the door to her room semi-closed. I could tell that she was chatting with my granddad Odell. So, as I grabbed a beverage from the refrigerator, I heard her entering the kitchen behind me. When I looked over at her, she appeared to be bothered, which encouraged me to ask if she was alright.

"I'm fine, but I need to talk to you, Mark."

"Okay, what about?" I asked.

"I know your Dad is trying to help you get into OU and that's fine and all, but after seriously thinking about this even more, today, we think you should stay and enroll at UAPB. You'll get the same education and play the same level of football, son."

"But I don't really wanna go to UAPB.... They didn't even recruit me!"

"Neither did Oklahoma, but you're considering going there if your Dad can get you in!" She fired back. "So why not consider UAPB if your mom can get you in, Mark?"

I just dropped my head in disgust as she went on and on and on selling UAPB's football program and why it should be the program of choice. And as you may have figured, this is the university that *she* attended and graduated from. Does this still sound like a lil competition going on, here? I thought so.

"Mom, we're talking football here," I replied.

"Mark, UAPB's football program is just as good as any other school in the country. Don't let all that junk you see on TV and what Danny keeps saying to you, fool you. You don't have to go to a big school to make it, son."

"First of all, he's not saying that, mom. Second, I've seen the difference in the two programs, there is a huge difference in a football program like OU's than one like UAPB's.... And if I can get into a major program where there are better resources to prepare and protect their athletes, why wouldn't you want that for me?"

"You're starting to sound like your damn daddy," she said sarcastically.

"But it's the truth mom," I replied. "I've seen these facilities with my own eyes, it's just not the same.... I see why its so easy for those schools to recruit!" I said, knowing that had LSU or Florida, or even Arkansas offered a scholarship, they would have rushed me up the road and out of Pine Bluff with the quick. The big schools is all they talked about until I didn't get an offer from the many letters they thought were scholarships, and mind you none them came from UAPB.

But as expected, she began to raise her voice, getting emotional. When she got like that, it was hard to talk to her, so I would just shut down. And with her voice starting to quiver, she said, "I did the best I could with you when your sorry no-good daddy was no where to be found, and this is the thanks I get!"

"Mom," I said, in an attempt to calm her down.

"Don't mom me.... Do whatever you want—but when it doesn't work out, don't come running your butt back crying to me!" She said, as she exits the kitchen.

And suddenly she hits the floor and appears to be hyperventilating as I jumped up to help her. Then she let out a loud scream, hollering, "Lord I've done all I could—I can't take another step with this anymore—I've gone the distance!"

Seeing her get like this, just sent me over the edge as well and before I knew it, I began crying uncontrollably, too. I then rushed out of the room just as my step-dad was coming in the front door. He then rushed over to his wife, asking what had just happened? And she hollered, "I'm tired! I can't do this anymore.... I just can't do it!"

"Do what?" He asked, as I paused listening in, before storming out the house.

"I'm just tired of fighting with Mark and his daddy! All I asked him to do was consider staying at home and go to UAPB, but his Dad got his head messed up with all this big school stuff! And I'm just tired, Braylon!"

I then took off, jogging up the street. Moments later, Braylon drove up alongside me about a quarter of a mile from home, trying to talk me into the car as I walked.

"Mark, come on man, we can work this out—your mother loves you."

I didn't respond—I was done talking.

"She's only trying to do what's best for you, Mark. Come on, get in the car—let's go check on her, she wasn't lookin too good when I left the house."

I was done talking, I still didn't respond.

"You don't want your her to be sick, Mark.... She loves you.... Get in let's go check on her," Braylon said. "We're family, Mark.... We can work this out."

Suddenly, I thought, *who in the heck am I fooling here—these guys know I'm one of them; they know I'm just bluffing; this craziness has only been going on for twenty plus years now—and we're still walking around the same freaking mountain.*

So I stopped, paused, and thought about it and got in the car.

A couple of days later, as my grandma Shelly was opening up her morning newspaper, she notices the headline that read, **"Bradley heads list of UAPB signees."**

She picks up the phone, calls Danny to share with him the news, who is not surprised, as she begins to read Mark's quote: *"It feels great—I'll be real close to my family. I know what the system (at UAPB) is like, and so I'll feel just like being right at home."*

Simultaneously, JB walks through Shelly's door and says, "I just heard Mark on the local radio saying that he's decided to attend UAPB because his mom and family wanted him to stay close to home."

"Denise just won't quit will she," Shelly said.

"Hey, maybe he'll at least get an education," Danny replied. "And again, it's not just Denise, mother, it's Mark, too."

"But Danny," Shelly said.

"Mom, to be honest, I think Mark feels more comfortable in that environment. And that's okay.... These major programs are not for everybody.... This may be the best environment for a kid like Mark."

"So what now—what do you plan to do?" She asked.

"Do what I've always done—be his father." Danny replied.

As you may have imagined, my mom and the family were on cloud nine, and all was well among us, once again. But sadly, I let my mother manipulate me into doing what she wanted me to do—not really what I wanted to do. It was never about me and what I might want—this was all about what she wanted—from him. And the more she felt me leaning towards my father, they would call me into the family office and reprimand me.

But I must admit, I was indeed much more comfortable at UAPB than I would have been at OU or UT. Not because I thought, by any means, that UAPB's program was superior or even equal to those highly decorated programs, but mainly because I was afraid of the challenge at those big schools. I hadn't really been raised to take on such a huge-huge responsibility. But I was willing to try it if she would have supported me.

And the hidden undercurrent to all of this madness was simple: I was trying to do this her way, even though we all knew that my father was my best way—out. But in my house, her way was the only way unless I was willing to risk losing the entire family. So, once again, I avoided my Dad's calls that entire summer. I guess you can say, I was prepared to never have that father/son relationship that I desperately needed in my life.

Simply put, I found myself helping my mom justify a multitude of wrongs that she obviously didn't want to make right between us. But in the midst, my father taught me that wherever you find fear, you find selfishness—and wherever you find love, you'll always find faith. My mother lived life out of fear, selfishness and resentment—and had raised me to do the same. However, I knew better, but I still couldn't or wouldn't do better by this man now known as my father.

As a result, I finally turned to that friend, who had convinced me that getting high was the way to deal with all this stress. So, despite all I knew to be right, I started smokin a lil marijuana to ease my pain. It was thoughts of my Dad that stopped me the first time, but it was the thoughts of my mom that drove me back the second time.

So with sex, drugs and now alcohol used as coping mechanisms to get me through, the more distant and alone I began to feel. And when my Dad got word through the grapevine that I was indeed using drugs, a trip to Pine Bluff, once again, was in order—and this time, the gloves come off.

28

Divinity at Work

It's now the fall of 2000, and while the Davis, Terry, and Mayberry families were thrilled that Mark had chosen to stay at home, which kept them *in control* of this senseless war, the Bradleys just remained prayerful. And although beaten completely down by it all, he was attempting to make a name for himself in the Southwestern Athletic Conference—known as the SWAC, a historically black college conference. While he would remember his dad's words of counsel, *bad company corrupts good character,* every time he found himself getting into a certain *Red Cutlass Supreme* with the high dollar rims, his character would soon begin to expose the multitude of emotional issues going on within his world.

Having become totally consumed by his mom and her family's manipulation, his Dad's words of wisdom were being overpowered by that of this friend, with this *Red Cutlass,* who was always ready with a, "what's up playa—you ready to hit this joint?"

But on this Saturday afternoon, as the game comes to a close, Mark's teammates are praising one another and giving him props for the two punts he returned for touchdowns, against Texas Southern University. As they make their way toward the buses, one of his teammates, Dante Wesley, catches up to him.

"What you got going on tonight?" Dante asked.

"My Pop's in town; probably just do dinner.... I might later hook up with my boy, RC," I replied.

"RC—Red Cutlass, RC?" Dante asked.

"Yeah—that's him," I responded offhandedly. "You know him?"

Stepping out and away from a few of our teammates, pulling me with him, he looked me in the eye and said, "Mark, that ain't you brah—break wide from dude. RC is a heavy smoker, man."

And in as confident and reassuring a manner as I could project, I replied, "Nah—I'm not using like that—I've only had a joint or two on a couple of occasions."

"I'm just warning you, dog—you don't want to go down that road," he said.

Later that evening, Mark and his dad were at dinner at their favorite spot in town—*Garfield's* at the Pines Mall. Mark ordered the usual, a hamburger, fries and a coke, as Danny does his usual—water and a chicken salad with UAPB as the appetizer.

"So, how's it going with the Golden Lions?" Danny asked.

"Its going okay," I replied.

"Decided on a major yet?"

"Not really," I replied. "But I'm leaning more towards Industrial Technology, your fraternity brother heads up that department. He's cool, and a really good instructor."

"Aright, Nupe—Engineer, huh," he said.

For the record, the term "nupe" is a term associated with Kappa Alpha Psi.

"I kind of like the engineer program," I responded.

"What about your teammates and coaches?"

I smiled as if thinking about one of them and said, "The coaches are cool—but comical! We have a lot of comedians in our locker room. But Dante Wesley is the most talented player we have."

The waiter stops by with their orders and politely places them on the table and refills their glasses with water, as Danny asked, "Where do you guys dress at?"

For the first time during the conversation I was noticeably less enthusiastic as I replied, "Well, we don't really have a dressing room-dressing room for either the home or the guest teams; so we dress at the old-old field house. And, by the way, you're right—they don't really have a rehab facility for *the seriously* injured players."

"Yeah—but it would be nice to see them raise enough cash to build the right kind of facility, and hire a good training staff to provide you guys with a chance to get prepared and stay healthy," Danny said, as if thinking out loud.

"Well, maybe you could help," I replied. "You're connected with all the right people with deep pockets, and I heard that there has been a few local people, with influence, trying to get you to come back and get more involved with the program."

"And where did you hear that?" He asked, with a light smile.

"Dad, it's a small town—people talk, you know that," I replied.

"That's an Athletic Director's job, son."

"Well—become the next AD and make that much needed difference—and while you're at it, you get the chance to spend a lil bit of time with all of us—at home."

At that, I took a healthy bite of my burger and sat back waiting for a response; confident that I had solved a long-term separation problem.

He replied, "Aright Chancellor Bradley, point considered, but in the meantime, just stay healthy and take your butt to class and get that engineering degree."

He then picks up the cell and makes a call to one of the power players in town, a well-known elected official, who had been encouraging him to come back and use his relationships, experience and skill-sets to help the university—a university that this power player had a strong relationship with. He informs him that he would apply for the position if he felt that he had a really good shot at getting the job. The power player's response, "It's nearly a guarantee."

As I heard those words, I took a deep breath feeling as if all of my family issues were over. I, too, believed, knowing what I knew about this man and our program, he could definitely make a major difference in our program, and had previously shown his interest, unbeknownst to many in this town, when he encouraged, then, Cowboys Coach Barry Switzer to consider UAPB as the school of choice when, Doug Switzer, his son, was looking to transfer from Missouri Southern, which brought a reasonable amount of visibility to the Golden Lions programs.

However, ten minutes later, as we were pulling out of the parking lot of the restaurant, he asked, "Which of your buddies you say owns that really nice *Red Cutlass* I saw you with a while back?"

"That's my boy, RC—I went to high school with him," I replied.

"Okay," Danny replies as his cell phone rings.

It's his brother, JB, which brings us to the *main* reason he made this trip to PB.

"I got good news and bad news," JB says.

"Go ahead," Danny responded. "Give me the bad news first."

"The bad news is, Mark indeed has been seen smoking a lil marijuana with a couple of those same guys you ran upon him with a while back named RC."

"Can you confirm that?" Danny asked.

"Yeah," JB replied. "The dude that sold the weed to RC, said he saw Mark gettin high with him and his boys—and this is the same guy with the *Red Cutlass.*"

"And the good news?" Danny asked.

"Well—the bright side of this is that Mark, according to my source, may not have had more than a joint or two or three. The guy said that the way Mark was handling the weed the other night, he couldn't have had more than an experience or two; his buddies were teasing him about his lack of dope smoking skills," JB said giggling.

"Aright—thanks for the update," Danny replies and hangs up.

At such point, Danny was approaching Denise's house and pulls into the driveway. After coming to a complete stop, he looked straight ahead—in silence, which prompted Mark to ask, "Is everything aright?"

He then turns and says, "I just got a very interesting call—confirming some very disturbing news, Mark B."

"What happened?" I asked with grave concern.

"A very reliable source has confirmed that he saw you smoking marijuana a couple of weeks ago with this guy RC—is that true?"

I frowned quizzically and asked, "He saw, me?"

"Yeah, you—is it true?"

"I don't know who could have told you that, Daddy.... as I told you and mom a while back, I wasn't using then nor...." Danny, then, put his hand up as if to cut off anything else he attempted to say and said with calmness but with firmness, "Don't lie to me Mark!"

"But you didn't let me finish Daddy," I pled.

"Don't lie to me, Mark.... are you gettin high or not?!"

I paused and then said, "I did, but it was only a few times. I only did it a few times, pops—that's it. And I wasn't lying back then about gettin high, Dad."

Suddenly he said firmly but softly, "Get out."

"Dad—it was only a few times!"

"Get out."

"Dad—seriously," I pleaded.

"I said get out!" He yells.

At that, I knew it was time to exit. Therefore, I slowly opened the door and eased out of the car, as he calmly backed out of the driveway and drove away. I just stood there not knowing how to even think about what just happened.

And surprisingly, despite his star-studded support and reference group, for some strange reason he did not get offered the position as Athletic Director, which kind of rubbed a few *local dignitaries* the wrong way. The Chancellor had mysteriously hired an AD without notifying the search committee, after making known that he was one of the final two candidates to be interviewed. And since a few members of my household seemed to be *pleased* that he was denied this opportunity, made me wonder what role *they* might have played in it. After all, my grandfather, Odell, works on this small campus, my mom knew several of the search committee members, and they both had a more than cordial relationship with the Chancellor.

This was an embarrassing situation for me, given the dynamics. The outcome had severed a few long-term relationships between the university officials and some of it's local supporters, which disappointed my father deeply. But being that focused father, he just kept his eyes on me, monitoring my every move, decision and activity off the field—even from a distance.

By the next fall, my days of smoking weed may have ended, but my inability to overcome my need to please my Mom and her family—didn't. And this, over the years, would be the drug, which prevented me from having the kind of relationship with my father that I desperately needed.

And by mid-October of '01, as we traveled to Louisiana to play Grambling State University, I realized that Saturday evening, I was sliding deeper and deeper into depression as the rest of the year unfolded.

Meanwhile, across town, the Bradleys were at home eating dinner when Danny surprises them by walking in the side door unannounced.

Hugging her son Shelly says, "Baby, you didn't tell us you were coming, I just got off the phone with Dr. Jensen, who was asking if you were going to the Grambling game in Shreveport?"

Duke, likewise, gets up to hug him and jumps right into the issue about this estranged relationship he had with his son.

"What's going on with my grandson, is he still dipping and dodging you?"

"Well, funny you ask—for the past three weeks I've been fasting and praying for a breakthrough.... We still haven't talked very much since the incident regarding the drugs, but I've been keeping up.... He doesn't return my calls too often, but I got the 411 on him."

"Well, what brought you to Pine Bluff and not Shreveport?" Duke asked.

"Its strange, but right about noon, today, I felt this strong urge to come home. I knew he wouldn't be in town but something in my spirit, kept pushing me to come to Pine Bluff.... So here I am five hours later, sitting here not really knowing at all why I'm here," Danny said.

Duke smiles and said, "I'm sure the good Lord will reveal it to you, but in the meantime, let's listen in on the Grambling game."

As the commentators came back from a commercial break, the sound of the world-renowned Grambling State marching band fills the Bradleys kitchen, as Denise, and practically most of her family are taking their seats at the Independence Bowl Stadium. And just as soon as this game gets underway, injuries began to take their toll. And by the middle of the first quarter, sophomore standout Mark Bradley was back deep to receive the punt.

As the announcer calls it, Mark makes a couple of great moves to elude tacklers, and just as he begins to make the last cut to be home free, he goes down and appears to be in great pain. This might be ugly, one announcer said over the airwaves, as the other one made mention that the cart is being brought out and Bradley is indeed in great pain. As the announcers continued, Danny's parents noticed tears begin to fall from his eyes as a smile began to also accompany it as well, for which Duke then looked at his son and said, "Well—it appears you have your answer big-boy."

Shelly, who'd been leaning back in her chair with her feet propped up, just smiles and said, "Well I'll be."

"So, what's the plan now? You think he'll call?" She asked.

Danny wipes away a tear and said, "He'll call."

"You trust they'll let him?" Shelly asked, her tone filled with years of past letdowns.

"He'll call—divinity is in play, now," he said, as he stood up leaning toward the kitchen.... But in the meantime, I'm hungry.... Grits, eggs and bacon would work just fine—the fast is over!"

Shreveport, Louisiana

A security guard was manning the door to the locker room. I could hear my mom and my step-dad frantically telling the guard who they were—my family. He finally relents and when he opens the door they storm into the room. One of the trainers informs them of the severity of my injury, a torn Anterior Cruciate Ligament (ACL), which will require surgery.

He went on and mentioned that I wouldn't be playing football for a while if ever again—these kind of injuries can take time and affect different players differently. He suggested that I be taken to a local hospital in Shreveport immediately before heading back to Pine Bluff.

As I lay on the training table with ice on my knee, I could hear the voice of my father, *Son, whatever you do, stay healthy. A serious injury at a program like this, that lacks rehabilitation resources, could end it all.*

I replayed and reflected on all the discussions I'd had with him in my head; the prayer sessions; the pep talks; the trip to UT; Valley Ranch; and the one to OU that never happened. I began to question all my decisions, my family's decisions, even the pet dog's decisions. I questioned everything, which caused me to suddenly slam my fist into the table in disgust, which brings the entire room to a stop. They thought that my reaction was pain related, but this was more anger related.

After I made this agonizing walk on crutches to the car, we were on our way to the hospital. I kept thinking, *we were told over and over and over again what the consequences might be.... Time after time after time he had offered his wisdom on many of these issues of life, but I wouldn't listen—we wouldn't listen.*

Little Rock

Two days later we were at the Arkansas Sports Medicine Center in Little Rock. The physician had my Magnetic Resonance Imaging (MRI) pictures in a large yellow envelope. He then slid what looked like a large picture of negatives onto the monitor, which illuminated the negative and began examining them. He then says, "Yes—it appears you do *indeed* have an ACL tear—which will require surgery to repair the damage. You plan to continue playing football?" He asked.

"Yes—I would like too," I answered now thinking that there may be hope after all. So much of what was happening had made me doubt anything positive, let alone playing football again.

My mom who is there too, jumped in and asked, "Is there a possibility he won't be able to play again?"

"Well, with all the new procedures and rehab programs available today, he can definitely return to the field. But it will take him perhaps about four to six months to get back to a hundred percent. This is an athletic injury, which will require a serious athletic course of therapy and treatment to make it back."

Doc paused as if to make sure we were truly listening before he went on, "It takes time, commitment and mental toughness to come back from these kind of injuries."

"How much will something like this cost?" My mom asked.

As he opened my file he replied, "Well, usually, the scholarship covers the cost for the athlete, but it appears that it's your personal insurance that will be providing the coverage, not the university, which simply boils down to what plan you have him covered under—you would need to contact your insurance company about that."

As he made that comment, I dropped my head in disbelief and asked, "So, the program is not even paying for this, mom? So, I'm playing ball at my own risk?"

"Mark, we can talk about this later.... Doc, when will he have this surgery?"

"The target date is usually five-to-eight weeks from the time of the injury, after the swelling has subsided," Doc said.

I thought, *You gotta be kidding me! My Dad had straight up called this thing and it was starting to unravel on our clock.*

As we made our way to her SUV to head back to PB, she said, "Don't be so quick to judge, Mark.... All university athletes must have their own insurance."

"Mom—if that's the case, what would be the sole purpose of a scholarship?" I asked disappointedly. "Which means, I'm probably not even on scholarship."

"Well, complaining about it won't change anything, Mark," she said testily.

"You right—what am I complaining about. I knew; you knew; we all knew that this could happen; we know about this possibility!"

"Mark, please don't start with me about your father! Every time something happens you want to throw up your Daddy! Danny ain't here! Do you see Danny anywhere around here?! You ain't even heard from your damn Daddy!"

While she took a breath from her rant, I whispered, "I wouldn't come around either, if I was him, with the way y'all treat the man."

"Excuse me?! What did you just say?!" She asked.

"I said I don't blame him with the way y'all treat him."

"Boy please, you have a torn up knee, bout to have surgery, why are you trippin?!"

"I'm just saying, mama, how can the man be here if he doesn't even know?!"

"Well—its not my fault that he doesn't know! If he would've had his butt at the game he would have known—don't you think?"

I'm thinking, *Mama please—you don't really want me to respond to that. This man can't win for losing with you.*

Looking disgusted at me in her rear view mirror, she barked, "Mark, your daddy don't come around because he don't want to come around! It's just that simple—so deal with it.... Live with it!"

I said to myself, again, *you don't really want me to respond to that, mama.*

So as she went on and on, I just shook my head and didn't say another word the rest of the way on this thirty-five minute drive. By the time we made it back home, I was an emotional wreck. I crutched my way inside, past my step-dad, who quickly asked, "What's wrong with him?"

And as I worked to get settled in, I could hear him asking her, "What happened?"

"A little bit of everything," she replied. "He's upset that the school is not paying for his surgery.... He's upset because he's not on scholarship.... He's upset because the school doesn't really have a rehab program on campus.... and he's angry because his dad is not here.... Mark is just trippin as usual!"

My step-dad tried to softly whisper, but I was able to make out what he said.

"Well, he is in town.... or at least he was a couple of days ago. I ran across him about 6 a.m. at the convenience store on East Harding near your parent's house while patrolling the area. I don't know if he was comin or goin, but he is or was in town."

My mother paused and replied, "I'm sure he knows by now, somebody has perhaps called him and told him about the injury."

Overhearing that my father was indeed in town, didn't calm my emotions, they sent them out of complete control. Despite everything, this man loved me, people; and I knew I needed him more than I needed anybody in my life at this point.

So I grabbed the cordless, paused, took a deep-deep breath and I dialed grandma Shelly's number to see if he was still around town. When she answered and heard my voice, she looked over at Danny, and asked, "Mark, how you doing baby?"

Barely able to get it out, I asked, "Is my Dad still in town, Mama?"

"Yes, Mark, he's here," she said sadly with concern.

"Is he there, can I talk to him?" I asked, as the tears begin to build.

Shelly then began to weep as she handed Danny the phone while whispering, "Its your son, Mark."

Danny, then, grabs the cordless, pauses, takes a deep breath, and said, "Talk to me, son—how you doing?"

"Daddy," was about all I could get out before totally breaking down, which pushed Danny over the emotional edge a bit too.

"I'm here, son," Danny replies tearfully but with strength.

"Will you please come get me out of this house—I can't take it anymore?" I said, as I cried through my whisper to keep my mom from hearing my plea. Danny pulls the phone away from his ear in an attempt to maintain his composure, to which Shelly says, "It's aright baby—perhaps this is the answer to your prayers," while Duke, the once-upon-a-time deadbeat father, began to pace and pray.

As Danny placed the phone back to his ear he could hear Mark saying, "Daddy, Daddy—are you there?!" His voice was racked with pain, fear and uncertainty.

"I'm here son," Danny replied warmly.

"I know I've let you down—I've lied to you—I've hidden from you—talked about you—disrespected you—but if you'll give me one more chance, Daddy, I promise I will make you the proudest father any kid could ever have," I said, crying in agony.

"Where are you, son?" He asked.

"At my Mom's—can you come get me—I just can't do this like this anymore?!"

"I'm on my way, son—hang tough," my father said as he rushed over to come deliver me from the bondage that has so easily beset me through my own family's despicable behavior.

29

Divine Intervention

As the doorbell rings, I can see the looks on my mom and my step-dad's face wondering who that might be. And for the first time, as my Dad entered the house, despite this spirit of confusion and division within my family, I felt as if serenity had just walked in.

Exuding peace in a hostile setting appeared to be a way of life for him. In the fifteen years I've known him, I'd only seen him totally lose it and physically go completely off on a relative, who had, for years, verbally abused his parents without cause. And even then, he repent before all family members who had seen him fall.

Nevertheless, with two parents holstering guns on their hips by profession, my Dad walks into the house, by himself, unconcerned of what could potentially happen if my step-dad, who was now a police officer, or my mother, a well known probation officer—just snaps.

But my Dad was bold, yet gentle, kind and respectful toward them. And it was this approach, I believe, that kept my mother and her support group turned upside down. They couldn't stand the fact that they couldn't get him to fight their war. They saw it as a fleshly battle; but he viewed it as a spiritual one. *'For we wrestle not against flesh and blood,"* he would often say, *'but against spiritual wickedness in high places,'"* And he had to be correct, because how could anyone, in the natural, have the wherewithal to withstand the kind of pressure we put on this man, and not snap.

So with UAPB not being able to provide the necessary rehabilitative support I needed to successfully recover, my Dad readjusted his life, once again, and took over the monitoring of my physical therapy. Health South and a local workout facility became the places which we used to work toward that full recovery. Behind the scenes, he became my trainer, physical therapist and nutritionist. I would often think during those days, how badly we miscalculated this man's character. I didn't have anybody that had the know how or the ability to wear so many hats, not to speak the number of commitments and sacrifices he had to make seemingly without much thought.

He would fly or drive into town each week to assist me with a very difficult rehab program, which also provided him the time to spiritually rehabilitate me as well. He not only helped rehab my body, but he also help rehab my mind. And it was this combination of *Spirit, Soul* and *Body* to which I found *the hope* to believe again. His input, began to help me understand what made him do the things he did, say the things he'd say and respond the way he responded. Again, he was not perfect, by any means, but this man trusted God and never made any excuses for his failures or shortcomings. I discovered a multitude of mistakes my father had made over the years through these sessions, but by faith, he learned to lean on God's mercy and grace, as he searched for a better way.

Having spent all my life in the church, I'd never been taught the *Grace of God in detail* the way my father laid it out for me at this point in the game. I never knew that God, through His grace, had already made provisions for me to experience life guilt free—to the full—til it overflows with His goodness. All this time, as a believer, I thought God was angry with me and that I had to *do something* to move Him in order to be blessed. But God, according to scripture, had already provided everything I needed in life to win. But I could only partake of these blessings by Faith in His grace as a believer—not by works or performance, which had never been explained to me.

For by grace you have been saved through faith, and not of yourselves; it is the gift of God, not of works, lest anyone should boast. [Ephesians 2:8-9]

This changed everything in how I viewed God; talked to God; and approached God, even though I knew I had a ton of changing to do before God. But this man helped me understand, in more detail, what God thought of me; how much He truly loved me; and how much He wanted to bless me.

But what was tragically ironic, the same man the good Lord used to teach me these truths, is the same man my family worked overtime to keep me away from. I realize, at this juncture, too, that the *real enemy* was not just in the flesh, but rather in the spirit. Satan was the adversary here, he helped me conclude, not my family. The family was merely being used as a vessel to not only minimize the blessing on my father's life, but to also keep me from fulfilling my own destiny.

Now with frequent Bible study and prayer sessions implemented into my daily routine, I began to believe I could truly make a comeback, as I started confessing the word of God, daily, regarding my health, family and circumstances, to combat these demonic forces that had already robbed me of a multitude of blessings.

Morning and evening, I would come into agreement with my father, as he quoted and paraphrased scriptures: '*You are highly favored Mark B; You can do all things through Christ who strengthens you; No weapon formed against you shall prosper; by His stripes, you were healed; He shall supply all your needs according to His riches in glory,'"* to name a few. And my faith began to get established as my confidence slowly but surely started to rise.

However, reality set in as the need to address my current issue became more evident. He asked, "Have you heard from anyone at UAPB since your surgery?"

I thought about it and then said, "Actually, no.... Wesley and a few other coaches called, but no, I haven't heard or talked to Coach Hardman. Maybe he sent word through my mom or granddad but I never heard from him directly."

"How do you feel about it?" He asked.

"Not hearing from the Head Coach bothers me a lil bit.... But I understand that, hey, he didn't really recruit me, that's a deal my mom cut with him."

"You ready to move on or you want to work it out?"

"What do you think?" I asked.

"I think its time to move on.... If he didn't even recruit you, you might not have much value to him.... But don't sweat it, he's a decent man, who just happens to think you can't really play."

"Well, if a small program like UAPB didn't recruit me, and I'm right here in their back yard, apparently I can't play," I said sarcastically.

"Apparently, but that chapter of your life is probably over.... It appears that they have moved on and its time you do the same big-timer.... and the way you jump start that, is by requesting your release papers—and if we're right, he won't waste anytime trying to talk you out of it."

"I'm at least good enough to be on scholarship at UAPB. My performances clearly documents that though Pops!"

"True, but selecting football talent is like choosing a date, son.... What one man might think is beautiful, another might think she's just aright.... So, always remember, *one* program's trash can be *another* program's treasure—understood?"

"Understood," I replied.

The very next week, I was at the football offices requesting my release papers from Coach Hardman. And just as my Dad had predicted, he didn't ask why, when, or what for. He just said, "Sure—no problem," and gave me my release papers and sent me on my way.

Meanwhile, Danny was on the phone with the University of Oklahoma, again, checking the possibility of Coach Stoops taking Mark in as a walk on, which is the route he was attempting to push a couple of years earlier, independent of a scholarship offer, but his mother persuaded him to enroll at Arkansas Pine Bluff instead. They both understood that mothers generally win those battles whether the father is inside the home or not.

He made known to Merv Johnson, Director of Football Operation, that Mark was only about 85% healthy from an ACL injury that took place mid-October the previous season. But if Coach Stoops would consider the idea, Mark would be elated, and it would mean a lot to his father, having played and been a part of that great historical program and institution.

"He understands what it means to be a walk-on," Danny said. "And if he's talented enough to earn his keep, great, if not, I'll continue to help fund his way."

"Has he received his release from Arkansas Pine Bluff?" Merv asked.

"Got the transcript, release papers and his MRI report," Danny readily replied.

"Sounds like you guys are prepared to make it happen. So send me what you have and I'll be in touch within a few days."

And as promised, a week later, OU called with a thumbs-up response. Coach Stoops agreed to take me in as a walk-on. I was now headed to Norman to join the Sooners of Oklahoma.

The packing had begun and I was trying to keep from being conspicuous, given the fact that I wasn't quite ready to have that conversation with my mother. For the past few weeks I had been taking my packed things over to Grandma Shelly's little by little. But on this afternoon, while packing and eating a bowl of cereal, I heard my mom enter the house. It was early afternoon and usually she was at her office or in court this time of the day. So I quickly grabbed my bag and threw it in the closet, picked up my half-eaten bowl of cereal and pretended to be watching television.

Standing in the doorway, she looked at me, then the TV, and asked, "What are you doing at home in the middle of the day—eating up all the food, Mark?"

"I'm just having a bowl of cereal, Mom," I replied.

"Which reminds me—I heard recently you haven't been going to class much this summer—what have you done, quit school altogether?!

"No, Mom, I haven't."

"Aren't you supposed to be in summer school to make up for all these classes you missed behind this injury? Are you a college dropout now, Mark?!"

"No, I didn't drop out of college, Mom."

"I told you this once before, Mark, if you're not careful, son, you gon be just like the rest of these once-upon-a-time talented athletes, who are now just complete thugs around this town with no education and no job," she shot out.

“I didn’t drop out of school, Mom,” I replied again, as her comment once again digs into me just a little deeper.

“Yes you have Mark! I’ve gotten word from several people on campus some that said they haven’t seen you. So, since you’re not interested in going to school anymore,” she said, “get up, get dressed, and go find a job,” as she looked at me with disgust while exiting the room. But she wasn’t done, she returned shortly with what she’d apparently come home for, a file in her right hand. Using it to emphasize her point, she says, “And be at this house by seven tonight, You and I are going to have a talk about this stay over you been doing at the Bradleys and what you seem to be doing with your life!”

She stuffed the pointer-slash-document in her briefcase and stormed toward the door and slightly yelled, “And stop eating up all the doggone food!”

Once I heard her car pull off I called a relative on my Dad’s side of the family, who was the manager at a local department store, and told him I needed a job. And his first question was, “Why do you need a job when you’re about to leave for OU in a month or so, Mark?”

“I need some shut-my-mama-up money. She’s giving me a hard time about school and food—so can you get me hired?”

“For a month?” He asked.

“Yeah—for a month or so,” I replied.

“Mark, come on man, why don’t you just call your dad?”

“He’s done enough already—I just need a job for now.”

“You serious?” He asked.

“Can you help me get in or not?”

The relative pauses, sighs, and says “Come see me this evening.”

We hang up, and as hoped for, this relative hooked me up with a job. And suddenly, I became the kid that once was a local star, who is now just simply trying to make enough to afford a car. In my family’s eyes, at this point, I was just *a nobody,* once wishing I could be *a somebody.*

So after being on the job for about a month, the time had come. I had avoided that conversation with my mom by using the job schedule as my escape. But as I was getting the last of my things together from the house, I had called Grandma Shelly and asked her to pick me up in about thirty minutes to help me with the rest of my bags. And as I was about finished packing most everything, I heard my mom come in, again, and yelled, “Mark?!”

I wanted to hide but couldn't. So I then tried to hide my bags again, but unfortunately, she stepped through my bedroom door too quickly this time.

"It's time to have that talk—now!" She said with agitation.

And then she notices my bags, looks in the closet and sees that all my belongings—are gone, and says, "And where in the heck is all your clothes, Mark Anthony?!"

"I'm moving over to Grandma Shelly's house," I replied solemnly.

"With everything?!" She asked.

"Well—it's obvious you don't want me around here, Mom."

"It's not that, Mark! But to stay here, at this point, you had to get a job!"

"I understand that, but I couldn't go to school, rehab and work too, especially if I was gonna try to play ball again," I replied with emptiness.

"Does your daddy know you quit summer school?!" She asked.

"I didn't quit summer school, Mom.... I did drop a few classes because of my rehab—but those folks didn't want me on their team anyway!"

"Well—I hope you're smart enough to keep your lil job because your lil football career is over—don't ya think?"

"Maybe," I replied.

"Well while you're settin your hours at work, you should at least try to finish college!" She fired back. "I worked and finished, you can work and finish."

"Who's going to pay for it mom?"

"Apply for financial aid, ask your beloved Daddy," she said, as she exits.

I wanted to ask so bad, *What happened to that vow you guys made, while posturing in front my father, that you were going to pay for my education, regardless?*

So, for the record, if I needed any further proof, I now had it. They never had any intention of helping me pay for my education. They were just posturing with my Dad to shoulder up themselves. At this point, they now saw me as a failure in comparison to my father, which broke my heart even more as I hung my head in distress, hoping that her reaction to my next decision of resurrecting this all-but-dead-football-career, is not the opposite.

So I took a deep breath, said a short prayer, while listening to her go on and on scolding me from the next room. But as she reentered my room to chastise me even more, I lifted up my head, looked her in the eye, and said, "Mom—I decided to transfer."

She stopped, thought about my comment and just ran right through it.

"Mark, get yourself together, son; keep your job and think about re-enrolling back in school and get an education of some kind!"

"I am enrolled in school, Mama."

"Well why you're not in class then, Mark?!

"I'm transferring to OU," I soberly replied.

"Boy please! You and you're daddy need to get on with that mess... If you failed at UAPB, what makes you think you'll make it at a program like OU, Mark?!" She shot back as a matter of fact. "At this point, you owe ME—not OU!"

However, not willing to back down at this stage, as she begins to exit the room, I made myself clear again, "Mom—I've decided to transfer to OU."

She then stops, pauses, and says, "Mark, its over, son! We've already been down this road before with your Daddy! Its over!"

"Mom, I'm transferring to OU—that's why I've been packing my bags over the past few months—I'm leaving mama," as tears began to well up in my eyes.

"Well, you might as well unpack'em—football is over, son.... So wipe your face, get yourself together and try something different!"

I then paused, again, now knowing that she's not going to make this easy. I took another deep breath as the tears flowed heavier, and said, "You're right Mom, I can't do this anymore, its time for me to move on."

Suddenly, she pauses, and then she takes a deep breath, as if she recognizes my seriousness, and said in a much calmer tone, "Mark—why are you doing this, son?"

"I got to do this, Mama—I can't live like this anymore—it's time for me to go."

"Mark," she calmly said.

"Mama, I have done everything you wanted me to do, how you wanted me to do it, when you wanted me to do it and where you wanted me to do it. But it's now time for me to do what I need to do, Mama."

As she ponders his words, tears begin to fall from her eyes, too. She then backs herself up against the wall, shaking her head slowly from side to side and serenely begins to plead, "Don't do this to me, son."

"I gotta go Mama."

"Please don't do this to me," she said with brokenness.

As much as I hated to see my mom fall into this state of condition, I knew I couldn't turn back this time. The window of opportunity was about to be completely closed, and now was the time—this was the moment to break free, so I pressed on.

"I can't ignore my dreams anymore, Mama. And I can't keep disrespecting my father just to please you and the rest of this family—it's time for me to go," I said with tears heavily streaming down my face.

"Mark, I'm begging you not to do this son," she replied, her face full of anguish.

"I gotta do this, Mama.... It's all I got left."

"No—Mark, don't do this to me baby," she cried out, as she began to slide down the wall, weeping uncontrollably, "We can work it out, son—we can work it out!"

I then thought, *Nah Mama—you guys gotta work it out—I gotta get out.*

"You are going to be the death of me!" She says through her painful tears. "Lord, what did I do to deserve this from my own son!" She cried out. "I did the best I could.... I don't know nothin else to do!"

Suddenly, I hear the sound of a car horn. Grandma Shelly was outside honking and as soon as my Mom heard it she looked up at me with a face flooded with twenty plus years of agony, pain and defeat, and said, "Go—just go—get out—get out!" She yelled, pointed towards the door.

So, I grabbed my two duffle bags and stepped past her, heading for the side door, thinking about changing my mind about this once again. But something on the inside told me not to look back, or else I might turn back. So, right before I exited the house, I stopped and whispered, "I love you, Mama," and then turned the door knob and stepped out, feeling as if my heart had just been ripped out.

The minute I got into grandma Shelly's car, it was like all the strength I used to stand up to my Mom had all but dissipated. I totally lost it, which seriously startled my grandmother, who then began looking towards the house, as if she expected someone to come running out after me.

"What's wrong baby?" She asked frantically.

"Let's go grandma—let's go!"

"What's happen Mark—talk to me." She said, as she took her time putting the car in gear. I was so choked up, I couldn't respond. I tried, but all I could do was take deep breaths and blow—my jaws filled up as I rocked back and forth in the passenger seat of her car. But when I finally found my voice I said the words that I thought I would never be able to say to my beloved mother, "I told her, I finally told her that it was it over—I can't live for her anymore, grandma!"

And grandma Shelly, in her attempts to console me begins to cry, too, as she drives away while trying to empathize with her emotionally wrecked grandson.

30

Divine Force

Two days later, the phone rings at the Bradley house. It's my grandfather, Odell.

"Shelly—I'm trying to reach Mark. Is he there?"

"Yes, he's here but I think he may be asleep," she replied.

"Would you check please? I need to talk to him."

"Hold on," she said as she enters the room that Mark had crashed out in the past two days—stressed and depressed. "Mark, baby, it's your grandfather."

I immediately cringed at the idea of having to hear more of this nonsense. And even though I expected this call, I waved her off. But she then encourages me to take the call if I didn't want them to start showing up at her doorstep. So I decided to hear him out.

"Mark—this your grandfather. Your Mom tells us you decided to leave us," he said.

"Yeah—somethin like that," I replied.

"Well, if I were you I'd think about this thing a lil while longer, Mark.... Your mom is just sick about it.... Why don't you call her and see if you guys can work it out?"

"I've tried working this thing out, granddad," I replied with a lil agitation.

"Well, she's really struggling with this, Mark—we considered taking her to the hospital last night. She's stressed out about this thing—why don't you call her and work this thing out with her?"

"I've said all I can say about it," I frankly replied.

"She's still your mother, Mark, and don't you ever forget that," Odell shot back.

I just shook my head in disbelief, thinking, *they have been condoning this craziness from day one, and still trying to guilt trip me, while trying to protect her—please!*

So, to end this call, I told him that I would reach out to her, but he went on.

"Mark, we raised you—we're still your family, and as long as you live, she will *always* be your mother! Do you understand me?!"

"I said I'll call her granddad." I politely replied.

"Alright—you do that soon," he said. "But I'm telling you, that's still your mother and don't you ever forget it.... And come by and see me sometime, you don't have to stay at Shelly's. You can always come live with me like you used too.... you know you're always welcome here—we're family, Mark, and don't you ever forget that."

Now, I didn't want to disrespect my grandfather, but come on man! All I did was make a decision to transfer to another school—not another country; at the suggestion of my father—not some criminal. And by the way, I wanted to say, *aren't the Bradleys my family, too?!* And shouldn't *my father* be just as remembered, honored and considered as my mother?! Of course! But this wasn't about fairness or justice or respectability with them, this was about control and competition and contemptibility.

After we hung up, Grandma Shelly walked back in the room and asked was I alright. I assured her that all was fairly well. But informed her that I was really tired and still restless. She makes known that my Dad had sent my itinerary, which had me scheduled to leave in a couple of days, as planned, as she handed me the envelope. And I suddenly realized, I was finally holding in my hand the ticket to a new life. It had all now become very real to me. I was about to take the one step I should've taken a long-long time ago.

However, I must admit I was still a little terrified of doing it. I was just days from being free from all this division, strife and envy I'd been raised in. I didn't know how my mom was ultimately going to deal with it, but I was done being so overly concerned about it. At this point, it was down to one single hurdle—did I truly have the *guts* to get on that plane and become all that I could be, or just stay put and just be, whatever?

It's about time, don't ya think?! Because if I were you, reader, I would've already reach through these pages and slap the taste out of my mouth, you know what I'm saying?! And perhaps some of you have already done just that; I'm starting to feel the need for a couple of ice packs right about now. But hang in there with me. I'm trying to work it out—it's hard on the youngster, especially without having the right guidance.

But it was now departure day, and my father called a second time to make sure I was on the way to the airport. There was a little more than an hour and thirty before my flight was scheduled to leave. And grandma Shelly informs him that I was still asleep—that this ordeal with my family had simply worn me completely out the past few days.

"Okay, I understand.... Let me chat with Mark," Danny says with gentleness.

Shelly goes in his room and wakes me, holding up the phone, "It's your Daddy."

"Hello," I said woozily.

"Mark—what are you doing, son?! Do you know what time it is! Your flight leaves in about an hour thirty—you're not going to make it if you're not leaving right now!"

"I'm sorry—I guess I overslept."

"Overslept!" He said with volume. "Get up—it's 2 o'clock—it's time to go!"

"I said I'm sorry, daddy, I was up all night."

"Doing what?!" Danny asked, sounding highly upset.

"My Mom and my grandpa, they giving me a hard time about this." I replied.

"Tell me something I don't know, Mark! That's the oldest doggone news in Southeast Arkansas.... Now get your butt up and get to the airport—now!"

As I begin to get emotional, grandma Shelly notices and intervenes; she takes the phone from me and says, "Danny, listen son, this kid is struggling with this right now—his folks has been fighting him on it and he hasn't slept much at all—so why don't you lighten up and give him a few more days to get himself together."

"Mother, I appreciate your concerns but let me handle this—please," Danny said respectfully but firmly.

But grandma Shelly stood her ground, knowing my emotional state, was real.

"Danny—I'm telling you to lighten up and give him a few more days, son!"

"He doesn't have a few more days, mother! Mark has to be in Oklahoma at the Bursars office in the next 48 hours. Furthermore, I've given Mark fifteen plus years to get himself together—his time is UP!"

But grandma Shelly was like a mama bear protecting her baby cub at this point.

"Damn it Danny, listen to me, I'm your mother—and according to my birth slip, you're not my daddy.... I'm telling you this child needs a few more days to get himself together, now don't make me clown! This kid has way too much pressure on him right now.... He doesn't need this from you too."

As I listened to my grandmother fight my case, I began to question, again, if I really had the courage to make this move after all. As she pleaded with him, I started feeling relieved about not having to exit town right now, hoping it would give me time to be absolutely sure that I was *totally ready* to leave my family in small town Pine Bluff for the big-time lights of Oklahoma. And by her closing remarks, it appeared that he had conceded. She then hands me back the phone.

"Mark," he said meekly and with calmness. "Are you listening to me, son?"

"Yes sir."

"You sure?" He asked.

"Yes sir," I replied humbly.

"First of all, don't upset my mother with all this moping and whining, son. Life is hard but its fair. But listen up, I'm going to say this one time and one time only—you understand me?" He asked.

"Huh uh," I replied now with concern.

"I'm changing your flight from 3 p.m. to 6 p.m., today.... which means you got three hours to get up, get your thoughts together, your belongings together, and get your butt to the airport.... Do you understand me?!" He asked, as his voice started to rise.

"Yes sir." I answered as I began to feel lil numb.

"I didn't say three days or three weeks—you have three hours to get your stuff together, and get to the damn airport young fella—am I making myself clear?!

"Yes sir."

"And if I don't see you get off this 6 p.m. flight, today, in Dallas, Texas, then you might as well strap it on, spread your shoulders, and call all yo family and the local law enforcement, because I'm kickin yours and anybody else's that wants to step! And if you think I'm bluffin this time Mark B., then do what you've always done—stand me the hell up.... and let the chips fall where they may!"

And all I heard next was a dial tone.

So there you have it, folks. If I didn't understand anything he said, I understood this: Have my butt on that 6 p.m. flight or else he would be forced to make good on *this* particular threat—in its entirety.

Dallas, Texas

Later that afternoon, the plane that Mark was scheduled to come in on is pulling up to the jet-bridge at D/FW airport and Danny is patiently waiting at the gate. He stood in a position to have a good view of all passengers as they deplane without being seen. And yes, as you might have expected, after it appeared that most of the passengers had exited the plane, there was still no Mark.

Danny closes his eyes and takes a deep breath and says to himself, *come on son.*

As the ticket agent began making an announcement about the next flight, it was evident that all passengers had indeed deplaned this flight from Little Rock—even the *pilots* and *flight attendants* were now emerging from the Jet-bridge—which always meant that there were no more civilians left on board.

Danny looks at his watch and takes in another deep breath as he stares at the jet-bridge tunnel as if willing his son into view. And once it's apparent that Mark has not made the flight, Danny drops his head in disappointment, knowing what his next step has to be. But then raises his head as if he refused to believe his son had quit on him again. He began to stare at the Jet-bridge once more, hoping for at least one more passenger to exit.

And suddenly another flight attendant emerges with her bags, as if moving in slow motion. And seconds later the last passenger appears wearing jeans, tennis shoes and a white hooded tee-shirt covering his head—it's Mark. As Mark looks up, his eyes like a radar go directly to his father as if he knew where he would be standing. And as he calmly makes his way over to his Dad, carrying a dejected posture, he drops his bags, hugs his father and bursts into tears as Danny begins to console him.

"It's alright son—it's alright," Danny says. "I know this was a huge-huge step for you—but you did it.... Everything is going to be just fine."

But Mark wouldn't let go, as he continued crying while hugging his dad, Danny begins to shed a few tears, too.

"It took some big faith to make this step," Danny said. "But you did it—the toughest part is over, son.... I got cha, not gonna leave you hanging, son."

But Mark just kept on hugging his father and crying, so much so that even passengers began to take notice. They were watching fifteen-twenty plus years of pent up emotions now being released in overflow, as Danny continued consoling him, rubbing his back and attempting to calmly talk him through it.

Taking a step back from Mark in order to look him in the eye, he says, "She's going to be just fine, son—trust me.... The good Lord brought me through—he'll bring you through. So let's go home, relax and watch a movie or two; besides people are now look at us as if we're making a movie...and I don't see either a director or a camera—do you?" He jokingly asked, as he got Mark to smile a bit while wiping his eyes.

Danny then pulls out his sunglasses, gives them to Mark and said, "You know—you do kind of look a lil like Nick Cannon with the attire and all.... so cover your eyes with these, keep your hood up, and wipe your nose—and then we just might receive some applause as we exit this stage."

And sure enough, as they turned to make their way out the terminal, a few people nodded their head and smiled as if to applaud.

A couple of days later, we are at Joe's Crab Shack, a beach-themed restaurant known for its lively staff. My Dad informs the waiter they'll need one more place setting. I didn't know who might be joining us, but knowing my father, it had to be somebody special. As I look over the menu, I'm suddenly wrapped in a bear hug from behind and when I turn around, I see none other than Darren Woodson, Cowboys All-Pro Safety!

Excited to see him, I get up, hug him again and give him dap, as does my Dad.

"How you doing youngster?" Darren asked.

"Hangin in there," I replied with a lil enthusiasm.

"Look at you, boy—all grown up, now—you good?"

"Better now," as my smile got brighter.

After more small talk, the chat turns to my impending enrollment at OU, and Darren senses some uncertainties in my voice, and takes a moment to encourage me.

"You'll be fine, Mark. Let that situation in Arkansas with your family work itself out. I know I'm echoing several things you've already heard from your Pops, but it's always good to hear it from someone else who's been through this process too," Darren says. "But you're about to enter into a fast paced environment, keep your head in the game socially, athletically and academically. Never take any of it for granted, you feel me?"

"I understand," I responded, receiving his advice with humility.

"I know you've gone through a lot with your family, but there comes a time, as with every young man, if we're going to be the best we can be, we gotta step out on faith. I'm not saying let your Mom go, by any means, we need our mothers—I have a great relationship with my mother, but we, too, your Dad and I had to let go when it came time to leave home," Woody shared.

"Appreciate the encouragement," I replied.

"OU has a great program, Mark, but their locker room is no different than every other program in America, filled with young guys that have gone through some kind of family situation that broke their heart in some way.... Unlike yours, many of them were broken *by* their fathers—not necessarily their mothers. So enjoy yourself and take your butt to class; it's a lot of distractions on these major college campuses that can get you twisted."

Woody soon had to break. The Cowboys had a pre-season game the next day just down the road at Texas Stadium and it was now close to his check in time at the team hotel, which was also just about a mile up the road. But by the time my Dad and I ate our dinner, Joe's Crab Shack begins to live up to its reputation as more patrons begin to file in and the staff embarrasses one of the diners by singing Happy Birthday to her at the top of their lungs—it was indeed time to go.

The next day, we were making good time up Interstate 35 en route to Norman, Oklahoma, to begin this new chapter in my life. And with each mile marker, it was becoming more and more real. Not having any idea what OU would be like except what I'd seen at the Cotton Bowl, the Red River Shootout, my father noticed early in the trip that I was extremely quiet, but waited until about midway through this two-and-half hour drive before he initiated a conversation.

"You aright?" Danny asked.

"Yeah—I'm good."

"You've been awfully quiet," he said.

"Just thinking about it all," I replied softly.

"Have you talked to her today," he asked?

"No—not since I left—she hasn't answered my calls."

"Well, if it helps any, I caught up with her this morning at her office to see how she was doing after our talk last night. She didn't appear to be to bothered. Whatever her concerns might be, she might not really share them with me, but I told her I'll take care of you and that you're going to be just fine, son; and that OU is a great university academically and athletically. She thanked for the call and told me to keep her updated."

"Wow, she sure didn't sound that way when I talked to her about it."

"Well, son, it takes time to make certain adjustments in life.... Denise is going to be okay.... This is all new to her, too," my Dad replied.

"Well, apparently, she not talking to me," I shot back.

"You think she's avoiding you?" He asked.

"I don't know, probably.... But its just interesting that when I was with her, she avoided your calls, and now that I'm with you, she seems to be avoiding my calls."

Reaching into the console, my father hands me the cell, and said, "Why don't you try her again—maybe she'll pick up this time.... And if she answers, sound confident and let her know that all is well."

I make the call but get the answering machine again. And did leave a message; one that indicated all *was not* well. I didn't really know what I felt. I guess I was enthusiastically fearful about life in general at this point.

"She is going to be just fine, son," he says again. "In due time, this move will be a blessing to both you and your mom.... I believe God sends the provisions to where we are suppose to be—not necessarily where we choose to be.... In fact, I'll go on record, right now," he said with confidence, "if you handle your business; do what you're suppose to do; be where you're suppose to be and believe that you receive, your entire family will see a much different outcome at Oklahoma than they ever would've seen at Arkansas Pine Bluff. But you gotta walk this thing out *by faith* and not *by sight.*

"It wouldn't be so bad if she would just support me and give me a chance to better myself, Dad.... She's not even willing to give us a chance," I said disappointedly.

"I understand—but if she doesn't *ever* support your dreams and/or our relationship, just remember, you can still go on and fulfill anything the good Lord calls you to do, son. His blessings are not predicated on her support of you," my Dad said.

"But she don't approve of anything I want to do," I replied with sadness.

"And I'm saying you don't need her approval or their approval in order to move on and be productively happy with your life, son. God doesn't need your mom's approval to bless you, Mark—you are His masterpiece, not hers or mine. However, He does command us to honor our mother's in order to walk in the blessing."

"But I thought I was doing that?" I asked.

"On many levels you were.... But unfortunately, its hard for a person to appreciate honor if they don't have a genuine respect for it themselves."

"She treats me like I owe her something," I said with grief. "She even said before I left, 'you OWE ME, not OU.'"

"You do owe her, son.... You owe her honor," he replied. "But from a pure debt standpoint, we are to *owe no man nothing, but to love him.* But we are required to honor our mothers, *that our days may be long on this earth,"* he said. "So, hang on in there."

"So how do you think I'll do in the classroom?" I asked with major concern.

"You'll be fine, although I will admit, it will be a bit more challenging, but the good news is OU has a great academic assistance program for their athletes, which will help keep you above the eligibility line, if football is your biggest concern."

"And you truly believe I have the ability to really make it at this level?"

"Absolutely! No question! No doubt!"

"Even with just two years of eligibility left?"

"Even with just two years of eligibility left," he said with confidence. "You won't get many chances as a walk-on, but the Mark Bradley I believe you can be doesn't need many chances—just a chance," he replied. "But football is my least concern, you'll be on scholarship by the end of this semester and maybe in the starting rotation by the spring—and that's a guarantee.... My concern is that you don't get so caught up in football that you forget about your academics—if you don't accomplish anything else, get your degree, Mark Bradley.... Anything less is just totally unacceptable," he said.

"I understand." I replied.

"If you can see the invisible, you can do the impossible, son," he said as we were exiting I-35 North onto Lindsey Ave—in Norman, Oklahoma.

I, then, took a deep breath with a great deal of uncertainty, and in sort of in disbelief of the confidence my father truly had in me. He had finally loved me out of an unproductive environment, knowing it would initially cost him a ton, if an athletic scholarship wasn't earned quickly. Which left me wondering, again, what my family might be now thinking about this *sorry-no good-deadbeat-dad-of-a-father* of mine, who *allegedly* didn't even want me.

31

Divine Confession

As we made this entrance into the campus, I suddenly felt extremely hot. My heart was pounding with both excitement and uncertainty as my Dad began to point out various landmarks as we approached the university grounds on Lindsey. And suddenly there it was—right smack dab in the middle of campus—Gaylord Memorial Stadium, also known as Owens Field, decorated with a banner of seven National Championships atop the south end zone—and should have been eight, if my Dad's '84 Sooners team had brought their 'A' game into the '85 Orange Bowl.

And it's mid-August and football practices had begun for this storied program. And yes, as usual, the Sooners are once again atop the pre-season college football polls and were currently in session preparing for opening day, I notice as we drive by.

We pull up to a high-rise dormitory building for non-athletes where I would be residing, and people were all over the place—excitement was in the air everywhere—it was vibrant. We go in and get checked in without any hassles—and just as we were exiting the dorm en route to Target to pick up some much needed items, suddenly here comes *The Pride of Oklahoma Marching Band* playing the Sooners fight song.

Students began gathering all along the side of this campus road, clapping and cheering them on. Then I started noticing block party signs and billboards all over the place. I look over at my Dad, he winks, and says, "There is no place like home, son."

Now, I wasn't sure what to expect after visiting UT but this campus felt more intimate, smaller and cozier. UT felt like a campus for the big-city boys; OU seemed to be the perfect environment for a small-town southern boy—like me.

However, Texas was indeed a special-special place and Coach Mack Brown and his staff left a tremendous impression on me. I could quickly see why my Dad thought so much of him and their program. And listening to him talk about Coach Brown, you would have thought he was still coaching at OU. But after having visited both schools, I instantly saw why this rivalry, this feud between these two programs, is the best in college football. These two giants had the ideal environment for the perfect storm. And I was about to walk right into the middle of it carrying the last name—Bradley.

The next day is all about business. First the admissions office, then to the campus infirmary for a physical examination, and then on to the Switzer Center to be fitted for the uniform of all college football—OU.

As we pull up to Gaylord Memorial Stadium, again I was in awe with all the National Championship Banners. And once we entered the Switzer Center, I remember thinking, *it's going to be hard to beat UT's facilities—so let's go Sooners!*

The first person we meet is Merv Johnson, who is waiting for us. We greet and my Dad informs him that I was set and ready to go; been to admissions; checked in at the dormitory; and just finished my physical.

"Great—practice starts in fifteen minutes. Let me show Mark to his locker, and introduce him to the equipment manager," Merv said.

Before they head into the locker room, one of the trainers, Scott Anderson, approaches them. He and Danny shake hands and he introduces Mark.

"Mark, it's great to have you and we'll catch up tomorrow and discuss where you are with the knee, in the meantime, welcome to OU!"

I thought, *Dad really did hook me up—this transition, so far, has been effortless.*

Entering the doors that finally lead to the locker room area, Mark couldn't help but notice a few of the past Sooner players hanging on the walls: Billy Sims, Joe Washington, Leroy Selmon, Steve Owens, JC Watts, Brian Bosworth, Tony Casillas, Keith Jackson, Spencer Tillman, and wouldn't you know it, a picture of his dad—Danny Bradley.

Once inside the locker room Merv says, "I see your name badge is already up and since we didn't know what jersey number you might want to try, we figured we go the safest route and allocated your dad's old number, if that's okay with you."

I looked at my nameplate and then at my Dad with an embarrassing shy-like smile and thought, *wow—what are the chances that this, ever so popular number, would be available with a team with already so many flashy players?*

"Apparently, we guessed right, huh?" Merv says.

"Yeah—I think so Coach," I replied."

Merv then looks at his watch, and says, "Practice is about to start, let's head that way before Mark gets fitted for his uniform. Coach Stoops would like for you, Danny, to share with the team before practice, if you don't mind. Every now and then he asks past players to stop in and encourage our guys, so, I'm sure he'd appreciate it."

"Sure," my Dad said with enthusiasm.

As we were exiting the locker rooms, he looked over at me and smiled, winked again, as I proudly smiled back. The last time I had the privilege of witnessing this invitation was at the University of Texas, when Coach Brown asked if he would do the same at one of their practices too.

So, as Merv introduces my Dad to Coach Bob Stoops, he reaches out and shakes my hand as well, and said, "Hey Mark, you ready to go?" He asked.

"Yes sir," I replied nervously.

"Did your Dad get you all checked in?"

"Yes sir." I answered while trembling on the inside.

"Well, the equipment guys will get you all fitted up here shortly—we're happy to have you," Coach Stoops said.

"Thanks Coach," I replied, with tremendous uncertainty.

Then he turns to my Dad, again, who was now being introduced to a few other coaches and personnel people.

"Danny, you mind sharing before we start practice?"

"Absolutely Coach," Danny replies.

"Everybody up!" Coach Stoops yells.

Once all were gathered, Coach told the players to take a knee, as he prepared to get things underway. He began talking about being one week away from opening day and that it's time to get more focused on our game plan and zero in on the little things.

Then, he says, "I've asked one of our past players to come share—he was a terrific player who handled himself well on and off the field…. The Conference Offensive Player of the Year in 1984 and led the Sooners to the '85 Orange Bowl for a shot at the National Championship. His son Mark will be joining our team this year as a walk-on out of Arkansas Pine Bluff. So we're excited about that and what the future holds for him, but in the meantime, welcome one of our own, quarterback—Danny Bradley!"

As Coach Stoops steps aside, I thought, *How many guys in America would be invited to share with both the Sooners and Longhorns football programs, especially a player that played a significant role in this incredible rivalry?*

My father stepped up and shakes Stoops' hand again, as coach takes a knee alongside his players too, as the squad's applause is accompanied by a few barks from within the group. One player shouts out, "Wishbone!"

My Dad pauses for a moment and smiles as if to blush and then waves off the comment to get into his talk. Back in those days the *wishbone offense,* although made famous by Coach Darryl Royal and the Texas Longhorns, a another great former Sooners All-American, *the bone* was mastered by Coach Barry Switzer and the Sooners, whose offensive coordinator in '84, is Texas' current Head Coach—Mack Brown. Add the recruiting war between these two dominant programs—yeah, you got it—it's on all day long to the concrete!

But this was a pivotal moment for me. As I stood watching my Dad being welcomed as one of the most accomplished players in the history of Sooners football, once again, was a very humbling experience for me. I really didn't know this side of my father or his career. All I heard from my folks were all the negativity, the slanderous comments. But it was during this time that I begin to *further* recognize that the people in his entire world that coached him, played with him and worked with him, *all* treated him with the same level of respect. And these are people who possess tremendous amounts of success, wealth and accomplishments. But the people in my lil world—despised him.

So as he shared, I reflected and suddenly realized that *my family really didn't even know this man.* They had no idea who Danny Bradley—really was. They knew of him but didn't really "know him." Yes, my mother spent a moment or two of ecstasy with this man, but she didn't spend time getting "to know" this man. She met him in the latter days of their teenage years, before he departed for a life in sports that would forever change his life, for which I now get the luxury of standing here today, as a benefactor.

As I tried to listen to his talk with the team, I couldn't help but replay the many events and conversations I'd had with my family about him. But as I fade back into the scene he closes with one of my favorite quotes, which he often used to help change my perspective on life along the way: "This is a once in a lifetime opportunity. So take care of yourself and each other knowing that *"with God all things are possible to them that believe….* And, by the way," he says, "take it easy on my son, he's just a small town kid who's now trying to find his place at a big-time program—be blessed and Go Sooners!"

And suddenly from the midst of the throng one player could be heard saying with emphasis, "Oh—we gon get him!"

Another shouted out, "Got to get got, Pop Bradley!"

Coach Stoops steps up and shouts, "Let's go to work," and practice was underway.

Then, Merv grabs us, again, to head to the equipment room. But as we make our way, about five members of the Oklahoma local media sidle up to my Dad requesting an interview. So he motions to Merv and I to go on, but before we do, I gave him dap and said, "Great job, Pops."

Danny recognizes a couple of the reporters from his days at OU. They pepper him with the usual array of questions. "Tell us a little bit about your son—why did he decide to transfer? Why wasn't he recruited? Is he healthy, tell us about his knee injury?"

He answers all of them with both analytical and political correctness as a smooth QB would. But it wasn't his cogent responses that made the headlines—it was his prediction that shocked the Sooner nation after one reporter simply asked what he thought about my chances of making this very talented Sooners team, with only two years of eligibility left loaded at every position?

"Honestly, I think Mark's chances are great," Danny replied confidently with no hesitation. "He's a smart kid with a tremendous amount of athletic abilities; one of the nation's best track-n-field athletes; capable of playing every skilled position on the field.... In fact, this kid might be the best athlete on the OU roster—right now. Once he's healthy, he'll not only be one of the top players on this team, he'll perhaps be one of the best in the country," he said and heads towards the door of the Switzer Complex.

The next morning, we were headed to the training facility as my Dad pulls out a new cell phone from the glove box and hands it to me and says, "Under all circumstances, stay in touch and call your mom and give her your number."

"Man, you have got to be the coolest Dad a twenty year old could have," I said.

"Just trying to eliminate as many distractions as I possibly can so that you can focus academically, Mark.... As I told you once before, football is my least concern—but you have absolutely no excuses to not perform in the classroom.... your academics comes first, not second or third—but first.... so keep that in mind at all times, please sir."

"Yes sir," I replied kind of nonchalantly.

"Mark, listen to me, son, don't underestimate the importance of your class work—getting a degree is the ultimate goal here.... and anything less than that, again, is unacceptable—are we clear here?"

"I understand," I replied with a more serious tone.

"I'm serious, Mark," he said with concern.

"I got it, daddy." I replied with assurance.

"Okay, you're not here on the University of Oklahoma's dime—you're here on the University of Daddy's dime.... I'm having to figure out now how to get some additional financial aid to help pay for all of this—so I expect your best, Mark."

"I understand and I appreciate the sacrifices," I sincerely replied. "Had you not drug me out of Pine Bluff, none of this would have been possible."

"Well, then, lets not let your history affect your destiny," he said.

"I won't," I replied reassuringly.

Once inside the training facility, the first person they see is assistant Trainer Jim Hillis. He calls them into his office, hugs Danny and introduces himself to Mark. Jim was in possession of Mark's MRI as well as his knee surgery notes from the Arkansas Sports Medicine facility in Little Rock who had performed the surgery.

While he reviews them with us, Scott Anderson, the head trainer, whom I met earlier, walks in. Scott and Jim were both assistant trainers on the OU staff during my Dad's playing days in the '80's.

Scott remarks, "A little politicking going on, huh?"

Danny smiled and asked, "What are you talking about—what's up?"

"Rumor has it *that Dad thinks son is the best athlete on Sooners roster."*

"Now where could you have possibly heard such rumor," he asked, smiling.

"Well—you know the walls talk around here when those kind of bold comments are made.... and it's starting to spread throughout the locker-room," Scott replied.

"Which means practice will be like game day everyday for you, Mark," Jim said grinning. "So, it appears that you have one choice—cook or get out the kitchen."

As I smiled with them, I wasn't really shocked that my Dad thought such was the case, but I was floored that he had actually said it, publicly, knowing that it would no doubt echo throughout this locker room with arguably the most talented football team in America. So, I'm thinking, *is my Dad trying to help me—or punish me?*

Later that day, I was exiting the Switzer Center complex, this time in uniform, to attend my first OU practice. Players are scattered about as I make my way on to the field. The barking among players had begun and they were chomping at the bit to a get a shot at *bringing to naught* that ridiculous statement made by my father. And wearing jersey #1 only *maximized* this confrontation.

The wide receiver coach pulls me aside to make sure I understood what to expect as I began making the adjustment from UAPB to OU, which was an enormous difference.

"First—stay close to me," he says, "so that I can point out, as we go, how we do what we do; second—this is a red shirt year for you, so get very acquainted with our offensive scout team unit, this is where you'll spend most of your practice time.... But be aware, the scout team unit gets pushed around a bit, but it will you give you a chance to show us what kind of skills you have as a receiver—cool?"

"Cool," I said nervously as I ignored many of the wolfers who were making mockery of *the rumor* as the warm-up session of practice began.

Out of nowhere, Tommie Harris, the All-American defensive captain, the heart and soul of this team, approaches me. As I began to brace myself for the encounter, he suddenly said, "Don't pay these jokesters no mind—I'm the one you need to be concerned about—so come out here and do your thing, everyday.... and by the way, FCA Bible study starts tonight at seven thirty—be there."

As Mister Harris walked away, I exhaled and thought, *did he just invite me to bible study or am I in heaven?*

Once the whistle blows, I'm ready to see what it's like to be a part of one of the most adorned college football programs in the country, with a chance to perhaps prove—I belong. And as you can imagine, yes, I was indeed, terrified. Over the years I tried to envision what it would be like to play ball for a Oklahoma or Texas—but never in my wildest dreams did I believe it could possibly come true with the multitude of self esteem issues I possessed. So, thanks to my father, all I had to do now was figure out how to live up to this hype he blew into the atmosphere among these giants.

And to make matters more difficult to deal with emotionally, he knew I wasn't totally healthy, nor had I heard from my mother. And that saddened and terrified me, even more. So to say the least, my spirits were down and under despite having this new chance at life, which my mom seems to have decided that she didn't want any part of, this new life.

Fortunately, my Dad was astute enough to recognize the emotional and psychological effect this reality had on me, so he decided to hang around Norman a few weeks to ensure I got in sync. And to be honest, I really appreciated his presence—it helped calm my nerves while I made these life-changing adjustments academically and athletically. This was a major transformation for me. And his network marketing business had allowed him liberty to control how and where he spent his time.

But after about the second day of practice, in the midst of my struggle to cope, one of the most interesting and unexpected revelations took place that even took my Dad by complete surprise. Another Sooners player, who happens to play the same position, which I had been given the assignment to learn, approached me in the locker room and asked if I knew any Fordham's that lived in Pine Bluff. I told him I did. I noticed how much that got his attention, which prompted him to ask, if I knew a Hubie Fordham. And again, I informed him I did, "Hubie is my Dad's uncle," I replied with interest.

Then I started naming off all the other Fordham family members, which were many, before he stopped me and said, "Hubie Fordham is my dad!"

"Are you serious?" I asked.

"We kinfolk fool!" He said, as he gave me dap and a half hug. "I'm Travelee."

Not knowing the Fordham side of the family that well, I didn't know anything about Travelee. So I asked, "How did you end up at OU without anybody knowing?"

"Well—it's a long story dog.... My mom left Pine Bluff for Tulsa when I was about five, and since then I've only been back once or twice to see Hubie."

So we trade numbers as we got acquainted, and he promised to get me caught up on the happenings around campus, the do's and don'ts in the locker room, if I would get him caught up with the goings-on at home with Hubie and the Fordham family.

And for starters, he said, "Just so you'll know, a few players on the team is a lil heated about the comment your Pops made.... And a few of them are looking to get after you at first chance.... So beware, know whadum sayin?" He said with a smirk like grin.

That bit of news further dampened my spirits. By days end, my father met Travelee for the first time ever, and was even more excited that I now had someone inside the program to show me the ropes so to speak, which created a natural opportunity for him to vacate Norman. But unfortunately for me, the time had come, I either had to cook or indeed get out the kitchen.

32

Divine Results

And no sooner had my father arrived back in Dallas, I was leaving the offensive team meeting room at the Switzer Complex when one of the scout team coaches, Brandon Hall, pulls me into his office and told me that the staff have been evaluating the approach to this weeks preparation. Iowa State has a stud at quarterback by the name of Seneca Wallace—a Heisman Trophy candidate, who creates a lot of problems with his speed, his ability to throw on the run and his decision making. He's the most complete quarterback in the country. Then says, "And since we think you might be the most talented *scout team* player we have, Coach Stoops thought you might be able help us by emulating Seneca this week in practice against our first team defensive unit—can you handle that?"

"I'll give it a shot," I replied with fear rumbling in my bones.

"You sure?" He asked, perhaps sensing my uncertainty.

"Yeah, I'll give it my best shot," but wanting to say, "hell no!"

"Aright—get yourself prepared, this session will be live as if in a real game—so tighten your chin strap and give us a good look," he said, as he pats me on the shoulder and leaves me standing right there in his office.

As I exit the facility, I'm thinking, *Yeah, it appears my Dad has set me up for failure.... And I'm sure they won't have any mercy, after having a chance to marinate on the comment he made a few weeks ago.*

Meanwhile, just as I was entering the chow hall, he calls. I took a deep-deep breath before answering, not knowing how I should address this humongous problem.

"How was classes?" Danny asked.

"Classes were good, I don't think its going to be as hard as I thought," I replied.

"So, after a month, you think you got this academic thing on lock?" He asked.

"Yeah—I think so," I said with assurance, but yet very concerned about the athletic piece, not the academic piece.

"Okay—Phi Beta Kappa," Danny cautioned. "Just remember—the academic assistance program is there for a reason, son—take full advantage of it—cool?"

"Cool," I replied. "But on another note, Pops, I have a huge-huge problem."

"What's up?" He asked with concern.

"You know I'm only about eighty-five percent healthy with the knee, right?"

"Yep—is it starting to give you some problems already?"

"A little—and I haven't really done much on it just yet," I replied.

"You getting treatment?" He asked.

"I am but the bigger problem is, they asked me to emulate Seneca Wallace in practice this whole week, ON SCOUT TEAM, at quarterback, LIVE, against the FIRST TEAM DEFENSE—starting tomorrow!"

"Really?! That's great, Mark!" He said with enthusiasm, with no hesitation. "So what's the problem, you concerned about the knee?" He asked.

"My knee! I'm concerned about ME!" I replied with seriousness.

My Dad just chuckles a bit at my response and says, "Don't be, son—you'll be fine—you're the best athlete they've got—trust me on that.... So don't sweat it," he replied with this level of certainty that both confused me and angered me a little.

"Even at only eight-five percent?"

"Even at only eighty-five percent, Mark, you'll be just fine.... In fact, once the horn sounds and the sessions begin, you won't feel a thing.... You'll be zoned in on proving that you belong," he said as I pull the phone away from my ear and looked at this cell as if he was speaking Hebrew or an unknown tongue of some kind.

And he went on preaching this greek to me, "This is exactly the stage you've been looking for, Mark Bradley.... They get a chance to see you close-up live and in living color against the best in the country—so handle your business—it's show time."

"Dad—come on, man.... The scout team unit gets beat completely down every day in practice—you know that! And I haven't taken a snap from center in three years!"

"All the more reason why your performance will leave them speechless," he replied.

"Well, I think all they're doin is settin me up to fail—to prove you wrong!"

"Maybe so, but by week's end, they'll know that Pops was right.... And yeah, it was a set up, but only to give you a chance to prove you belong—not to be sent back home."

"I understand.... But couldn't you have waited until I was healthier?"

He then paused and said, "Mark, all jokes aside, listen to me, son, if the truth be really told, quarterback might be *your best* position—not your *scout team* position. Furthermore, I could have waited but I didn't. Why? Because this is your appointed time—your divine moment—*all things are possible to them that believe."*

"But Dad, I'm tellin you...." But he cuts me off, "Have I led you wrong yet?"

"No," I soberly replied.

"Have I let you down yet?"

"No."

"Do you think I might know just a little bit about this business?"

"Yes, Pops, but...." But cuts me off again, and said, "Then get yourself ready to go handle your business, Mark Bradley, like the set apart man you are—God has not given you *a spirit of fear, son, but of power, love, and a sound mind."*

"But I feel so uncertain about this, Pops," I replied.

"I understand," he said. "But the remedy to those feelings of fear is faith and prayer, Mark B.... So go home, open up you bible and read a lil bit, then get on your knees and thank the Lord for this opportunity; then get up, get some sleep and go make believers out of everybody who said you weren't good enough to play any position—let alone *the quarterback* position—and call me with those results."

And BAM, he hangs up, leaving me speechless. I thought to myself, *My Dad is either crazy—or a prophet, or both.*

I didn't know anybody that saw in me what my father saw in me, especially athletically, or else I'd been highly recruited. But this is also what fascinated me so much about this man. And trust me, despite my disappointment in his comment, I knew he truly believed it, and had been around enough players and evaluators of talent to perhaps know a lil something about this business.

So, I took his advice, went to my dorm room and opened up my bible, got on my knees and thanked God for the opportunity, and then sat up *all night* wondering if he'd protect me. That's how much faith I had! However, it meant everything to me to know he believed that I could do this.

The next day, the stage was set and the buzz was out. The defensive unit was ready to finally prove that my Dad's comment was bizarre and way off base—and that I needed to be humbled and brought back down to earth. But what they didn't know, emotionally, with all I had been through in life, I felt as if I was already under the earth.

A million things were going through my mind, as I watched the kicking game drills. I kept talking to myself quoting that scripture, *"With God, all things are possible."* And suddenly, I hear my name called, "Mark Bradley—let's go baby! Its time to show us what you got," the scout team coach yelled as all heads turn toward that particular practice field. The moment had come.

I, then, pretended to be stretching, contemplating on how I might get out of this ready made destructive war zone, as I hear my Dad's voice, *'God has not given you a spirit of fear, Mark, but power, love, and a sound mind.'"*

I took a deep breath, decided to give it a shot, and slowly jogged onto the field, as the defensive unit, filled with great players, barked and scolded me; confident in their ability to make mockery out of this situation. They had been highly insulted and were now ready to send me back home to my Dad with perhaps a change in career. And let me remind you, this was practice at OU, people—practice! But yet the biggest game or event I've ever participated in.

So, as the scout team coach was giving us instructions, I looked over to my right and there he was, *the man,* Coach Bob Stoops, down on one knee, waiting to see what I could do, too. After all, I hadn't thought about whether my Dad's comment had insulted this incredible evaluator of talent also, given the fact that he didn't recruit me, either, with a roster already loaded with talent. I then looked across to my left and I see Hall of Fame Coach Barry Switzer, the great evaluator of talent, whom I hadn't seen since I was about thirteen years old at the Cowboys complex at Valley Ranch. I then began wondering, *where is the man that got me thrown into the middle of this hot spot.*

But instead of being upset with him, I began meditating on his voice, again, *You can do all things through Christ, which strengthens you — all things are possible to them that believe — this is your divine moment — make believers out of all who said you weren't good enough.*

"Bring it on Bradley!" They yelled. "Don't get scared now! This ain't the SWAC baby! This the Big Twelve! It's time to put up or shut up!" They shouted.

As I broke the huddle with my little scout team unit, made up of other walk-ons like me, who were not good enough to be on scholarship, either, I suddenly see, out of the corner of my eye, the *silhouette of a man* who looks instantly familiar to me. Another couple of steps and I realized its my Dad. I wasn't expecting him to show up, but suddenly as he raised one fist in the air as if to say, again, *this is indeed your divine moment.... All things are possible to them that believe,* something came over me. I then smiled behind my tinted helmet visor and shook my head, and said to myself, *Oh, yeah—now, it's on!* And suddenly, the eyes of fear had turned into the eyes of faith.

And from first whistle to last, Mark dominated the Sooners top-ranked defensive unit. He picked them apart with passes of both short and long; he eluded and escaped tight situations in ways no coach or player on that Sooners team had ever seen; he scored with his feet; he scored with his arm; he began to successfully execute each drawn up play to near perfection. And despite the inferiority of his small *untalented* scout team unit, this *scrub team* and *quarterback* was simply—no contest.

Finally, after about twenty plus plays of embarrassment, the Defensive Coordinator, out of frustration, had seen enough. Mike Stoops cuts the session, which he had already extended in an effort to stop this walk-on kid from Arkansas Pine Bluff that may have just proven to everybody on this roster that his Dad's comment might indeed be true.

So as practice came to a close, he turned to give props to his Pops for believing in him, and noticed that he was not there. He rushes to the locker-room grabs his cell and calls him to see what he thought. But he could suddenly tell by his response that his Dad was still in Dallas—not Norman, but had already heard about his performance through the grapevine. Mark suddenly realizes that the *silhouette of a man* was not his father in the flesh but perhaps in the spirit—an Angel there to root him on.

And if we needed any further confirmation, just a few days later, after Oklahoma won big at home against Heisman trophy candidate Seneca Wallace and the Iowa State Cyclones, Coach Bob Stoops, during his post-game locker-room celebration, did what had never been done in Sooners history—he presents Mark Bradley, the *redshirt walk-on that nobody recruited,* with the game ball as his Sooners teammates erupted in support! Mark was now officially a Boomer Sooner and inaugurated, that day, as perhaps the best athlete—on the roster!

Later, speaking to the media during his post game press conference, Stoops commented on Mark's performance in practice and his ability to play anywhere on the field—including quarterback, which meant that what the local media and this very talented Sooners coaching staff may have been unprepared to face, joyfully, that this **Dad Really Did Know Best!**

And to cement the above, every player who was asked about Mark Bradley's abilities gave a similar response—amazingly talented! After the game, Danny, as usual, was waiting for Mark outside the player's entrance in the SUV, who gets in the car with a confident smile on his face, and humbly says, "Thanks for all the encouragement, Pops."

"Are you convinced now that you belong?" He asked.

"Now I feel like I belong," I replied.

"All things are possible to them that believe," he said with faith laced in his tone.

"You think?" I sarcastically replied. "At this point, I'm convinced that you got somethin divine going on with you, Pops.... I can't quite put my finger on it just yet, but you got a lil something-somethin celestial going on with you, man."

"No, no, no, son.... Its no big deal, I'm just working the word."

"Well I need to learn how to work this word, then," I replied, feeling renewed, as we head to celebrate.

After finishing our postgame dinner, the waitress leaves the bill as my Dad, being the focused father, asks, "How's your mother doing has she returned your calls?"

"No—not in the past two-three weeks.... We talked maybe twice since I left, she doesn't seem to be too interested in what's going on with me," I replied.

"Well—you gotta be patient and keep reaching out to her," he said concerned.

But unbeknownst to Danny, Mark had avoided his Mom's calls the past week in an effort to avoid being teamed-up on by his grandparents, especially Odell, who seem to be just as bothered by Mark's decision to leave home as Denise was, despite his destitute state.

"I'm startin to have mixed feelings about talking to her, Dad, its startin to drain me."

"Son, call your mother and see how she's doing."

I dial her up, and as usual, the first few minutes were civil, but then it turned south.

"Well—we want to come visit you next weekend," Denise, sputtered out.

"Who is we?" I quickly asked, knowing that I did not want to be attacked and smothered by the rest of the family about my decision to leave that chaos in Pine Bluff.

"What do you mean?" She asked agitatedly. "Like we—us—your family, Mark!"

"I'm just asking, Mom, because I only get four ticket slots to each game; two for you and two goes to my Dad—the rest of the family will have to purchase tickets."

At that comment, let the fussing commence.

"Two tickets slots!" She shot back. "What does that mean, Mark?!"

"It means I only get two tickets to each game."

"Why we only get two tickets, we're your family?!"

"That's all we get, Mom!"

"Well—ask your Daddy to get us some tickets. Isn't this *his program*," she shot out.

Before she could get on a roll, I put her on speaker so he could hear her too. After about thirty seconds of listening to her rip him up a bit, he signals for me to politely end the call, but I had another plan. I decided to disruptively continue the call.

"Mom, I'm not asking my Dad to pay for no doggone family tickets!"

This prompted my father to lean over and press the mute button. He then looks me dead in the eye and said sternly, "Don't you ever let me hear you raise your voice to your mother like that again—do you understand me? I don't care how wrong or unfair she may be—or whether she ever approve of me, you, or us—do you understand me?!"

Crestfallen, I said, "But I'm just saying—Dad!"

"Give me the phone, Mark," he demanded.

I give him the cell, he releases the mute button, and said, "Dee, this is Danny. I overheard some of Mark's conversation and I thought I'd try to help resolve the ticket situation. You guys can have my two tickets, and if you need more, just let me know—I'll do what I can."

"Oh, okay, thanks," she replied. "It may be about five-six of us coming."

"That's fine—but for the record, just so you'll know, the NCAA rules regarding game day tickets work a little different at OU than maybe at perhaps Arkansas Pine Bluff. They don't give out physical tickets anymore—you have to be on the player's guest list to get access into the stadiums, and they do only get four slots."

"Okay," she replied slowly and suspiciously.

"So he is shooting straight with you about the tickets, Dee, and the one thing he didn't say is the university would need to know by mid-week of each week who might be attending a game," Danny politely explained.

"Okay, thanks for clarifying it, I appreciate your help," she said. "Tell Mark we'll see him next week and let him know who's all coming by mid-week."

Mark waited till he disconnected the call before saying, "Don't give up your tickets to them, Dad—make them buy their own tickets."

"Mark—I'm good, son."

"They never shared any of their Arkansas Pine Bluff tickets with you!"

"I realize that, but you got to let this thing go, Mark—unforgivingness is destructive."

"I just don't like how she's always trying to take advantage of you in someway."

"Mark, you gotta learn how to *forgive, if you want to be forgiven, son,"* as he gets up, leaves the tip and heads for the door.

True to her word, a week later, my mom indeed made the trip, but she only brought one relative not the five or six she spoke of. And since they didn't get into town until late on a Friday night, I didn't get a chance to spend any time with them until after the game on Saturday night. And no, I wasn't really avoiding her, red-shirt players were required to follow certain pre-game team rules, too, which condensed my time down significantly the night before the game.

However, as soon as the OU/Colorado contest had ended, I called her to discuss where we might be able to meet up. After we agree on a local landmark, I then call my Dad to give him an update, to which he had one word of advice, "Whatever you do, son, **do not** get into any heated discussions with your Mom about anything, Mark—be kind and always take the low road, son,"

I promised to do so as I made my way to our meet point, a local restaurant.

As we finished dinner, my cousin was getting me caught up on the gossip at UAPB before her cell goes off. She then excused herself, which left me and my mom, alone, with time to chat about anything we so chose. And right in the middle of a really good conversation about other news in Pine Bluff, she changes the subject, "Mark, don't believe everything your daddy is saying about me and your family."

I'm thinking, *What?!* Then replied, "He hasn't said anything about you or the family."

"But your *sudden change* of attitude towards us says that somebody has been messin with your head, son, and its still likely to be your daddy," she shot back.

"Well, he hasn't said anything derogatory about you, Mom. In fact, its the opposite."

"You don't know your daddy," she fired back again, as she conveniently jumps to another hot subject, "So what's really up with the ticket situation, Mark?"

I pause for a moment thinking, *here we go again.*

"Mom, it is as he told you."

"But what are you telling me?" She asked. "Cause I know your daddy."

And man I wanted so badly to say, *"No Mom, clearly, you don't.... And what about all the apologies you made a few months ago.*

But I didn't, the goal was to stay out of any heated discussions, right?

So I replied, "Mom, these Division I programs just deal with these issues differently, he's already explained that to you. I only get four slots—not tickets—but slots. I gave you two slots and him two slots. And I'm pretty sure you saw his name on that same guest list you signed to get in the game."

"Well, Danny can get some extra tickets whenever he wants a few."

"Perhaps he can, but this ticket situation is out of our control, too, mama."

"Well—it all sounds a bit shaky to me," she replied.

"You can always call the athletic department and inquire about it yourself."

"I just might do that as a matter of fact," she replied sarcastically, but serious.

Unfortunately, this was the norm with us. She just couldn't seem to function if she was not completely running the show. And this thing she's got going with my Dad was unbelievably insane to the tenth power.

Then she jumps to even another hot topic, making it more difficult to stay the course.

"So who's paying your tuition—I hear you still not on scholarship here, either?"

"Who else would be helping to pay for my stay, Mom? You asked me that already."

"Well, just wondering, since you cried so much about UAPB not having you on scholarship," she replied with sarcasm. "Plus, we raised you and provided for you the past twenty plus years...it's time your Dad participate."

Now, this is the part about my mom that really disturbed me. She always treated me as if I was the *most clueless* person on the earth, especially with anything regarding my father. And what she'd failed to realize is that I'd been taking notes on this situation over those same twenty plus years, and had come to an understanding that this man has done more for me, *by himself,* than my whole family combined, and she knows that.

But the problem was he didn't do it through her. And rightly so, with the way my Mom had this house set-up. I had learn not to trust her, too, so why should he be required too.

But, yet, she still spoke of these things as if they were *The Gospel Truth.* However, I was determined not to get into a heated discussion with her. So, I then decided to jump to another subject to avoid the inevitable, "When are y'all headed back?"

"After what I saw on that field today, I might not go back," my cousin shouts out as she makes her way back to the table.

"Girl please, we are out of here first thing in the morning," my Mom said as she then looks at her watch, "Which means it's time for us to get some sleep right about now."

"Well—I'm hanging out with Mark tonight."

"You need some sleep so you can help me drive," Mom said in return.

"And I'm hanging out with my bed," I went on to add.

"So you gon do yo kinfolk like that, Mark?"

"Yes," my mom says, before I could respond. "You gotta help me drive, girl—and by the way, where is your daddy, Mark?"

"Not sure—somewhere chillin. He's a big shot in these neck of the woods," I replied.

"Hell, he's a big-shot in our neck of the woods, maybe I need to go hang out with yo daddy," the cousin said.

"I don't think so, sunset, yo hangout buddies are in PB," I shot back.

"Let's go get some rest, girl," Mom said. "And maybe Mark will show us around the facilities tomorrow before we go."

At first I thought, *No Mark won't,* but then again, I thought, *That might not be a bad idea—given the fact that my mom is completely naive about programs of this magnitude.*

Once we came together the next morning, I took them to see the Switzer Center before they headed back to Arkansas. And since it was still early Sunday morning, the building was fairly empty. And since the stadium sits right down in the middle of campus, they had already gotten an expanded view of the university property site.

But as we started the tour, my cousin, being flirtatious, was all over me again about meeting a few of my teammates that she had scoped out in the media guide. And thank God that most of them were not at the facility just yet, not even for treatment. But my mom on the other hand, was quiet, wearing a somber expression as she observed the program's immaculate facilities, which had to be at least one of the reasons she was speechless. All she would say was, "Nice.... Okay.... Nice...."

And I was praying that I didn't run into anybody of importance from the coaching staff or Athletic Director's office. I just wasn't sure what she might say or do. As we make our way out of the complex, a couple of teammates were finally making their way in as my cousin gets excited. By the time we made our way to her car, my Mom remained reserved and in deep thought. I was hoping to hear something encouraging or positive from her about my new program; the campus; or even about me.... But instead she goes back to her main pitch, "Call your granddaddy Odell—he's upset that he hasn't heard from you."

"That's not true, Mom, I've talked to Daddy a few times since I left."

"Call your granddaddy, Mark!" She fired back. "We still your family. So don't get too beside yourself and forget where you came from, son."

I'm thinking, *Mom, come on, get too beside myself? Don't forget where I came from? How about I'm proud of you.... I love you.... OU appears to be all of what we see on TV.... I'm with you, behind you, rooting for you."*

But that would be asking just way-way-way too much from my mother. And again, the only reason she was pushing me to stay in contact with granddad Odell was because she knew he was committed to helping her continue fighting this unnecessary senseless war against my father. And you would think, at this point, that grandpa Odell would have squashed this nonsense going on with his daughter, but to keep the peace, I simply said, "I'll give him a call, Mom."

My then cousin shouts, "Can I also get a call, from one of your fine teammates?!"

That comment made me laugh as my Mom giggled a little, too.

"What?" She shot back. "Y'all playin—I'm tryin to make it happen!"

"Girl—if you don't get in this car," Denise said with a grin, as they say their good-byes and go their separate ways.

I left this weekend get-together still feeling very empty and even more disconnected from the one person I have trusted all my life as the hand that guided my steps, wondering, *where in the world do we go from here? How do we right this ship? How do I get her to see her err? Or better yet, how do I possibly move on without my mom being a integral part of my life? Could jealousy and envy be that strong of a venomous thread that my own mother would be willing to really throw me totally away simply because she refuses to join forces with the truth? This was definitely the time for her to make amends, not pass on it again.*

But unfortunately, the more this new light began to illuminate the potentials of this new life, the darker it seemed to get between me and my family.

33

Divine Revelation

It was now mid-December 2002 and the Sooners are crowned Conference Champs by defeating the Colorado Buffaloes again 29-7 in the Big XII Championship Game in Houston, Texas, at Reliant Stadium, which meant this team was headed to another BCS Bowl Game—The Rose Bowl—to take on the Washington State Wildcats in Pasadena, California. And since red-shirt players don't travel with the team, I spent this Christmas *in Dallas,* for the first time ever, with my father—elated that he rescued me from absolute total destruction, just in the nick of time.

He took me to the Potter's House for the Christmas and New Years Eve Celebration, and I had a blast—a bit emotional but very uplifting. I had never experienced a church environment quite like this place. Bishop T. D. Jakes was incredibly good—and so was Kirk Carr and his musical group. And just as this awesome event was about to come to a close, Kirk began introducing his back up singers, and he mentions the name Smokie Norful. And the guy walks up to the edge of the stage to take a bow, and I then look at my Dad and say, "That's my history teacher from Jack Robey—in Pine Bluff!"

"Really!" He replied.

"Yes!" I replied. "I didn't know he was a singer!"

Then I rushed down to the stage and got his attention to tell him how impressed I was to hear him sing like that—he was amazingly great! I immediately felt inspired by Smokie's courage to pursue his dreams, just as I was beginning to doubt whether or not I had the courage to pursue my own dream, especially with all the strife and division going on within the midst of my family. This was the moment that I perhaps realized that the good Lord is indeed *no respecter of persons.* What he had done for Smokie Norful, He was willing to do for me, a message my Pops often preached.

Of course Smokie went on to become a mega Gospel superstar after that night, while I had only managed to survive my first year at a major program, right? But, hey, given the fact where my head was growing up, surviving was huge. Not to speak of how tough it is, I'm discovering, to be a productive a student athlete at a big program.

Nevertheless, on one end, life was now starting to make sense, which encouraged me to dream in ways I'd never dreamed, but on the other end, life was starting to make even less sense to me. It had become apparent that my beloved family didn't wish me well—they wished I'd fail. My mom had slowly but surely distanced herself to show her disapproval of my decision to team up with my father. So instead of being excited for me, she mourned and grieved at the idea of me potentially succeeding without her. So as I embarked upon this opportunity of a lifetime, my mother had practically deserted me.

And the reality of totally losing my mom began to take root, again, which produced a whole new wave of stress inside me. I understood that my relationship with my father shouldn't have ever threatened my relationship with my mother, but it did. Not because of his irresponsibility or his disinterest in my well-being, but on the contrary. It was my mother that operated irresponsibly, proving over the years that she was more concerned about her well-being, not mine.

I loved my mother dearly and always wanted the best for her, evident in the number of years I protected her and hung in there with her even when it hurt and harmed others; doing things her way knowing that they were not God's way. But her behavior at this juncture, made it clear that she really didn't want the best for me. And yes, I knew that such was probably the case long before now, but accepting it was still incredibly hard.

So, after the Sooners Rose Bowl victory, my Dad drove me back to Norman in the newest model of the Mercedes SUV ML Class. He had traded in one for the other. Along the way, he made sure, again, I understood the significance of my academic work, especially since more would be required of me now that I'm eligible to participate and compete for playing time on the field. He would often use these road trips to often warn me of the do's and dont's of life, not that he had all the answers, but believed he knew where to get them. And his story telling abilities would always inspire me in someway, which pushed me to seize these opportunities the good Lord has given me. And that your mother, in due time, would be fine; not to lose hope.

We pull into the driveway of this newly built trac-home, he gets out and says, "I gotta run inside for a minute to visit a friend."

But when he walks up to the door, he takes out a key, opens it and enters the house. Not knowing who lived there, or what the deal was, I get out the car and step through the door too, as he began flipping on lights. I then eyed the furniture, the pictures on the wall and the general layout of the place and said, "This stuff looks familiar, is this one of your rent houses? Who'd you say live here?"

He then tosses me the keys and says, "Go get your bags young fella—you do."

"Huh!" I replied, startled.

"This is you for the next twenty-four months," he said.

"Dad, come on man—you serious?!"

"Mark, get your stuff, son."

"Pops—you serious?!"

"Your family will need somewhere to stay when we come to visit, right?"

"Yeah," I excitedly replied.

"Well, they can save a few dollars on hotels...now go get your bags."

"Dad, you serious," I said as I began trying to process what's going on here.

He stops all movement and said, "Son, yes, and maybe this will keep you from crashing on the sofa every night at your teammates house."

Surprised by his comment, I asked, "What do you mean?"

"Mark—don't play me. You've only spent about two weeks in your dorm room since you got here. And that is just way too much distraction—academically."

"I apologize, that civilian dorm kept me so disconnected, Pops, but I got this academic thing under control," I said, as I gleefully take a tour of my new place of residence.

And as I make my way back into the house with a few of my bags, he tosses me another set of keys.

"What's this for? I ask, puzzled.

"You gotta get back and forth to campus, don't you?"

"Yeah," I said curiously.

"All I ask is that you take care of this house as well as I know you will this car?"

"Dad—a Benz?!"

"It's just a car son—it does the same thing any car will do—just better. So go get the rest of your bags and let's get going.... You need a refrigerator and a washer and dryer."

I suddenly take a seat on one of the bar stools as tears began to well up in my eyes. I really didn't know what to say, accept, "Thanks Pops," as a tear fell.

"Son, all is well.... Thank me by maintaining a 3.0 or better.... Now let's roll."

I then got up, hugged him, and thanked him again for believing in me. He told me he loved me and was just doing his reasonable duty as my father. And that he knew staying on campus would keep me isolated but close to where I needed to be. But he wanted to see me prove myself, after I'd stood him up so many times. And once he learned I'd been hanging out at the teammates place, catching rides back and forth to campus, he decided to change the circumstances rather than try fighting me about it. I learned that day, how my father strategized his authority when dealing with the many issues in my life. There were some battles he just chose not to fight, which kept me a bit off balance. So, I never knew what to expect next.

However, after a couple of nights of dinner and shopping for appliances, he took a flight back to Dallas and you know it—it was party time. I called my newfound cousin,

Travelee, who was already on his way over to check out the car and the crib for the next couple of years. And he immediately started calculating as soon as he stepped through the door, "Hey, ask your Dad if I can move in with you kinfolk."

As I was about to answer him, I got a rare call from my mom, which prompted Travelee to then ask, after I hung up, "Your Mom be sweatin you like that?"

"It's a long-long story, brah," I replied, not wanting to really talk about it. He sensed that but went on to share how wonderful his mom has been in his life despite not having a relationship of any kind with his father. And that the locker room seemed to be filled with his kind of story. And he recognized off top, that such was not the case with me.

But suddenly I said, "Looka here—enough with all that, let's go party!"

And party did we! But semester classes was about to begin, which meant it was time to get refocused. And all was well until the weekend of the Spring Game. My beloved Mom and half the family decided they would just show up. No, not totally unannounced, but their behavior was once again—totally unaccepted.

They get in town on a Friday evening but I didn't get a chance to see them until the next day, after the game. I met them at their hotel after they had gone to dinner. We made plans to do breakfast before they headed back to Arkansas, which meant I was to arrive back at their hotel about 10 a.m., but during our visit, they discovered I was no longer in the dormitory, and as expected, they decided that viewing my new place of residence would be more important than doing breakfast.

So by 9 a.m. Sunday morning, on this April 2003 weekend, my cell phone goes off and it's my Mom, asking for directions to the house. After giving them, I quickly strolled over to my Dad's room, who was still asleep before he was to head back to Dallas, to inform him that they were on their way. And he decided that he would step out to give us a chance to spend some quality time together.

"You leaving me here by myself?" I asked.

"Yeah, why, what's the problem?"

"You know they have a tendency to team up on me when I'm alone, Pops," I replied.

"Well, son, you said it went well last night—maybe they'll be as cordial today."

"I would be much more at ease if you stayed just in case it gets hot in here."

Danny paused, thought about it, and then said, "Okay, but anything past 12 noon, I'm out; I got to be back in Dallas by 4 p.m."

"Cool," I replied with relief.

And then the doorbell rang. *Man, they must have been in the car when they called.*

So, I head for the door, while my Dad heads for the shower. I admired my father's patience when it came to my family, especially my Mom. But I was ready for this craziness to be over, more than over wanted over. I said a short prayer before opening the door, and then there stood my mother, granddad, sister, and a relative that made the trip too. But strangely, there was no grandma Leola.

Maybe she stayed at the hotel or was making her way from the car, I thought.

As they enter, my Mom and the relative immediately start scoping out the house, opening nearly every door and cabinet, whispering comments to each other. Curious as to what happened to grandma Leola, I asked the relative, "Where's mama Leo?"

"She's out there in the car," the relative replied.

"In the car—why?" I asked with concerned.

"Oh, she's just tired, Mark," my mom jumps in and replied.

"This sure is a nice place Mark," Odell added, seemingly in an attempt to divert the conversation, which was followed by a rapid fire of questions from my beloved mother.

"So, whose house is this? And where did you get this furniture from?" She asked.

"For real—this is nice stuff boy," the relative said. "But what I wanna know is who those two Mercedes Benz's in the garage belong too?" She asked, smiling perhaps hoping I'd say one of my teammates. And as they all stood waiting for answers to their questions, I decided to drop the grandma Leola situation for the moment to respond, knowing at this point, this visit has the potential to get out of hand.

"The E-class is my Dad's, the SUV is mine; the house and the furniture is mine."

"Boy please—both those cars belong to your Dad and so does this house and the furniture too," my mother replied sarcastically.

Pausing, not knowing how to respond, created a fire inside me. But I kept my cool, took a seat on the sofa and pretended to be watching TV. However, I was still curious as to why my grandma Leo won't come in, especially since I haven't seen her since I left home. And my sister who had been fairly quiet seemed concerned about her too, asked the relative, "Go check on Mama," as the others began taking seats in the living area near to the kitchen, where Odell had already taken his seat, at the kitchen table.

My Mom, finally, sits down next to me and softly asked if I would go and invite mama Leo inside. Not liking the sound of that suggestion I asked, "What's really up with Mama Leo?"

"Well—she doesn't feel at ease coming in what she believes to be *Danny's house."*

I thought to myself, *Wow! Mama Leo has finally flipped sides completely.*

So, if we needed any more validation regarding my previous comment, let me reestablish it again: *My family didn't wish me well—they wished I'd fail.* This kind of behavior from one of the main leaders of our family, was just unacceptable. Even after all they've seen for themselves, knowing without doubt that things were much better in Norman than they ever were in Pine Bluff, and they still not rooting for me? Come on family, this thing has now reached a serious level of insane stupidity.

Nevertheless, before I attempted to coax my grandma Leo into the house, to which she was obviously against doing, I decided to update my Dad on the matter, first. As I entered his bedroom, knocking as I stepped in, he was partially dressed and close to completion. I then gave him a blow-by-blow of the situation.

"Can you believe my Mom is strugglin with the car, the house, and the furniture?"

"What did she say?" He asked, as he continued to get dressed.

"Well—once I told her that all these things were mine, she shot back with, '*boy please, this stuff all belongs to your daddy.*'"

"Really?" He asked, seemingly surprised.

"Can you believe that?!"

"You sure you didn't misunderstand her, son?" He asked.

"Positive!" I loudly whispered.

"Denise is going to be fine in due time son, just hang in there," he said, nonchalantly.

"I don't see it.... I think my Mom is going to change, Dad.... I don't."

Danny pauses to look at him, and said, "Mark, keep in mind, *Life and Death is in the power of your tongue,* son.... Don't negate your prayers by speaking words of hopelessness.... At one point, I could have taken the same attitude towards you, but I didn't.... I loved you through, so let's love her through it.... You know the drill, only speak words of life, not words of defeat."

I then took a deep breath and brought him up to speed on the other major issue.

"The other problem is grandma Leo is outside, refusing to come in."

Danny stops all movement again, and asked, "Why, what's going on, son?"

Suddenly, I was too embarrassed to even say it. I just couldn't get it out. How do you tell this man something like this, knowing that all he's done was love these people with kindness while they lynched him daily! So I just said, "I don't really know—and I hate to even think about why she may have chose not to come in."

"Tell her I said please come inside, there's no need to sit in a hot car!"

Fortunately, by the time I reentered the living room area, grandma Leo was in the house. And thank God I didn't have to deal with that situation. Nonetheless, my mother, on this day, had taken me to a whole new level of frustration—a level I didn't quite even know how to process. I hadn't achieved that level of spiritual understanding to know how to deal with this kind of behavior, just yet.

When my Dad finally emerged, they were taking pictures of the house and each other. Since his room was closest to the kitchen, the first person he sees is Odell. And they exchange pleasantries and shake hands.

He then waves at my Mom and family before making a point to go over to Mama Leo and personally greeted her with a hug, and then makes his way back over to the kitchen table to grab a seat across from Odell to properly man the room.

And my grandfather, who'd seen my Dad right before the spring game, leaned over and whispered, "I just want to say again, what you're doing for Mark is just wonderful—the blessing and doors you've been able to open for Mark—its just wonderful."

"All is well, Odell," Danny replied.

"But Odell went on, "I told that girl a long time ago to stop this craziness, but she just wouldn't listen…I apologize again for any role I may have played in the matter—I just didn't know what the real deal was between you and Dee."

"And as I told you, Odell, you don't have to thank me, sir, Mark is my son. I'm just doing my reasonable duties as his father, not seeking approval," Danny humbly replied.

Eavesdropping on their conversation, I was hoping my grandfather understood the magnitude of my Dad's response, but it would have been really cool if he had recognized this man's fatherly efforts fifteen plus years ago. But his apology was a step in the right direction even if his motives were wrong, too.

But now with everybody wanting to get in the snapshots, they ask my Dad to take a picture of all of us, except Odell chose not to join in, which prompted mama Leo to head for the exit after the pic was taken. But instead of trying to stop her, they simply said their good-byes and trailed her out the door too. But my sister, being impressionable, hangs back a bit and whispered before exiting, "I wish your daddy was my daddy," and then rushed out.

Although a bit surprised by her comment, I understood why she felt that way. She noticed, as I did, at an early age, that there was just something *uniquely* different about my father than the other father figures in our family. So as I closed the door, I turned and said to my Pops, who had slightly overheard her comment, "I think the hotel is the best place to meet them in the future—not the house."

And he paused, and said, "Maybe so, but whatever you do, son—be patient."

"Dad—they should know better. Even Cassie can see somethin is just not right."

"Perhaps, but we've all wished that we were somebody different at some point over the course of our life after having been wooed and impressed, son," he humbly replied.

And once again, as he talked my eyes filled up with tears of disappointment in my mother. I felt like I had forgiven her, but every time something like this happened between us, I felt that anger and rage building all over again.

"But it just seems like a never ending story, Daddy!" I replied with frustration.

"I understand, son...but trouble don't last always, Mark—keep the faith."

"But the sad thing about this whole situation, Dad, is that you are my Mom's biggest fan, and she don't even know it."

Danny paused and then said, "Honestly—I think she does, but she's not quite ready to accept that just yet…so hang on in there. I assure you the good Lord is working overtime at turning this thing around—*nothing shall remain the same."*

"Well I just don't see it and I don't know how you do it," I replied, flustered.

And he paused again before saying, "Mark, I figured out a long time ago, son, *hatred stirs up strife, but love covers all sins....* Remember, this is a spiritual warfare—not a fleshly one.... So let's not start *leaning on our own understanding* about this thing.... We must trust that the Lord will work this out if we stay the course."

And as usual he would close these sessions with a short prayer as I, as usual, wipe away a few tall tears. Afterwards, he hugged me and persuaded me to continue to be *strong* and be of *good courage,* the Lord promises to *never leave me or forsake me.*

He then exited en route back to Dallas.

However, by the time he had made it to Texas, I was on my way to Oklahoma City with a few teammates to party—on crutches. Yes, in the midst of it all, I had-had my second knee surgery, a scope to clean up debris from spring ball, which seemed to only add to my stress. I knew what my father was teaching me was divinely correct. And I had studied these biblical truths with him and knew them to be written in text. But I guess I was still trying to reason it all in my head from a humanistic viewpoint, which caused many of these up and down mood swings I seemed to be trapped in. But he tried to keep me focused with our bible study sessions, usually by conference, which helped a great deal as the spring semester session comes to a close.

But shortly thereafter, as the 2003 summer session was about to get underway, the biggest party yet, was being held in another small town right outside Norman—Pauls Valley, which made it one more given for me. But suddenly, right in the midst of all of the hype at this "couldn't miss" party, gunshots rang out—**Bang! Bang! Bang!**

34

Divine Support

Everybody scattered. Fortunately, I just happened to be near the only exit door in the building. I rushed out running on crutches as if I didn't need a crutch. I had ridden with another teammate who had parked about a half-mile away because of the sea of cars in attendance. And I didn't look back to see which direction traffic might be going, I just pent-my-ears back and rolled through this crutchful sprint back to the car. I suddenly hear my Dad's voice: *Choose wisely the company you keep, son, and the places you go, it could be a matter of life and death.*

Once I made it to the vehicle, one of my teammates had already arrived waiting for me, and Travelee, who had also ridden with us. Suddenly, someone ran right by us and shouted, "Mark, I think your cousin Travelee got shot, he might be dead!"

I then begin to pray frightened out of my wits! We started making phone calls to some of the people that caravanned down with us. We managed to locate most of our friends that made the trip, but we couldn't reach Travelee. So I decided to call the only one somebody that I knew could guide us through this serious-serious ordeal.

"Dad," I said frantically! "Travelee—Travelee got shot and **may be dead!**"

"What?!"

"Yeah, this guy just ran by, I'm at this party, and said Travelee might be dead!"

"Calm down, son, tell me what party you're at," as he looks at his watch.

"I don't really know—some lil town outside Norman!" I replied terrified.

One of my friends then yelled out Pauls Valley, we're in Pauls Valley!

"Pauls Valley!" I repeated.

"Mark, listen to me, son.... Get in your car and head back to Norman, now."

"I can't, Daddy—I didn't drive. And Travelee rode with us.... so we're just tryin to locate him before we get out!" I replied as Danny could hear the frenzy going on in the background. "I tried callin him but he's not answering."

"What's Travelee's cell number?" He asked calmly.

I quickly and precisely shot them out to make sure he got every number.

"Get inside the car and stay there until I hit you back—do you understand me?"

"Yeah—my battery is low and I don't have my charger."

And suddenly, my cell went dead. So I took the battery out, prayed over it and put it back in my phone, and thank God, I still had a lil juice. And simultaneously, one of the other friends that rode with us arrived at the car and said, "Let's roll, Travelee did get shot, he's being rushed to the hospital."

They jump in the car and began weaving our way out of this chaotic situation. I began praying that God would spare Travelee's life and anybody else that might have gotten hit or injured by the stampede of folks rushing out of the place.

In the meantime, my Dad calls back but my cell went dead again. I then started reflecting, wondering how I could have put myself in such a dangerous situation—on crutches, knowing the risk of what could happen at these kind of *hole in the wall* get-togethers. I didn't have any excuses—I knew better.

About an hour later, I rushed into the house, placed my cell on the charger, grabbed the land-line and began making calls trying to find out what Travelee's condition might be. Then I called my Dad to see what he may have discovered. He knew a few people inside Oklahoma law enforcement who would have the real 411 on this matter by now. Hospitals are usually pretty private about giving out any information. And such was the case. My Dad answers, but was on the phone still gathering info and had to call me back.

However, a couple of hours later, Travelee was walking through the door bandaged up around his left quad and hamstring area. I then exhaled. He said it was just a flesh wound, nothing really serious, but was obviously looking to retaliate against the one who pulled the trigger. And before we could get into a heavy discussion about it, surprisingly, my Dad walks through the door. He had driven from Dallas to Norman, to put eyes on the both of us.

He was fully aware of Travelee's situation by the time he arrived and was definitely expecting to see him at the house. After patiently hearing Travelee's side of the story, which was filled with anger and revenge, and my side of the story, which was filled with stress and resentment, he decided to talk, and said, "I've listened to both of you guys for nearly thirty minutes, one with a gunshot injury looking to get back at the gunmen, and another with a knee injury, looking to get back at life, which he thinks has been so unfair to him.... And quite frankly, both of you need your butt kicked for not only putting yourself in this position, but also for thinking that retaliation is a viable solution to these kind of problems, when you know better." Then said, "Mark you could've lost your life stepping into an environment that carried death—on crutches, son! And Travelee, you will eventually lose yours, if you don't stop trying to defend every friend that might be justifiably gettin his butt kicked.... The graveyard is full of men with *great potential* who decided that they're not going to be punked."

He went on and encouraged us to investigate and *examine our minds, our interests*, and even *our friends*. I mean he was all over us—but he shared these truths without doubt, in love.

"Mark and Travelee," he said, "you can always judge the character of a person, by the company they keep....the question is, which one are you? Are you *the good company or the bad company?"* He asked, as he gets up from his seat. "I suggest both of you decide which one you're going to be—your life depends on it," as he exits, slamming the door behind him, only to reenter moments later, and said, "And by the way, both of you represent one of the finest programs on the freaking planet, act like you appreciate it damn it!"

And Boom! He slams the door again en route back to Dallas without even saying, bye. But sadly, for me, the slide had begun. Instead of this event and wise counsel turning me, the emotional pain of being ousted by my family caused me to regress even further. I continued socializing with some of the wrong people, hanging out in the wrong places and started dating many of the wrong women, which led to more emotional distress, sexual encounters, which caused even more psychological hardship.

I began oversleeping, missing classes, tutoring sessions and assignments, making it that much more difficult to stay eligible to do what I came to OU to really do—play ball. And with the tight ship that Coach Stoops ran, he was not going to tolerate anything less from me than he would a scholarship player. And that kept me somewhat focused. Plus, I was here *on Daddy's Dime—not the University of Oklahoma's Dime.* Therefore, I was getting it from both sides, Coach Stoops and Coach Bradley.

So I was fully aware that my eligibility to participate in sports was predicated solely on my ability to stay academically above board and out of trouble. Nevertheless, despite my many emotional and social setbacks, I somehow managed to survive the spring semester of '03, but I would still need fifteen plus hours of summer school to be eligible to play ball in the upcoming fall.

There is no doubt I was struggling with this new life and the heavy responsibilities that accompanied it. But for some reason, unlike my mother, my father just refused to quit on me. This man just kept encouraging and challenging me to be the best I can be with a love I had not known before.

So as the 2003 fall practices began, even though we were still loaded with All-Americans and future NFL draft picks, I wasn't happy with just being on the roster anymore, I wanted to play—and play now! But my father pressed me to be patient and just focus on learning the game. He believed that in due time, Coach Stoops would give me a chance to contribute. But on this call, I thought I'd press a little deeper, "It would be nice if he could start by at least giving me a scholarship."

Danny paused and then asked, "Where are you going with this Mark?"

"I'm just saying, Dad, he's had a whole year to evaluate my abilities, he knows what I can do—they give scholarships to high school kids whom they have no idea what kind of player they'll be once they put this uniform on. But I'm here busting my butt and performing every day in practice—against the best players in the country—and it still appears as if I'm not getting any love."

Danny knew his son had some great points about the scholarship situation and he obviously wanted more than just proving he belonged. He wanted Coach Stoops and the University of Oklahoma to validate it, publicly. And he knew one of the last things Mark needed was one more negative emotion, especially one associated with rejection. So he decided to squash this line of thinking, right there on the spot, in an effort to keep his son focused on the bigger picture and the opportunities within.

"Mark, here is my position on this—first of all, I agree.... I clearly understand how you feel. However, let's not focus on what hasn't happened just yet, let's keep our mind focused on what's going to happen in the near future, son."

"I'm just sayin, Dad!"

"And I'm just sayin, Mark.... As it is with most collegiate players, being accepted and counted among your peers is important—I get that! But what's more imperative, right now, is to be content with the opportunity Coach Stoops has given you," my Dad said.

"But I do appreciate him giving me a chance, but....." Danny cuts him off, "Mark, listen, son.... There is a much larger testimony, here, than you being on scholarship. Your ability to succeed despite that scholarship proves to a lot of young men out there that *all things are truly possible to them that believe."*

Not having considered the spiritual slant, I then said, "I understand and appreciate that angle, but at this point, Dad, you shouldn't have to help pay for this anymore, especially with both of our blood, sweat and tears left on that field."

"I appreciate that, son—but that's insignificant to me.... All is well.... You just stay focused on your assignments on and off the field."

I paused and then conceded my position: "I don't like it, but I get it."

"Mark, stay away from this topic, especially with the media—do you feel me?"

I paused with no response.

"Do you understand, Mark Bradley? He asked again.

"Yes sir," I replied dejectedly.

"Be patient.... Good things come to those that *wait*.... And by the way, God promotes more on *character* than He ever has on *skills.*"

"But Dad, I've seen how much this has already cost you, man.... I've watched you downsize to an apartment while paying for me to live in a house."

"Parents make those kind of sacrifices, son.... I understand that you believe that you deserve to be counted and accepted beyond the game ball—and I agree that you have proved your ability to perform on the field, but right now, you need to focus on following leadership—not seeking out a scholarship.... Focus on making the grades, learning the game, and stop being concerned about your name, Mark."

"Dad, don't you think I've made a name for myself already around here?"

"Yes, you have, but sometimes *where* you are in life, son, is more important *than who* you are in life.... I'll be in touch," as he hangs up on me.

This man hasn't led me wrong yet, and I had no reasons to think that his position on this scholarship thing was off base. So, with a bit of humility, I took his advice and began focusing on my studies and my defensive playbook, after being moved from receiver to the defensive secondary during the spring.

But as opening day got closer, the offensive coordinator convinced Coach Stoops to move me back to wide receiver to help stretch the field the week of the first game, which meant that all the time I had spent learning the position of defensive back was seemingly all for naught. And with only one week to prepare before a national televised audience, in Tuscaloosa, Alabama, I was running routes again, instead of covering them.

And since my father was such a student of the game, I would call him in the midnight hours to help me understand concepts, terminology and philosophy—and that made this last minute adjustment much easier to deal with for which he often did with reluctance, I might add. He was always cautious about interfering or overstepping his boundaries with any coach, especially a staff he had such great respect for as OU's.

My father's primary focus was not on preparing me for the game of football, but for the game of life. But, hey, it was still a huge advantage having him to call on in the wee hours of the morning with football questions, too. And knowing that I would have to fight for more playing time with an already very talented receivers' group led by Mark Clayton, Brandon Jones, and Travis Wilson, my father made a suggestion in week two of the season that would forever change my status with the Sooners.

"Mark, as you await your opportunity to get into this starting rotation, it would be advantageous for you to learn to play in all phases of the game," he said. "NFL scouts love guys who can play anywhere, especially the kicking game—you follow me?"

"Yeah, I'm with you," I told him.

"Go seek out Bobby Jack Wright, your special teams coach, and tell him that you want to play in every phase of the kicking game he can find a spot for your talent; from punt team, punt return, to kickoff coverage and kick return.... I mean anywhere he can better his group, including holding for extra point and field goals—you do it.... **and then** you'll be in a position to make your presence known as one of the best football athletes in the country. And at that point, the OU football offices will be flooded with NFL scouts inquiring more information about Mark Bradley—are you with me?"

"I'm with it and on it," I replied with excitement.

The next day, I did just that. And after about two weeks, I had become one of the special teams captains. And through this avenue, I indeed began to make a lil noise while I waited patiently for more playing time at receiver.

"It was now starting to make a lot of sense," I often said to my Pops.

But while my Dad's advice was timely, my Mom was starting to take untimely shots at him, again. Most every time we talked, she still had to say something negative and derogatory about him. So, even though life on the field was now even brighter, life off the field, with my family, was now pitch black.

And by week five, after sharing with my mother the multitude of struggles I was having mentally, physically and emotionally behind all the warfare going on between me, her and the rest of the family, she fired back and said, **"Mark, nothin is gonna go right for you until you get right—with me."**

That floored me! I couldn't even think after she made this comment. For the life of me, what have I done to my mother that could have been so wrong, that would cause her to say something like that! This aggravated me so much that I became extremely depressed, which caused me to lose my whole focus. And just a few days later, I was late for our team buses headed to the airport for Iowa State, upon which I informed Coach Stoops, that I was thinking about just giving up football, entirely.

He was obviously disappointed in me but he persuaded me to reconsider, even though he also had to discipline me. He was gracious enough to allow me to make the trip and even play, which gave me a chance to refocus and reposition myself a bit. In doing so, I returned my first ever kickoff for a touchdown, despite having to fight off thoughts of wondering again, if life was even-really worth living.

And by week eight, after becoming the special teams lead skipper and starting to contribute on the offensive side of the ball, the coaching staff, *out of nowhere,* decided during the Texas A&M pregame preparations that they were going to go in a different direction—without Mark Bradley.

I had suddenly gone from being a major contributor, a captain and perhaps the most talented player on this roster, to not playing at all with no explanation as to why. As you could imagine, I was crushed, especially given the magnitude of all the other family issues I was already dealing with emotionally. I didn't believe in superstitions, but I suddenly felt jinxed by my Mom's comment.

So as I stood there in uniform, *clueless* as to what went wrong, the A&M game came to a close. I didn't know what to think, what to say or what to do.... I just stood there in a clean uniform, zoned out, speechless, staring into space, knowing that going back home was not remotely a possible option for me. *I really would rather die than go back into that confrontational pigsty,* I recall thinking. And I knew my father truly loved me but, yet, I didn't know after another major hiccup if he could ever really trust me again.

And as expected, he had a lot of questions and I didn't have any answers to give him. I made it clear that there was no indication throughout the week that there would be any changes in our game plan.

But his thoughts were, "Mark, this is way too sudden, harsh, and deliberate for this not to be either a serious *team violation* or a serious *academic related issue.*"

And I assured him that all was well with my grades and knew of no such issue with the team or coaching staff. So he backed off for the time being, and suggested I stop by Coach Stoops' office and seek an answer. Nonetheless, I was confused, my teammates were confused, and the media seemed somewhat confused by this sudden demotion of someone who appeared to be making a name for himself.

Meanwhile, as my Dad got prepared to head back to Dallas, I got prepared to chat with Coach Stoops as to what caused my sudden demotion. So on early Monday morning, as I headed to see coach, I noticed this message posted at my locker, which read, "Please see academic counselor before practice," as I simultaneously see that my locker had been cleaned out, the cubicle was empty. So I just stood there wondering, *what in the world is going on here?*

In the interim, my Dad was home going through his mail when he notices a letter addressed to me from the University of Oklahoma. He opened it and read it. And as he had assumed, *the Arts and Sciences department had officially suspended me and charged me with academic misconduct until further notice. The charges were associated with three counts of plagiarism, which is strictly prohibited as stated in the universities rules and regulations. A hearing had been scheduled for about mid-January.*

Danny immediately calls his business associate Jackie to inform her he's got to get back to Oklahoma to handle an emergency situation that can't wait and won't be attending their scheduled business meeting. He then quickly packs a bag and heads to Norman. While in the car, he places a number of phone calls, one of them to the Athletic Academic Director, who was unavailable. So he's transferred to one of the assistant AD's. They talk about the charges leveled against Mark, charges of plagiarism, as the assistant AD voices his disappointment over the situation, commenting on how well he thought Mark was doing otherwise. He suggests they stop by his office as soon as he arrives in town.

The next call is to Mark who is still sitting in front of his locker, in shock. Danny was aware of his son's emotional state and wanted to be as productive as possible without losing his ability to reach him. He tells him about the notice and of his disappointment.

Mark is stunned and says, "Daddy, I don't even know what plagiarism is!"

"What do you mean, you don't know what plagiarism is, Mark?!"

"I'm tellin you Dad, I have no idea what the term even means!" I replied.

"Son, saying that you don't know what plagiarizing is, as a student, is like saying you don't know what a goal-post is as a football player—how is that possible?!"

"I don't know, but I have no idea what the term means, Dad!"

"Well—I'm on my way to Norman and I highly suggest you have your butt at the house waiting with a better damn answer than that!"

And after a short man-to-man session at the house, I discovered in detail exactly what the university has charged me with and minutes later we are sitting in the assistant AD's office, as he begins to explain the gravity of my academic situation.

"Plagiarism," he says, "is the copying or stealing of someone else's material without citing or giving credit to such person(s)…. Unfortunately, Mark, you have three counts in the same class within the same semester, which makes it extremely difficult to even begin a discussion about the possibility of probation. In fact, I don't think we've ever seen anyone overcome charges of this magnitude without an extended suspension. The only thing you can hope for now, is perhaps a reduction in fines. But suspension time from the university, will be lengthy, which will probably absorb all of your remaining athletic eligibility, given the time lost from the transfer from Arkansas Pine Bluff."

"So—a suspension is inevitable?" Danny, asked pointedly

"I'm afraid so," he replied. "But here's the name of a local attorney who is experienced in dealing with these cases. It would be extremely wise if you give her a call. She's going to be your best route at this point. It's totally out of the Athletic Department's hands—I'm sorry."

Danny takes the number and asks, "Who is the instructor leveling the charges?"

"That would be instructor Cathy Kelser, isn't it Mark?" He asked.

"Yeah—I think so," I replied solemnly.

My Dad turns and looks at me and asked? "So you knew about this?"

"Now that he mentioned her name, yeah. I received an e-mail from her after my summer school session. I tried to reach her back a few times but she said she didn't see a need to talk about it anymore since the deadline had passed." I replied, broken.

Danny drops his head in disappointment.

"Well, Mark," the assistant said, "once it gets to this level, most instructors, if not all, detach themselves from the equation, especially if you ignored her several attempts to discuss these charges with you.... These are serious violations.... It's now in the University Legal Department's hands—not the instructor's hands, which requires that you go before a panel to a hearing. So hiring an attorney is highly recommended, and the quicker you do—the better off you'll be."

Danny paused for a moment then asked, "So, the possibility for reinstatement is completely out of the question?"

"I'm afraid so," he replied.

"And hiring the Attorney, you're saying, would only be an effort to reduce the fines, but the suspension time is likely to be extensive, correct?"

"That would be correct," he replied with empathy, obviously taking no pleasure in being the bearer of such bad tidings.

"Unbelievable," Danny quietly said underneath his breath.

"And unfortunately," the assistance said, "it's my understanding that these legal fees could be very expensive."

"How expensive?" Danny asked.

"Somewhere in the neighborhood of *seven-eight thousand dollars* is what I hear."

I then look over at my Dad and thought to myself, *Seven-eight plus thousand dollars?! This can't be happening to me!*

Danny stood up and extended his hand and said, "Thanks—I'll be in touch," as the assistant AD walked them to his office door and said, "Good luck to you in the future, Mark," as he pats him on the back.

35

Divine Faith

As they exit the parking garage of the Athletic Academic Center, Danny knew his son was in serious trouble. He opened his cell phone and called the Attorney the assistant AD had suggested, as Mark's facial expression said it all—*this was just not meant to be, maybe my mom was right,* he thought to himself. *Maybe I'm just not smart enough to make it at a program like this. I'm being thrown out of school for a violation that everybody seems to be aware of—but I'd never heard of. However, I am not going back to Pine Bluff.*

"Laura Leslie, please?"

In less than fifteen seconds his call was connected.

"Ms. Leslie—this is Danny Bradley. I've been given your number by the OU athletic department.... My son, Mark, has received an academic misconduct notice from the University, charging him with three counts of plagiarism...."

"Oooh—that's a pretty serious one," she replies as she briefly interrupts him.

"Yeah—we've been briefed and told such is the case.... But I just drove in from Dallas to tackle this thing—do you have a minute to get together?"

"Absolutely," she politely replied.

"I've already been informed of what your fees may be, but for the record, can you confirm what his defense might cost?"

"Well—all legal fees can vary, Danny, but with a case of this magnitude, it's probably going to be anywhere between seven and ten thousand dollars."

"Understood—but if you don't mind, counselor, I'd like to get coached up a bit before I write a check for such a large amount."

"Sure—we handle student academic misconduct cases all the time.... we are very familiar and successful in defending our clients.... But, yes, I can be available in about twenty minutes if that works for you?"

"See you in twenty," Danny says and then hangs up.

He checks the address on the business card and proceeds on to her office. Knowing Norman, he figured it would be ten minutes or so before he'd be walking through her door, which was just enough time to have a chat with his wayward son.

"Is there anything else I need to know before we walk into this attorney's office?"

"No—there isn't," I replied somberly.

"You sure?"

"Not that I'm aware of.... But at this point, I don't know.... I didn't really know the seriousness of the instructor's e-mail. And even if I failed the class, I figured I had enough hours to still be eligible to play, Dad."

"Understood, but you asked me to bail you out of a negative and defeated situation, son, with nowhere to go and no way out.... And I rushed to your doorstep, as I have on several occasions to help you help yourself.... And the one thing I made absolutely clear is don't allow *the academic* side of this deal *run you up out* of this deal!"

"I'm sorry," I replied dejectedly.

"And to make this transition easier, I eliminated all possible distractions to create an environment that would be conducive to your success, by moving you out of the dormitory into a brand new three bedroom house, fully furnished with all utilities paid; a fifty-thousand dollar vehicle; a cell phone; cable TV; and the privilege to dine anywhere in town you like—and you still fail to make academics your top priority—really disappoints me, son."

"But Dad," I said, trying to get a word in but he throws up his hand to cut my response to finish his statement: "OU has one of the best academic assistance programs in the country, Mark—and I'm certain the coaching staff has made plain the need to use these services, but nooo you chose to do your own thing, even though you desperately needed help, especially if you don't *have a clue* what plagiarism is, son!"

Trying to get a word in again, he cut me off by the raising of his hand to my face, and then shot back, "Don't interrupt me!"

I dropped my head, knowing he was right. He had every reason to be highly upset.

"The last thing you can afford to do with me right now, is lie and play games.... your academic counselor says you've only used the academic center twice since you've been here, Mark! Oh, let me guess—your Mom kept you from going, right? Well, for the last damn time Romeo, you can't run these streets all night, play ball on another night and do the academic thing on any ole night.... I know because I made many of these same mistakes on this same campus twenty years ago," he said as we pulled into the attorney's office.

As he exited the car, you can imagine how I felt. This was perhaps the lowest moment of my life with all that has happened. He had warned me on several occasions about taking advantage of the academic resources available to student athletes but apparently I thought I could survive without the extra assistance. And yes, he was right, I didn't want to miss out on anything happening around campus. Plus, it appeared that the academic assistance program was full of freshman and sophomores, and being an upperclassman and all, I felt out of place. But, nevertheless, he knew me—and knew me well.

And I kind of did want to blame my mother and family for these setbacks; for making life so unbearable for me, which really did affect many of my erroneous decisions. But my Dad wasn't buying into any of these excuses anymore, even though I thought of them as legitimate reasons. But as the old saying goes, *it's hard to fool an experienced gamer.* He's been here and done this. But, I admit, failing to take advantage of the academic services was ridiculously stupid. I had embarrassed him, myself, and those who had given me a chance to breathe again.

After making our way into the office building I kept asking myself, *how much more will my actions cost this man? Since he's been in my life, it seems like I'm just one big financial burden to him—what else will he have to endure to help me?*

We shake hands with the attorney and took a seat in the guest chairs in her office. And it appears that she had already spoken to the school about my case, and makes it pretty clear, "That it's going to be darn near impossible to overturn this one, which is not unusual given these level of charges," she said.

She too believed that the only thing she might be able to negotiate was the reduction of the fines. But the suspension time *would certainly* eat up the rest of my eligibility altogether, which was only about one year.

At that, my Dad said, "Let me ask you a question, Laura, hypothetically, if this young man is innocent—and I'm not saying that he is, but for clarification here—if he is perhaps innocent, who could overturn a charge like this prior to a hearing?"

"Well," she says, as she paused. "That would most likely be, the instructor—but I'm not totally certain about that. However, I must say, Danny, in the twenty-five plus years I've been trying these kind of cases, I have never seen an instructor overturn a decision of this magnitude, or even meet with a student or his parents at this stage of the game.... The instructor, at this juncture, is generally out of the loop; this is solely a legal issue with the University, and I can't be more clear about that."

"I understand, and I appreciate that insight," Danny said. "But just so I'm clear about this, counselor, the instructor, even though this is now a legal issue with the University, would have the power to overturn this, if she could validate such reasons?"

"Perhaps, since she filed the charges. But again, at this point, I doubt very seriously if this particular instructor would even pick up the phone, much less be willing to meet with you guys. Furthermore, if such was the case, she'd better have a damn good reason as to why she would drop three counts of plagiarism for which all occurred within one semester against the same student, or else she could be on the hot seat—if you get my drift," she replied.

My Dad just shakes his head as if to say he understood, while yet in deep thought.

"Unfortunately," she goes on to say, "it's just not a real hopeful situation. Academic misconduct is a serious-serious issue, especially one of this magnitude," she repeats.

Suddenly, we all sat silently for a few seconds while my Dad seemed to be pondering on all this mess I'd gotten myself into. Then he says, as he stood up, "Laura Leslie, I respect your legal opinion. You come highly recommended.... Thank you for seeing us on such short notice, but I would like to explore one other option before hiring an attorney to represent him, is that okay?"

"Sure—absolutely," she said. "Just keep in mind, time is of the essence. The quicker we act the better chance we'll have at reducing these huge fines that will be levied against him."

"Understood, we'll be in touch," my Dad said.

We shake hands and exit.

Once we were back in the car, I quietly asked with tense curiosity, "What do you plan to do? It's pretty obvious I'm out, and it sounds like I definitely need an attorney."

"You don't need an attorney, you need your butt kicked!"

At that comment, there was nothing but silence in the car as he drove back towards campus, again in deep thought. However, his wheels were turning, he was apparently considering an angle that no one believed would turn this dead situation around. It seem to appear, they may have quit on me, but he hadn't.

We end up back at the Athletic Academic Center, in hopes of seeing, Dr. Gurney, the AD of Academics, and this time he's available. He reiterates to us the seriousness of these charges, with empathy too, and felt likewise that hiring an attorney was definitely in my best interest, legally. And with me, not knowing much about much of anything to do with this, I'm starting to get really concerned about all this talk about suspensions, fines and charges—this started to sound like I could possibly go to jail.

But my father seemed to be determined to play out this other option that no one believed that there's any such option left to play. He says, "Dr. Gurney, you know I respect and value your opinion, but let me ask you a question, do you think that this instructor, Ms. Kelser, would meet with Mark and I about this matter, at this point?"

"I doubt very seriously at this point, Danny," he, says. "Once it gets to this stage, it's very unlikely.... It's my understanding that Mark failed to get that sit down after he chose not to respond to *several* of her e-mail's regarding these charges this past summer.... It's now in the hands of the University legal staff," he concluded.

I'm now thinking, *Yeah, Dad, let's hire this attorney and get this over with. I screwed up, its over, let's get on with it and get out of here. This was never meant to be.*

But amazingly, my father was persistent and finally Dr. Gurney relents. He decided to give him the instructor's contact numbers so that he could explore this dead option. And graciously, my father promises to update him as we exited his office. He then pulls me into one of the vacant rooms, and asked, again, "Is there anything else you would like to tell me about this ordeal before I make this call, Mark?"

I'd held it together from meeting to meeting, but now in this vacant office with my defenses down, tears began to fall from my eyes—heavy.

"I'm so sorry, Dad—I apologize for embarrassing you.... I really am sorry about all this.... I know you built relationships with people who trusted that I would do my part based on your word.... You have lost so much over the years tryin to help me, but I'm telling you, Daddy, I really didn't know I was plagiarizing a paper—much less three!"

"Mark, you didn't answer my question, son, is there anything else I need to know about this situation, before I make this call?!" He asked, again.

"No—I've told you everything!"

"Everything?" He asked, once again.

"Everything," I replied, as I wipe away more and more tears.

"Okay, but if you had used these assistance services around here we wouldn't be having this discussion, son.... In fact," he said, "how does Coach Stoops' decision of not offering you that scholarship look to you now? What you need, son, is to learn how to submit to leadership, not be crying about a scholarship."

"Dad—you all I've got.... I don't have anybody else!" I cried out. "I thought I could do this without the academic assistance program.... I'm sorry!"

He then took a deep-deep breath, paused for what seemed like five-minutes, before saying in now a more calmer tone, "Do you truly and clearly understand what's going on here, Mark.... I mean do you really get what's happening right now?"

"Without doubt—completely," I replied with a heavy heart.

"Do you really want to do this?"

"Do what? I did, but they said its over, Dad!"

"I didn't ask you what they said, I asked if you really want to do this?"

"If I could get another chance, yes," I replied. "But that's obviously not happening."

"Says who?" He shockingly asked.

"Says everybody, Daddy!"

"But I didn't ask about what they said." He shot back.

"Well, then, yes, if I could get another chance to make good on my promise."

"Okay—convince me, son—because this next move I'm about to make could cost me everything I've ever stood for at this university, if you are not absolutely and completely sure that you really want to be a student athlete," my Pops said.

"I would not make this mistake again if I could get another opportunity, Dad. I told you a couple of years ago, if you gave me a chance to make right in my life what my family helped make wrong, I would make you proud of me."

Danny pauses and takes another deep breath, and then pulls out his cell and dials the instructor. He steps out of the room to chat, but quickly reenters and looks me directly in the eye and says, "First of all, I believe you. I believe that you didn't have any idea of how to write a paper and properly cite it.

My tears fell even more when I heard these words.

"Look at me, Mark," he said as I raised my head from a position of dejection to a humbled posture of attention.

"I love you—I believe in you, so hold your head up—innocent men don't slump their shoulders and drop their head in defeat.... Hold your chin up through adversity—Everybody else may have quit on you, but I haven't, and more importantly, God hasn't. So stand up straight, and keep your chin up.... Ms. Kelser has agreed to meet with us briefly.... And though she was reluctant, she did agree to at least listen. But we only have about five minutes, if that, she says.... And based on her tone, she does appear to have her mind made up about this matter," he says, as I shook my head in disappointment. "But if you're serious about getting a chance to redeem yourself, son, and once again prove that you still belong, then I think we can get her to reconsider and drop these charges, despite the expert advice we've been given—you up for it?"

Now, I know this man had confidence, but how in the world is he going to get this instructor to drop these charges? So my natural response was just that, "How do you plan to get her to change her mind?"

"Simple—by telling her the truth," he replied. "You're going to look her in the eye and tell her what you failed to tell her this past summer. Ask her to forgive you with a *contrite* spirit, and ask her if she'll give you a second chance to make your last and final impression, you with me? He asked.

"Yes, I understand."

"Look her in the eye and apologize to her and make sure she knows that this is all new to you, that you had no idea what the term plagiarism even meant until now—and that you would make it a point to be the best student athlete on campus if she would give you another chance, understood?" He asked, while coaching me up.

"Understood," I fearfully replied.

"And if you stumble, for any reason, I'll step in and help you explain—cool?"

"Cool," I responded with reservation, to which he then said, "Come on son, I need your faith to pull this off.... You still believe in divine favor, don't you?" He asked.

"Yeah, I need to at this point," I replied.

"I know you're still a lil rattled right now, but is that a yes or a no? I need your confession of faith on this, Mark…. Come on now, you know how this works, *life* and *death* is in the power of *your* tongue.... It's not just all up to God, you have a choice in this matter too.... So, talk to me?"

"Since you put it like that—yes, I believe God can do anything.... He said that He's *no respecter of persons."*

"Then show some faith; *believe you receive,* and let's go get you reinstated," he said with assurance, as he then bowed his head to pray one of the shortest prayers I've ever heard with so much on the table. He simply thanked God for being God; for the opportunity to meet with Ms. Kelser; and for giving me another chance to finish what I started—in Jesus name—Amen."

I suddenly thought to myself, *that's not enough to move the God, I know.*

He must have sensed my thoughts, he stops and says, "*All things are possible to them that believe*—its not how long we plead with God, but its the faith we have in our plea to God.... Now put your faith hat on and let's go get you reinstated."

I, then, said to myself, *well, I guess that cleared up that misunderstood thought about prayer.* And with his ability to call things before they happened, I really had no reason to doubt if he knew his stuff, spiritually. Most things he hit right on target, although, with such a short prayer, I wasn't as quite hopeful as he was about this one. I'm still thinking we needed at least an hour *at the throne of grace* with a few *halleluiahs,* especially after hearing the expert opinions about this all but dead issue.

So, we rushed across campus with urgency to make our scheduled appointment. When we walked into Ms. Kelser's office, there was only one chair in front of her desk surrounded by boxes on top of boxes and files on top of files, with barely much standing room; she was in the process of moving to another space. And such clutter didn't make me feel freer, but rather more intimidated.

My Dad told me to sit while he stood, as Ms. Kelser sat forward in her chair behind her desk with a stern look on her face, waiting for someone to talk. I knew then that this deal was over; she ain't trying to hear nothing I gotta say.

My Dad then thanks her for meeting with us on such short notice. And that he was very appreciative of her time and, as discussed, we would be brief, as her body language further indicated that while she said *yes* to this meeting, she might have regretted it the second we walked through the door, which was expected given the seriousness of these charges.

But he went on to say, that he wanted me to come and share with her face-to-face my position regarding these academic misconduct charges and why I had failed to get back to her promptly, which caused her to go from a straight faced look with him to a disgusted look with me.

So I paused, took a deep breath and said, "Ms. Kelser, first off, I'm really sorry I broke the rules—and even more regretful that I failed to get back to you within the deadline this past summer.... I don't really have any excuses as to why this happened. I obviously plagiarized my work and now understand why I was charged.... But the truth is, Ms. Kelser, I honestly didn't even know what plagiarism was until today…."

She cut me off immediately and said, "You stole material, Mark! And at this point you're going to have to take this up with the university's legal department!"

I dropped my head again and then looked over at my Dad, as if to say, *they said she wouldn't be willing to listen,* while tears began to well up in my eyes again.

But he nods for me to go on—continue.

"I understand that Ms. Kelser, I'm not denying that, but I really didn't know what the term even meant until today, after I discovered that charges had been filed."

"Mark, you stole material—it's as simple as that!"

"Ms. Kelser, I'm sorry. I made a naive mistake, and I wanted to come apologize to you face-to-face in the presence of my father, because without him I wouldn't be here," I shared, as my tears began to now rush out. "He is the sole reason why I got the chance to be a student athlete at OU.... I know this might be too much information, but my Dad is all I got Ms. Kelser, and I feel really bad for letting him down."

"Mark, you violated the rules," she said sternly. "And our rules are pretty clear…. plagiarism is against the law," with her expression clearly indicating that she really didn't believe me, nor was interested in hearing any more of what I had to say. So I withdrew and threw in the towel, as she began posturing herself to end this useless get-together, to which my father picks this moment to speak.

"Ms. Kelser—do you mind?"

"Go right ahead," she replied sarcastically, as would any university instructor who is serious about the rules, regulations and bylaws regarding academic integrity.

My father pauses a moment in an effort to gain her undivided attention and then began to represent his son, perhaps, better than any polished attorney ever could. He starts out by reminding her of the days he previously walked the OU campus, twenty-two years ago, as a freshman on a football scholarship completely clueless as to what to expect socially, academically or athletically.

He, like most first-year student athletes from small towns, often became enamored with the multitude of activities and events on a campus of this size. Fortunately for him, he told her, through many of the freshman orientation programs, he discovered that the University of Oklahoma was well known for its high level of academic excellence and academic integrity; its sense of family and unity whereby the terms we, us, together and our—stood strong.... an institution that took pride in its programs curriculum, looking for ways to inspire its students to excel—not to expel, he told her.

At that comment, I began to have a little hope, as his words of wisdom seemed to change her posture just a bit, as he went on to share: "Mark doesn't have an excuse, Ms. Kelser, but he does have a different set of circumstances that just might reasonably explain his situation."

Ms. Kelser then leans back into her chair as if to say, *continue—I'm listening.*

This is a small-town kid, he told her, who transferred in from a small-town college, may not represent the same level of academic integrity as that of an elite institution like what we have here at the University of Oklahoma. Even though this kid is listed as a junior on paper, technically he was a freshman on campus where everything is moving at a much faster pace. This may have caused these oversights including her all-important e-mail, which went unanswered, despite the numerous attempts she tried reaching out.

And that's an understatement, I thought to myself, as he made that comment.

He went on to say that he wasn't by any means making excuses for me, but was only trying to point out that there could be perhaps an *extenuating circumstance* to be considered here.

With no new change in her posture, my father, and now *attorney,* continued on.

"Mark is indeed guilty of these violations, but as his father, I don't believe he did this intentionally, knowingly, in an attempt to somehow skate through your course, which simply says to me that someone somewhere along the way failed to teach this young man what plagiarism meant and its consequences."

Hoping to get a glimpse of her expression on that comment, she didn't let me down, she simply had—no expression.

"I know this kid, Ms. Kelser," he said with conviction. "And I don't think for one moment that he would *purposefully* violate these rules knowing the consequences, because he knows without doubt, I would be the first to remove his butt from this campus and escort him back to I-40 East, to Arkansas.... Mark is not here on the University of Oklahoma's dime—he's here on my dime.... And it would be incredibly disrespectful to my Alma Mater for me to fund the activity of any student, let alone my own son, who would *deliberately* violate the academic integrity of this institution."

I looked again to see if any of this was getting through, but she still had—no expression. And in closing, he told her that despite the hopeless amount of legal advice we'd received today, in which many predicted with certainty, that this meeting would not likely take place, solidified that this institution still cares about the academic life and welfare of its students.... not first looking for a way to suspend them—but rather to educate them.

I'm thinking, *Now if she doesn't reconsider after that—just take me on to jail.'*

She pauses and then leans forward into her chair, again, looks across her desk at me and then back at him as if she was now working to regain our attention, and finally said, in somewhat more of a receptive tone, "Thanks for sharing—well said."

Then she looks down at a few notes and back at me, and paused again, and then said that I had a lot of guts bringing my dad into a meeting like this, and that most students wouldn't dare bring one of their parents into a discussion of this magnitude hoping for a turn around. And when they did, the parent(s) often came in with excuses, which makes it impossible to help the student. And she appreciated the fact that I didn't do that.

"But however," she says, "after assessing your father's comments and remarks, I don't think he would make such a huge investment in you if he didn't truly believe you were worth that cost, especially since he knows what it takes to be a successful *student athlete* at a major program."

She went on to say that she was *unaware* that I had transferred from a smaller college, which explained why I may have been taking so many hours over the past year, trying to become eligible to participate in sports. And after further evaluation of my transcript, she felt that her course, designed for advanced students who have completed certain other electives, was not quite suited for me. She then paused again, looking at her notes as the tension inside of me starts to overflow with anticipation.

"Therefore, Mark, I'm dropping all charges against you, and will notify all parties of my decision right away."

I just exploded in tears as my Dad stepped over toward my chair and began hugging me as I lean over in my chair in disbelief.

"So hold your head up, Mark," she said. "And go be that student you aspired to be," as she extended her hand to Danny, knowing she had given a decent young man another chance at redemption. "And after today, I'm pretty confident that you are my least concern, Mark Bradley," she added.

So, as the weight of the day's events poured out of him, Danny finally broke too and a tear rolled down his cheek as he thanked her for extending mercy to his son.

"We will forever be grateful to you, Ms. Kelser," he said, as he extended his hand likewise to shake hers.

"You're welcome," she replied with a warm smile. "And by the time you guys make it back across campus, the Athletic Department will have received an e-mail with my decision."

Danny thanks her again, as Mark finally makes it to his feet to properly do the same with a hug. After his embrace, she says, "When you're ready, you can re-take my course at any time.... And the only thing I'll require, is don't enter my classroom thinking that I will remotely remember that any of this ever occurred, are we clear?"

Mark thanks her too, for giving him that second chance to make the last and final impression. As we exited this office, I was overwhelmed with joy and relieved that the good Lord moved on Ms. Kelser's heart. And before exiting the building, Pops grabbed an isolated corner and began to thank God for deliverance in another short prayer, as we both felt the power of God at hand. I then looked him in the eye and said, "Thank you so much Pops, I don't know what I would do without you," as the tears just kept coming.

"Always remember, *prayer is the key to the kingdom, and faith unlocks the gate.* Now get yourself together we got a few people to see, and I'm sure you don't want your boys to see you all mushy like this, do you?"

"No—that would not be good," I said with a light smile.

"Well, wipe your face—let's go reclaim your locker and your spot."

So, we headed back across campus, straight to the Academic Center's office to track down Dr. Gurney to let him know an e-mail is on the way with a reversal of the previous decision—I had been reinstated and cleared of ALL charges.

Once we enter the Academic Center, I asked, "So how do you think they'll respond, given the fact that they saw my situation as being all but done?"

"They're smart people, son. They want to see you succeed," he replied. "I'm sure they may be a lil surprised that we were able to get this overturned, but maybe this encourages them to consider that sometimes the impossible—is possible."

After updating Dr. Gurney of the results but not the conversation in detail, his first response was, "Really—you sure?"

"Yes, sir—I'm pretty certain we didn't misquote her," my Dad replied.

He turns to his computer to check and doesn't see anything. But my father assures him again, and he checks again, and suddenly—there it is. As he silently reads this e-mail, his facial expression said it all! He turns and congratulates Mark with a smile, happy to see this kid get another chance and reiterates the importance of the academic center and their assistance program.

He then turns to my Dad, extended his hand, and says, "Well done, Mr. Bradley."

Danny nods in appreciation and asks, "So we good now?"

"It appears so," Dr. Gurney said with a pleasant smile.

So, over the next year, Mark buckles down and gets focused. He improves his study habits, became that better student, better teammate and even a better player. Mark Bradley, for the first time in his life, despite his family's lack of support, was beginning to live that dream that he had failed to accomplish while living under their roof and control. He was thriving both on and off the field as he helped lead the Sooners to the 2003 National Championship game in New Orleans to take on Louisiana State University, better known as the LSU Tigers. Thus, proving that *with God, all things are truly possible to them that believe!*

But unfortunately, believe it or not, this young man had another untimely setback that, once again, threatened to end it all—for the third time!

Divine Guidance

36

By the spring of 2004, the Sooners were licking their wounds from their loss to LSU as the Tigers gloated as the 2003 National Champions. And unfortunately, once again, Mark was one of the Sooners' wounded troops. He needed surgery again on that same left knee he'd previously injured at UAPB. This would be surgery number three and consequently would take place right before spring classes would begin. And because of the chaos still going on within his family, his Dad would be the only one attending this surgical procedure—and that was just fine with Mark.

Although, when the nurse entered his room with a needle that seemed to be as about as long as his arm—in all due respect to his Dad—Mark simply wanted, his mama! Even at age twenty-two, he still did not like needles. But with the intravenous ('IV') mixed with the anesthesia dripping, within about 6.3 seconds, he was out like a light with a smile on his face.

While Mark is in the recovery room, Danny respectfully calls Denise to inform her that Mark is in surgery and all was well. Mark hadn't seen or even talked to his mother that much since her *"nothing would go right for you until you got right with me,"* comment was made. And when he did make an effort to reach out, as usual, she took shots at both him and his Dad.

Nevertheless, she did make plans to come visit him, *but only after* Mark had somewhat recovered from the early stages of his rehabilitation program, which was great, because Mark didn't want to be on crutches when she came to visit to avoid other negative implications regarding his health, circumstances and situation.

But this time, only my Mom, Braylon and Cassie made the trip to Norman. And it wasn't until fall that she decided to drop in.. And as you may have figured, nothing had changed. It was just the same old-same old stuff between us.

However, with bible studies now re-implemented as a part of my weekly routines, my Dad focused on helping me to *finally* rid myself of some of this anger, fear and timidity that had controlled my life. He began to dig deeper into the values of forgiveness, confessing the word and how to meditate on it. And one of the first steps he pressed me to recommit too, was stop complaining about my family and mother's behavior and start speaking words of hope and life about her.

"And it wouldn't hurt to start inviting her to every game and family event that OU football had scheduled," he continued saying.

This was a major challenge for me, but as a result, I finally felt completely free and at peace about these long-term issues that had been going on for years with my family. And this move began to positively impact his play even more so on the field and his class work, off.

Hence, by week 1, the University of Oklahoma finally offered this young man a full scholarship; by week 7, he became one of the starting receivers for the Sooners, despite having one of the top receiving corps in the country; and by week 10, thanks to a suggestion his father made, regarding the special teams, Mark had become an interesting NFL prospect, with many of them flocking to Norman to get a glimpse of this rising star's performance against conference rival, Nebraska, as Dad sat proudly, watching his son live out the dream, while his Mom watched the conclusion of this wet and rainy game from her hotel room.

He's on center stage, and she chooses to exit the building shortly after being introduced at mid-field, along with Danny as the proud parents of Mark Bradley, on what OU calls—Senior Day.

And as it is with most seniors who are concluding their careers, Mark, as he was being introduced, wept heavily as he hugged his two parents, and thanked them both, especially his father. But, during the ceremony, he would gravitate more toward his Dad after suddenly feeling extremely awkward with his Mom. After all, this was only the second or third time in nearly *twenty-two years* that she's been willing to be around the two of them, together, at the same time.

So, as quickly as Danny recognized this undetected dynamic, he quietly reminded him, "All is well—your Mom is fine—this is your night—enjoy yourself and reflect on how good the Lord has been to you, me and your mother," he said, as the crowd noise began to drown him out. "Now go help Stoops go after another National Title!"

And that we did. This victory would help seal another Big XII Conference Title. It would send this 2004 Sooners team to its second straight National Championship Game, this time in Miami, to challenge the blazing Southern Cal Trojans. But before this game was over, Mark had already begun to feel a lil heat of his own—heat that began to affect his performance stemming from the presence of his mother who is now in attendance.

Afterwards, with a security guard escorting him to his car, Mark walked and signed a few autographs for a host of the beloved Sooner fans, many of whom were always very gracious and kind, reminding him of their memories of watching his Dad's career unfold on that same field, which also led to a shot at the National Title in Miami.

Once he got closer to his SUV and away from the reporters and supporters, as accustomed, he called his Dad on his cell to find that he had already made it back to the house just miles from the stadium.

"Glue—you're starting to look like an NFL caliber wide-out, son," my Dad said.

"You think so?" I asked.

"Without a doubt—you are becoming a Sunday afternoon kind of guy."

"Cool—but what's up with this thing, Glue?" I asked.

"Well, every ball I've seen thrown to you, seems to stick to you like glue!"

"Yeah—okay," I replied with a smile kind of liking this nickname. "So what's up, you going to dinner with us?

"No, no—you go ahead and do dinner with your mother and sister. You don't get to see them too often—it's the right thing to do, son," he replied. "Plus, let's not stress her, she's still not comfortable around the two of us together."

"Dad, I'm fully aware of that but at some point she's got to get over this non-sense," I replied. "Its crazy for me not to *ever* be able to spend time with my two parents without somebody in my family feeling uncomfortable about it."

"In due time, she'll be fine, Mark—right becomes wrong when it's forced."

"I understand. But let me ask you this: When did my mom leave the game?"

"Why you ask?"

"Because I could almost sense when she left the stadium."

"Really—how so?"

"Because—I just felt different the entire second half," I said with certainty.

"I think she and Cassie left a lil early, what's the problem?"

"Well, I'm with the whole idea of inviting her out more, but for some strange reason, I suddenly realized I don't feel like I play as well when she's in the stands.... It's almost like I can feel her negative energy."

"Did you have that concern in the past, prior to OU?" My Dad asked.

"No.... This is somethin I just began to feel." I replied.

"This may still be a forgiveness issue, Mark."

"Maybe so, but I don't think so, Dad."

"Well, if you are planning on extending your career, you better get adjusted to her being in the stands, because if I have anything to do with it, son, she will be there."

"I understand that, but I just feel stressed and anxious to perform when she's around. Almost like I start trying too hard to prove to her that I can make it without all that negative input coming from them."

"I get that, but you gotta separate your feelings from your faith," He said. "It sounds like you're having an emotional reaction when she comes around, whether you're on the field or not. That line of thinking is fear based, son, not faith based.... And what you need is to stand on your faith, knowing that all is well.... But give some prayer time to it before you walk into her hotel room—the goal is to stay out of strife with your mother and family at all times, Mark, do you understand me?"

I agreed to do so, but as soon as I stepped in their room, things began to get heated up almost immediately. And my step-dad had made the trip by the way, who was definitely the most civil one among my family members at this point. I think he had started seeing the injustice going on between me, my father and my entire family.

"Congratulations, Mark, we saw your touchdown on the news, we left at half-time," Cassie said.... My Mom then shot out, as Braylon was giving me a hug, "I also heard that you're *still* not on scholarship, is that true?"

"Why—you ready to contribute?" I asked politely, knowing she was picking at me.

"For what? You're doing aright—plus, most of our money goes towards your sister's modeling gigs," she replied.

Wow—some things just never change, I thought to myself, *if she only knew, as a parent what that really sounds like.* But hey, I must walk in love, speak words of hope and forgive moment-by-moment, right?

Meanwhile, I noticed a lot of shopping bags on one of the two beds, so what a great time to inquire about them, since we're discussing contributions. And like the Pine Bluff Commercial, my sister joyfully tells all the business.

"We went to the Mall yesterday and mama bought some nice stuff," she said as she begins to pull things out the bag and show them off.

My Mom then proudly asked, "Have you seen my new SUV?"

Cassie says, "Yeah—its sweet," as she walked over to the window, pulling back the curtain to point it out to me, "Its the red one."

"That is a nice ride," I replied, as Braylon sat back taking it all in.

"And we're also building a new room on to the house," my mom goes on to add.

"Really." I said agitatedly. "How can you afford to do all this but you don't ever have any money to help me with any of my stuff, Mom?" I asked, knowing her answer.

"Boy, please—what do you need money for? You say your daddy is taking care of you.... don't forget we raised you, it's time for your father to do his part."

As usual, so much for civility!

"Actually—you right, I really don't need your help," I replied.

Sensing my thoughts, she looks at me glibly and said, "Will you stop trippin?!"

And once again, I felt as if my own mom was competing, not just with my Dad, but now even with me. And it was this kind of craziness that made me not want to be around my family much—there was just way too much envy and strife and competition going on for them to be civilized. But after considering my Dad's advice, I chose not to bite the bait, but I did decide to opt out.

"Okay, I'll talk to you guys tomorrow," I said and walked out the door.

Moments later, my step-dad rushes up behind me to apologize for my mom's behavior. He tries to press a fifty-dollar bill into my hand, but I fought it off.

"I'm good," I told him.

But he insisted and asked if I would please take it. And I again informed him that I was good—it's just the principle of it with me, I told him. And he was patient and understood, but insisted I take the fifty dollars anyway. And as I approached my car, to keep this conversation from extending, I took the money, told him I appreciated it and to have a safe trip back. This was the moment I began to feel bad for my step-dad. He had walked right into the middle of a family full of undeniable chaos.

Leaving the hotel that night, I realized that I needed to stop taking what she says and does so personally. Because at the end of the day, until she forgives herself, and gets rid of her personal bitterness towards my father, she'll never be able to treat me right.

So over the next few weeks of trying to reason with my mother about all these lies, insinuations, and slanderous attacks against my father, I finally broke down again. And as usual, she was cold and disinterested in anything I had to say about it.

Therefore, after sharing my disappointment with my Dad for the five-hundred-and-fiftieth-time, regarding my mother's unwillingness to hear me out, he suggested an idea that would *forever change* how my family dealt directly with me, which brought to a halt, many of these silly games they'd been playing for the past twenty-two years.

"Documentation beats conversation twenty-four hours a day, seven days a week. So if you want to speak to your mother, uninterrupted, start writing her—send her an e-mail to voice your feelings about the situation. But make sure the tone of your words is that of love—not strife, Mark.... It's one thing to share your feelings, but it's a another thing to *argue* with her about your feelings," he advised. "So choose your words carefully, this is your mother you're talking about here. But be honest, straightforward and don't send anything until you've read it to me—you understand?"

I understood, I told him. So once I hung up, that same night, I sat down in front of my computer and did just that. And I thought this was a great idea, since I write *much better* than I best articulate things. This would be a good way to share what I'm thinking and feeling about my life—uninterrupted.

Mom—since it appears to me that you won't listen to me face to face or by phone, I thought I'd try writing you in hopes of getting through to you. I have come to accept the fact that you are in denial about many of the events regarding you, me and my Dad. And to be honest about it, I'm tired of being treated as if I'm completely clueless about these events. I know exactly what has and hasn't happened between us the past 22 years. I've been evaluating this thing ever since you made the announcement that this man was my father.... and I decided that I am not gonna allow anyone else in the family to continue to disrespect him while I stand by and do nothing.... The man has been a really good Dad to me for as long as I can remember, despite the family's attempts to keep us apart.

I am now fully aware that he didn't abandon me as you sold all of us on over the years—nor did he intentionally neglect all of his duties as my father to go play football knowing he had a son to tend too. I'm not saying he's perfect and hasn't made some mistakes, but the truth is the man had a wife and a ready-made life, when you decided to tell him about me—and I believe because he didn't instantly sprint to Pine Bluff to be whatever you thought he should be—it appears that you took it very personal—not realizing the multitude of changes and adjustments that maybe he had to make in his own life just to someday be involved in my life.

As a consequence, you began to slander and attack this man's character in an effort to protect yourself from the reality of what he might do or say next. I've said this once, and I'm saying it for the last time; my father has shown more love toward me and has taught me more about life than my entire family has shown and taught me altogether.

He made the sacrifices and put forth the effort that is worthy of respect. He forgave you and the family for all of the things you guys have said and done towards him—so why don't you forgive him? We ask God for forgiveness all the time—so why don't we practice at forgiving one another?

In closing, I must say, I don't know the Danny Bradley you guys keep talking about. This man provided opportunities for me that no one else in my family could've or would've provided.... But instead of you being delighted about that, you seem to have a problem with that. Why? Is it perhaps you, Mom, that neglected me—and not him. It seems to be you, mother, keeping this senseless war going—not him. And maybe it's also you, Mom, that's really struggling with loving me—not him.

So, despite this sad song you and the rest of the family keep singing, I've grown to trust the man, believe in the man, and quite frankly, I've grown to love this man. After all, he is my father—mother. And I'm copying him on this e-mail, so that there is no misunderstanding as to what was said or not said. If you wanna respond, please respond back by way of e-mail so that you can likewise share exactly how you feel—uninterrupted.... Mark

My Mom's first response, to no surprise, was a phone call—not an e-mail. She called my cell and I chose not to answer in hopes of her putting her thoughts on paper. I knew my e-mail would be explosive given the fact that I'd never shared these things in such detail with her. As you well know by now with my family, I wasn't allowed to talk much—just listen.

And after not being able to get through on and about her fifth attempt, she calls my Dad. "Danny—this is Dee, did you get an e-mail from Mark?"

"Yeah—I did," he said back.

"Can you tell me what's going on with him? I don't understand. Mark has had a good life; he was a happy kid; we kept him in church; he had great support from the family. I just don't understand! I tried to call and talk to him about this but he's not answering his phone. Can you tell me what's going on?" She asked.

Shocked and trying to pretend as if none of my comments were true, he simply said to her with kindness, "It appears to me, Dee, that Mark has a totally different take on his up bringing."

"But I can't even get him to answer so we can talk about it," she said desperately.

"Well, the e-mail I read requested that you respond back to him by way of e-mail, to avoid any misunderstanding of what may be said between the two of you.... So why don't you honor that request and get back to him by way of e-mail and likewise tell him how you feel about these statements he's made."

She pauses and then agrees to do so. Again, little did she know, the biggest fan my mother had—was my Dad! And at this point in the game, I believe most folks would have understood if he had chose to just smooth cut off any and all communication with her and anybody else associated with them. But instead, every chance this man got he worked diligently at helping me understand how to *forgive her* while trying to show her *how to love me*—now that's strong!

So as she tried playing the same *woe is me game,* he simply steered her back on point by saying, "Just meet his request, and respond by way of e-mail and tell him how you feel Dee."

Then there was a pause in the conversation; she's on center stage now. She's now having to deal directly with the source himself—ME.

"Just do what I've done, Denise—tell him the truth."

Surely, at this juncture, she would just let it go and apologize to this man and set the record straight before even responding to my e-mail. But she chose to hang on to the old, and said again, "I just don't understand what's going on with Mark—I don't get this sudden change in him."

In an effort to help her process this situation again, my Dad says, "Denise, here's the best advice I can give you...you can't conquer what you won't confront.... Don't let your past rob you of your future with your son."

"Okay, thanks for sharing," my mom replied, and just hung up.

The next day, I had an e-mail from my mom, fresh from the river of denial.

Dear Mark—I didn't get a book on how to raise you. I did what I had to do at the time, and God says we must forgive and let go. I have asked God to forgive me, now I'm asking you to forgive me. You got to move on past this, son. The past is the past, so get over it! It's over and done! Like I said over the years, one day you will understand when you have a few kids someday. As I said, its time your Dad start doing something, I've done my part, we raised you. I love you more than life itself son. So why don't you move on from this? — Love, Mom

Wow! I thought. *Are you serious? Why don't "**I**" move on?* Man, her denial was not just a pond—it was now a raging river! I forwarded her e-mail to my Dad and quickly began working on my response. I didn't want any grass to grow under this latest e-mail.

Mom—how can the past be the past when all you guys do is constantly bring it up? On this side, my Dad says very little about you or the family. In fact, I can't even recall one time that he made an effort to cut you down or discourage me about my relationship with you or the family. Has he defended himself, yes, but never has he intentionally tried to cut you down by reminding me of something you did in the past. If anything he encourages me to develop my relationship with you, not prevent me from having one.... And when I try to bring this to your attention, I'm told to shut up and stop lying, as if I don't know what's up. However, we do agree about one matter, you did what you thought was best—but you did what was best for you—not me, mama. And to be honest, I don't need to have a few kids to understand what mistakes not to make as a parent. That response is just another way to justify your actions, mom. And finally, this is one question I've always wanted to ask for quite some time. If you loved me so much, then why do you fight against my father and I so much, still? And why does it matter to you who does what for me, if you both love me? What you do with me and for me shouldn't be based on anything he does for me and with me—Mark

I checked my inbox periodically over the next few hours, but there was no reply. If I knew my mother, no new e-mail meant she was struggling with trying to wrap her mind around a multitude of things she now not only knew I knew, but now knew I understood. And as it turned out, two days went by before I finally got an e-mail response. But this time, her tone was just a little bit softer.

Mark—baby, I have read your e-mail's over and over again and I am now well aware of how you feel, and you have every right to be hurt and upset. There are no words to express how much my heart is in pain to know I have hurt you and your father like this. What I did was try to please everyone in the family and just got caught up. And you're right, it doesn't matter who does what for you. I am still your mother, and he is still your father regardless who has the most money or spent the most time. One does not replace the other. You are the son of both Denise and Danny. It was my choices that caused a lot of this confusion and for that I am sorry from the bottom of my heart.

I admit, my choices were not the best and I have learned from my mistakes through you and I pray that you can forgive me. As for your father, I never meant to cause him any pain when it came to you. And you're right, I am controlling and often have a problem with listening. I am too quick to try and explain away things and I didn't really listen to you over the years like a mother should have. Because I wanted the best for you, better than I had, I was overbearing and afraid. I wanted so badly for things to turn out right for you that it caused me to make some bad decisions along the way, Mark. And I would do anything to undo the damage I have caused you and your father. And I hope and pray we can get past this, together.

I promise I will do better by trusting in you and your ability to make responsible decisions. And I will be there to help when you need me. I will also do better by your father. You belong to the both of us and communication is key. So thanks for letting me know how you feel because now I have no excuses. But with your help I can break the chains of control. So again I apologize and promise to do better—Love, Mom

Before I responded, I chose to call my Dad with the good news.

"I saw that—so it's time to back off—mission accomplished," he said. "Just love her and give her a chance to redeem herself, Mark.... And don't expect her to be perfect."

And I agreed to do so, but after thinking about it a lil more, I really only had two questions: Was she really being honest, or just saying whatever she needed to say to save face? *Which is it?* I thought as I pondered my last response.

Mom—people can change and I know you can change—I've changed. But I personally find it very hard to believe that this suddenly all makes sense to you. I am not that same little kid that my family thought was so clueless and dumb.... I've been trying to tell you how I felt for at least ten plus years, and you've known the truth about all this for the past twenty plus years, but now you're thanking me for finally bringing it to your attention? I'm now concerned about your "sudden change." Nevertheless, I love you, mama, and all I ever wanted was for you to genuinely love me in return—Mark

I wasn't expecting a response back from her but I got one, and this time it was quick.

Mark—I have been praying daily, asking the Lord to give me the strength to change and become a better person. But you're right—I have been in denial. I wasn't trying to hear how you felt or what you had to say about anything, but after reading your e-mail's over and over again, I feel your pain. It brought tears to my eyes and sadness to my heart. I've been taking a class at my church about this controlling spirit I have. Even this past Sunday the preacher talked about change and that we can only change ourselves, and not anyone else. And with God's help, change is possible. And finally, I never thought you were dumb. I am so proud of the person you've become, and I will tell anyone, you can learn from your children, if you listen. I know I am on the right track now, and with prayer you and I will work this out, son, one day at a time. That way, the change will last. And tell your dad I said thanks from the bottom of my heart and I appreciate him for all he has done and is doing for you—Mom

I too decided to respond quickly to share my last thoughts.

Mom—I love you and forgive you, and thank you for finally-finally coming clean about this, it really means a lot to me—Mark.

As I sent this final e-mail, my emotions took over once again. I guess you might be thinking, this is about the crying-est dude on the face of the earth. But y'all just don't know how much pain and agony I've been feeling all these years. This is my mother man! And it's been so-so hard seeing my own family conscientiously discourage me from having a relationship with my father for twenty-two years, and for no just cause at all. That's a hard pill to swallow, especially when the father in question—*is a good man.*

So if there ever was a relationship between them, I now know why it couldn't have worked. I couldn't imagine my parents being married, or even being an item, they were just so different in areas that mattered so much. But as these emotions continued to leak out of me, despite what I already knew about my father, her admission caused me to appreciate him even more.

And I began to wonder even more, how he did it. How he managed to deal with all these years of *resentment* and *slander* and *defamation* from someone who should have been one of his biggest supporters—amazed me. Had she truly gotten over what has kept her in bondage where my father is concerned, or was she simply trying to pacify me, now knowing I could articulate these truths? Was this all just smoke and mirrors, to divert my attention in an effort to keep me from sharing my feelings with the rest of the family, which would no doubt, shake up the entire Davis household.

Whatever the case, I prayed that this would be the moment my beloved mother would rise above these trivial and senseless acts of *selfishness* and *division* and unify her thoughts; open up her heart and finally become that loving and caring nurturer the good Lord desires her to be just as He had molded my Dad into becoming that loving father who was willing to make these life changing sacrifices for me.

So, what will it be, I intently speculated? *Will it be love, life and a true loving relationship? Or just more self-centeredness, separation and division?*

37

Divine Reaction

It was now about 3 p.m. on Christmas Eve when I left Norman to go have dinner with my Dad in Dallas before traveling on to Miami for the 2005 Orange Bowl Game. I was somewhat excited that after twenty-two years my mother *finally* admitted the truth. Although I didn't quite feel her admission was *totally* sincere, it was a start. And believe me, I desperately wanted to believe her.

It had become obvious that as long as *"I"* didn't say anything, *"she"* would have kept right on doing perhaps everything she had previously done; attacking and blaming my Dad for the relationship she failed to foster with me, without even blinking. And sadly, I had covered for her for twenty years, without even blinking.

So as I entered the Dallas city limits, I was optimistically excited about our future together as a family, hoping that my Mom could finally get over these unjustifiable issues she have had with my Dad. And what better time of the year to express some of the happiness I felt than Christmas.

As I pulled up to my Dad's house in Colleyville, dinner was already set, laid out and ready to go. And surprisingly, Salena, his former fiancé was there to prepare the meal. She had relocated back to Dallas in hopes of reestablishing her relationship with my father, after having her marriage annulled, which further documented that this man saw forgiveness as a way *of life*, not just a way *to life*. And it was nice to finally see him able to move back into a house again, now that I was entering my last semester in school, and finally on scholarship.

Nevertheless, in the middle of dinner, as we began to share gifts, I passed my father a Christmas card that I'd been waiting for the right time to share. As he took it and began to read it aloud, Salena held on to her gift to present, as she listened in cheerfully. She was fully aware of the emotional wear and tear we both had been through.

Dad—After evaluating all the information that I've received from Agents around the country, I've decided that the best Representative I could team up with, if I have any shot at extending my football career—is you. And by the way, NO is not an option. Merry Christmas—Mark

He paused, looked up at me, and said, "I'll think about it."

"You'll think about it," I replied. "I'm your son!"

He glanced at the card again and then back at me, and said, "I'll think about it."

But unbeknownst to me, my father had already taken and passed the National Football League Players Associations rigorous and meticulous entrance exam, which also involves an extensive credit and criminal background check. His time as a front office executive with the Cowboys had familiarized him with the Collective Bargaining Agreement (CBA), which prepared the way for a smooth transition.

However, he was having second thoughts as to whether he really wanted to mix business with parenting. Again, he was my father first, and anything that threatened this privilege and responsibility would not be considered.

So after exchanging a few more gifts, being the focused father that he is, he asked Salena for some private time with me, which she respectfully grants, as we head upstairs to the media room to chat.

One of the many things I really liked about my father is that he was a communicator—always ready to listen first and then share, which flies in the face of my mom's claim that such was not the case. And though the hot topics with me were many, his primary focus was helping me heal and restore that relationship with my beloved mother. Reconciliation was the name of the game with him, but he worked harder to get me to understand that such was not possible without forgiveness.

"You good?" He asked. "You feel better about your situation with your mom?"

"Yeah—I feel a lil better about it," I replied.

"You sure, I sense some reservations.... Sounds like you still have mixed emotions about this new position she's taken?" He asked again.

"I guess it's just hard for me, knowing that my mother would take this thing this far, keeping all this mess going all this time."

"I understand, but now is the time to really focus on the positives, Mark.... *Forgiveness does not keep a record of the wrongs."* He said with concern.

"I think I'm walking in forgiveness, at least I hope I am.... But you saw in her responses, she had a tough time admitting the truth."

"But lets not negate how big of a step that was for her, son.... It's not easy for anybody to admit these kind of truths, Mark."

"I guess my concern is whether her admission was sincere, especially with the way she fought to hang on to all that garbage, Dad," I said, still slightly broken. "And what does that tell you about the rest of the family—who had to know what my mom has been doing was wrong, no matter how they viewed it," I replied, angrily.

"Perhaps," my Dad replied.

"If I knew, I know doggone well they knew! And in church every single Sunday!"

"I understand, but we've had this conversation before, Mark, it takes more than just going to church and accepting Christ, He must also become Lord of our lives, too. And yes, they should have known better, *but all of us are like sheep having gone astray, son, but the Lord laid on Jesus the iniquity of us all,"* he said, as my tears began to well up.

Then he went on to share that the problem with many of us in the church is we have an identity crisis, we don't really know who we are spiritually, which allows the world to pollute us with all kinds of things that lead to making many of these bad decisions, with a skewed perspective on God's word and viewpoint on these matters. Therefore, we never learn how to deal with life and death; success and failure; happiness and sadness; joy and pain, which always leave us stressed and depressed and even suicidal, unable to deal with the pressures of life. And our children are growing up in these kind of environments, leaving them damaged and torn.

"So you think that's where she's been missing it?" I asked with frustration.

"Its the same place we all been missing it, son—we either don't know God's word on these matters, or we're unwilling to be obedient to what we do know to be right," he said, as he raises his hand admitting his guilt in both areas.

"Well, I want my Mom to change, but I'm not sure if she will change,"I said.

"Are you not willing to give her a chance to make good?" He asked.

"I'm just saying, it bothers me that she had to be forced into admitting the truth."

"Understood, but you gotta give her a chance to make this right, Mark."

"But twenty-two years, Daddy! And she still struggled with admitting the truth? She should have been seeking me out, not the other way around."

"God will *forgive* any man for a lifetime of sin, if he repents, son. And if you expect to be forgiven, Mark, then you gotta practice forgiving others."

"Dad, I forgive her, but I don't really trust her sincerity."

"I respect that, but just be careful to not hold grudges, Mark.... You gotta give her a chance to make this right, even if you have to forgive her again, again and again. I'm not the perfect father either, but I don't have to be *the perfect* father to share with you God's *perfect message*.... That doesn't make me a hypocrite, it makes me human."

"Trust me, I am praying daily that my Mom and I can someday have the kind of relationship we have Dad, but she just keeps doing the same thing over and over again."

"And I'm saying, so do you and me for that matter. And thank God, He doesn't judge a man based on his performance, but rather in his trust in Christ.... Once your mom begin to truly trust the Lord in these areas where she's struggling, she'll turn from it."

"Well maybe he should judge us on our performance, because she's just not gettin it."

"If He did, son, who would be worthy enough to receive His blessings, Mark?" He asked. "No one, no not a one," he added. "But He loves us anyway.... And gave us His righteousness and took our sin.... We might see your Mom's mess, but God definitely see's her best, just remember that, son."

That comment seemed to strike a reasonable cord with me as I simply tried to understand more of this spiritual perspective on things in life. But, by the look on my face, he could tell I wasn't really grasping these words of wisdom. So he decided to take this lesson a step further, which is always what I ended up loving the absolute most about this man—his candid honesty. You see, my mom's telling of the truth was often meant to hurt, harm or hinder in someway, but my Dad's telling of the truth was often meant to bless me in someway, even if he knew it would hurt.

He then opens up his briefcase, pulls out an envelope and places it on the table. He nods for me to look at it. I picked it up and opened the envelope and began looking at these gruesome pictures of what appears to be a baby boy, a tiny-tiny baby boy. There were about ten of them. Being startled and stunned, wondering what is going on here, led me to ask without even looking up, "What is this? And who is this?"

I didn't get an immediate response, so as I looked up to get that answer, his face was flooded with tears, which caused me to sit back not knowing how to react to this. This was the first time I'd seen my Dad cry-cry. So as I sat there anticipating his response, Salena enters the room with water and sees his pain. She then sits down next to him and began consoling him by rubbing his back, as she, too, began to weep a bit as she notices the pictures I was holding in my hand.

Suddenly, my Dad said through his tears, "That's your baby brother.... He didn't make it.... Salena's amniotic sac ruptured at seventeen weeks and they had to take the baby at nineteen weeks because of the multitude of complications she began to have physically.... We didn't go down lightly, we swung for the fence believing we had the victory.... We may have lost this battle, but I assure you we haven't lost the war."

My own tears began to resurface as I tried to process this horrific story, obviously feeling their pain in every way I could feel pain.

But he went on, "I wanted to tell you a few months ago, but you had so many other issues going on I didn't want you to be bombarded with more distractions," he said lovingly. "But now seemed like the perfect time."

Then he goes on to share what no one in my family would have ever shared inside or outside the church. "Let me first say, I'm sorry for failing to live up to the higher standard.... *Sex, and the lust thereof outside marriage, is sin....* This was an act of selfishness not an act of love.... You should always be able to *see bits and pieces of God character in your father,"* he said.

"Pops, trust me, I do.... The fact that you would even share somethin like this, knowing that you didn't have too, is character," I replied.

"The point is, none of us are perfect, we fail by word, deed, and thought.... So give your mother a chance, son.... She doesn't have to be perfect for you to have a cordial relationship with her."

Suddenly, I felt compelled to come clean too, not realizing at the moment that his analogies were starting to change my heart right there on the spot.

"Well, I must also admit, I haven't been living right in that area either.... I don't know of any kids I have out there but I'm guilty too, Dad."

"Sounds like we both need to go a lil deeper into the word and right this wrong, son. The Lord is not trying to keep us from the good things He's given us to enjoy in life, but rather trying to protect us from the many pit falls that often accompany having kids out of wed-lock... But the point is, though my shortcomings appear to have only indirectly affected you, your mother's failures have obviously directly affected you, making it harder for you to forgive one versus the other, but both have failed you."

The doorbell rings as Salena gets up to go answer it, but says before exiting, "Only patience and walking in love with your mom is going to give her the courage to step through that door of reconciliation and restoration...God has already forgiven her."

"I understand," I replied, as we all wipe away a few more tears, thankful that I've grown a lil closer to knowing how to walk more upright in the fruit of the spirit.

As she exits, my father says, as he brings this much needed session to a close, "What I do might not *always* represent who I am, son, but I am in right standing with God; *justified by faith in what Christ did on the cross, not based on my performances.* Living right is a by-product of God's grace, not based in our own strength to perform it.... Your mom will get it together, Mark, so call her and delightfully wish her a Merry Christmas."

As he walks out the room, I just sat in deep thought torn between my flesh and my spirit; my mother and my father; and my anger and my love for my family. This session taught me something new, as they always do, but nothing stood out more to me than the old; my father is my mom's biggest fan and the best representative she had—with me.

A few days later, when our team plane landed in Miami, I was feeling pretty good after having Christmas in Dallas with my father; certainly a week to remember. This was the Christmas that may have gotten me over the hump. I was ready to just love my mother, regardless, after this visit. I'd seen him do it unconditionally, so I knew it could be done, even though I was still disturbed as to how one parent could share, *voluntarily*, his deepest and most painful sinful acts in tears, hoping to teach me something new, while the other would *pridefully* deny knowing of any such things, which always hinders the possibility for growth.

Nevertheless, I was about to play in my second consecutive National Championship game—a-once-in-a-lifetime opportunity. As we deplaned, I took my headphones off, shut down my iPod and called this *courageous* father of mine to let him know we had arrived. And again, being the *focused father* that he is, he made sure I understood the number of eyes that would be watching my every move. And to enjoy myself; being where I'm suppose to be; doing what I'm suppose to do, and doing it with class.

"Have you heard from your mom?" He asked. "Is she coming to the game?"

"Don't know…. but surprisingly, we haven't talked since Christmas Day," I replied.

"Well, have you called her?"

"No, she said she'd be in touch with me," I replied.

"You might want to call her again and see if she's coming down to the game."

"If you don't mind, I'd like to take the wait and see approach. I'm kind of hoping that she doesn't.... As I told you, I just don't feel comfortable when she's in the stadium.... I don't like that negative energy she brings, Pops."

"Mark, son, your feelings are coming from the way you are choosing to think about this thing.... So, change your thoughts and it'll change your feelings," he said.

"Dad, I'm trying to think right about it, you know that."

"I do. But you gotta see it right before you can do it right, son.... These are just negative responses to negative thoughts toward someone whom you had a lot of negative experiences with," my Dad said. "So stop trying to prove you can make it without her, less you get caught up into this game, too.... But I'll call your mom and see what's going on," he said.

A few days later, Danny is making his way through Miami International Airport when his cell phone rings—it's a representative from the nations newspaper.

"I'm a writer with USA Today, do you have a minute?" She asked.

"Yes, go ahead," as he stops to grab his pen and note pad.

"Thank you for your time, sir. Our production staff has selected the Bradley's as our game-day cover story and we are just fascinated with the uniqueness of Mark's path of playing at the *same* high school, *same* university, *same* jersey number, competing for the *same* National Title, in the *same* Bowl Game, in the *same* city, as his dad played in exactly twenty years ago. And we also hear according to Mark that you are not only his father, but soon to be his agent, is that true?" The rep asked.

"I guess so, if he said so," Danny replied, with his son's determination to hire him.

"Well, we think you guys have an amazing story! In fact, after doing a lil research, we discovered that you and Mark may be the first ever player/agent/father/son combo in the history of the NFL," she replied with enthusiasm. "So, we'd like to make you guys apart of our game day feature story—would you allow us to invade your space for about an hour tomorrow, to shoot some pictures for the story?"

As Danny pauses from taking notes, he asks, "Have you met with the University officials to determine when Mark might be available?"

"Yes, we have," the rep, replied. "He will be available between 1 and 3 p.m. But unfortunately, Mark said he could not commit to the story if you didn't approve of it, and that he would not participate unless you participated."

"Sure," Danny replied as he entered his taxi. "1 p.m. tomorrow is fine."

So we did the shoot and all went well—it was fun. The USA Today camera people were great and it indeed only took about an hour to do both the interview and photo shoot. And I must say, this was a special-special moment. How many guys get the chance to do something like this with their father, or are even in a position do something this special with their father? And how close was I of not ever having the luxury and privilege of experiencing this awesome moment with my father—*priceless!*

On another note, my Dad wasn't able to make direct contact with my mom and it's now a couple of days before the game. As we are having our traditional pre-game talk, my cell is ringing constantly from people I didn't even know. So, I stopped answering it.

We talked about the week's activities, how well the Orange Bowl committee managed to make this week a great experience for everyone. But after checking messages, surprisingly, there's one from my mom saying that she had an Agent that wants to represent me. I'm thinking, *Mom, come on—you are not out there talking to agents about representing me!*

Then I get this text from my mom, as we're chatting, saying that she and a relative have bought plane tickets to Miami, and that they had already talked to my father about tickets to the game.

I then began to read the first part of the text aloud. And his first response was no response, which then I ask, "Can you believe that? My mom has been talking to Agents!"

"The Agent more than likely contacted her, son, not the other way around," he replied.

"I understand that, but still pass his number on to me don't act as my liaison, especially with the kind of relationship we have. Furthermore, you'll like this, you know the ticket rules right?"

"I do," Danny replied.

"You know they know the ticket rules, right?"

"They do," Danny replied again.

"Well—listen to this text.... '*Mark, me and one of your relatives decided we are coming to the game and need two tickets. I've already talked to your father, I'll see you in Miami*.... I guess as usual, they're just gon Bo-Guard their way into this thing."

"Well, let me give her another call," my father said.

"She has had plenty of time to let me know if she wanted to come to the game, she knows doggone well she hasn't talked to you about tickets?"

"No, I didn't catch her.... But its now forty-eight hours before game time and tickets will be scarce and extremely expensive, at this point," Danny said with concern.

"I wouldn't have any problems, if you can't find any tickets.

"Mark, all is well, son, she's your mother."

Nevertheless, our buses were here—it was time for us to head to an undisclosed hotel, which is common the night before a Championship game.

"Keep checking your messages—just in case she calls again," my Dad says.

"I will," I said, as my cell seems to keep constantly ringing with unknown numbers appearing on the screen. "But in the meantime, please change my number?" I asked.

And he agreed to do so first thing the next morning, and said, "As soon as the old number is inactive, make sure you text your mother with the new, otherwise she'll claim *you* changed it to hide from her."

"No—she'll claim *you* changed my number to hide me from her," I said with a grin.

"You got a good point there, so, never mind, I'll text your mom your new number once the old goes cold, cool?"

"Yeah—I thought so," I responded with a smile, as my teammates, coaches and other staff people begin to emerge in the lobby ready to board the buses.

Once I got my bags from the concierge desk, he and I headed outside to the buses. I handed them to the handlers, who were loading them into the undercarriage, giving me a chance to hug my Dad one last time before we departed to the next hotel.

"We let the one last year get away, Pops, but if we come away with this one, this ring belongs to you.... I'll call you for our pre-game prayer once we get to the stadium," I shot out as I faded toward the team bus.

The next morning, game day, a delivery boy is dropping off a USA Today at every room at our team hotel, I noticed the front page as I was headed to breakfast. The headline read, *"At Orange Bowl; Football Dreams are in the Genes."*

The article featured the pictures they'd taken of us on the beach a few days ago. And by the time I had finished reading the article, I decided to give him a jingle.

"Have you seen the story in the USA Today?" I asked.

"No, not yet.... How they do?"

"I thought they did a good job," I replied while re-reading through again.

"What's up, you sound a little down?" He immediately asked.

"Well—for one, this cell rung all freaking night, until I flipped it off at about 1 a.m., and two, my Mom called."

"And?"

"She's *already* in town and needs both a place to stay and two tickets."

"Okay, where is she?" My father urgently asked.

"Not sure but I told her you might be able to help her find a place to stay, but I doubted very seriously if either one of us would be able to locate two tickets at such late notice. And, as usual, she didn't quite like my answer."

"I'll take care of it," he replied calmly. "You just go handle your business.... get your mind on your game, son.... I got this."

"And whichever one of my relatives she brought with her bout to get knocked completely da hell out."

"What happened," Danny asked.

"I heard him in the back ground clowning, running off at the mouth!"

"Mark, listen to me, son…turn your cell phone off…and get focused and ready to play…I got this!"

The first call Danny makes after hanging up with Mark was to the cell phone company, and then, he calls his business partner Jackie, who has flown in for the game to help Danny with marketing Mark's future endorsement platform, which would begin as soon as the clock strikes midnight. And she has worked with Danny long enough to know at least some of the deal between he, Denise and the rest of her family. So therefore she is not surprised that Dee showed up at the last minute practically unannounced, needing tickets and with no place to stay.

"Do me a favor Jack—call Dee and find out what's their location in the city, I'm a little too upset to make that call right now."

"What happened this time—I thought they had worked everything out?" She asked.

"It's a long story—but don't promise her any tickets or a place to stay just yet until I figure out both. Just tell her I told you to call and I'd see what I could do."

And she did so as asked. He then began making calls in search of two game tickets and a hotel room as Denise answers Jackie's call.

"Dee, Danny asked me to give you a call to find out what's your situation?"

"Well, we just found a place to stay, but we are in need of two tickets to the game."

"Okay—I'll pass it on, but just know it will be tough for them to locate two tickets for a game of this magnitude without somebody trying to get over," Jackie said.

And Dee replied plaintively, "Yeah, I figured as much. I've been trying to call Mark to tell him not to worry about finding us a place to stay, but apparently his cell number appeared to have changed."

In an upbeat tone Jackie said, "Well I'm sure they both would be happy to hear that you found a hotel room, and if anybody can pull off the ticket thing—it's Danny."

"That's what we're hoping," Dee responds.

Jackie's phone beeps, indicating another call, it's Danny. She clicks over and explains the situation to him.

"She said they don't need a place to stay now, they just need two tickets. And that she's been trying to reach out to Mark but said his cell appeared to have changed."

"Well, yeah, he requested his number to be changed to put a stop to several unknown calls, so she won't be able to reach him until after the game," Danny replied.

"Have they been harassing him, too?" She asked.

"Not necessarily harassing him, but she apparently brought a relative with her that made a few comments that upset him a bit.... And I'm just trying to guard the front door until he can make it out the back.... Mark needs to focus on his job, Jack.... he'll have plenty of time to spend with his mother after the game."

"Bless his heart, he's been through so much with Denise," Jackie replied.

"Unfortunately, but tell her I'm in search of two tickets, but she'll need to be where I need her to be, when I need her to be there." He said.

"Got it, I'll hit you back in a sec."

Two hours later, Danny had managed to locate a couple extra tickets through one of his university contacts, as he and Jackie were waiting in the lobby of the hotel for their good friends James and Mikki McKnight, who lived in Miami, and were picking them up to head out to the game. James was a former Miami Dolphins receiver, who knew the area well.

Danny turns to Jackie, and said, "Call Dee and tell her I got her covered and to meet you at the *'Will Call'* area of the stadium by three thirty sharp with their ID.... and be sure to give her Mark's new cell number while you're at it, please!"

Jackie immediately calls Dee to inform her of the good news and updates her with her son's new cell number as Danny simultaneously sends Mark a text to inform him that all was well with his mom, and not to answer any calls or check any messages until the game is over."

Later that afternoon, Danny, Jackie and the McKnight's are standing in the *will-call* line to receive their tickets. After receiving them, they hung around waiting for Dee and the relative to pick up theirs, and as he signed in, Danny notices that Dee's tickets were in the same row as his, just three seats down.

So, as the four are making small talk, Danny gets a call from Mark, as he is accustomed of doing for their pre-game prayer. He reaffirms that *all is well* again with his mom and relative; they had a place to stay, but he chose not to mention that he had provided them with tickets to the game...and Mark didn't ask for obvious reasons, knowing his father probably did.

As they closed out their traditional pre-game prayer, Denise and her relative have arrived at *'Will Call.'* And after Jackie had assisted them with retrieving their tickets, the three of them make their way toward the Stadium entrance, where the McKnight's were now waiting, and Danny was rapidly approaching the same area. But before he arrived, he spots Jackie, Denise, and the relative making their way in the same direction, which led him to veer a bit in an effort to say hello to Denise and family. But right as he is about to do so, Dee, and her kindred make eye contact with him and walk right past him without saying a word!

It was supposed to be one of the happiest days of their son's life, but yet there was still so much unnecessary drama going on between his parents, which was constantly fueled by Dee and a few of her family members. As he stood there, not shocked, but obviously disappointed, Jackie then said, "No this woman didn't just walk right by you and not even speak! You got to be kidding me! Her son is living out his dream, thanks to his father and she *still* clowning?!"

Danny took a deep breath, remained quiet in an attempt to keep from going off the handle himself, as Jackie says, "I agree with Mark, you are the biggest fan Denise Terry has—and she doesn't even know it."

Danny finally spoke, "All is well, Jack.... Let's go and enjoy the game."

And that they did! But unfortunately, despite all the excitement going on all around them, Denise and her relative, again, sitting just seats down from Danny, Jackie and the McKnights, just sat there as if they were at a very bad horror film for which they regretted coming too.

Nevertheless, we lost the game—USC beat us 55-19, and Coach Stoops, whom I have great respect for, felt my fumbled punt was the turning point of the game. And I must admit, it was a major mistake on my part—I simply reacted spontaneously, in an effort to make something happen. However, there were a lot of things that went awry in this game—not just that one play. We struggled in every area of the contest. But I must say, if I had to do it all over again, folks, I couldn't *imagine* playing college ball anywhere else in America except for the University of Oklahoma and Bob Stoops. OU is simply a great-great program with an incredibly gifted coach.

But the first thing that crossed my mind when I made this unfortunate mistake was that my mom had to, indeed, be in this stadium. And yes, I understand that her attendance shouldn't matter, and I do realize I must be able to play conscience free ball, regardless—if I ever get the chance to play this game again. But I knew she had to be in attendance at the very moment it happened.

So as you might have imagined, I apologized to as many of my teammates as I possibly could and rushed out of the locker room to get away from everybody to release all of my pent up emotions. But the minute I walked out, heading toward my Dad's party group, I heard these very familiar voices yelling my name from the crowd. I turned to see who they were—and indeed it was my mom and the relative. And they jump right into it—strong.

"Why haven't you returned any of my calls?!" She asks.

"Yeah—what's up with that!" He added.

"And why did you change your number, Mark?!" She asked.

"Yeah—why are you trying to hide from us?!" He shot out.

"Why you still trippin?!" She fired off.

"Yeah—we're your family!" He declared.

I paused for a second to quickly regroup and find a way to get my thoughts together. I was exhausted mentally, physically and emotionally. But once they stopped for me to get a word in, I just didn't have any energy to deal with another confrontation. And as I got ready to speak—they continued.

"Mark—why are you doing this?!" She asked.

"Yeah—why you treatin us like this?!" He said"

This is the time when I needed my mother most, not a confrontational debate with her. A blind man could see I had enough going on psychologically after this debacle. And for the record, as I suspected, this doesn't sound like the same mother that sent those *please forgive me—I love you—and I promise to do better by you,* e-mail's just weeks ago. So with all the strength I had left, I said to my beloved mother and my ill-advised relative, "I'm sorry, I just haven't had a chance to check my messages.... And I changed my number because I was gettin way too many unknown calls."

"Well, where are you headed right now?" She cuts in and asks. "We want to go to your team hotel because we need to talk, Mark!"

"For real—we definitely need to talk!" He added.

I then jump in and said, "I've already checked out of the team hotel.... I'm staying at my Dad's hotel tonight...plus I'm tired Mom, I need some rest," I replied.

The relative dropped his head as my mom said, "Oh, so it's like that," as she turned and walked away.

"We still your family, Mark," he added as he too turned and faded from the scene. So I just stood there wondering, *why does it have to be like this, Lord?*

And as I turned to head in the opposite direction, toward my Dad, I noticed he was already headed towards me. Once we met, he greeted me with a hug and the tears just rushed out as I began to let it out.

"It's okay, son," he said with confidence.

"She just seems so bitter and negative all the doggone time, Dad!"

Danny takes a deep-sigh and says, "She's going to be fine, in due time, son. Just hang in there, you have a bright-bright future ahead of you, still."

"Dad, after tonight football is over, and this situation with my mom, been over!"

"Its over if you want it all to be over, son.... Its not all up to God.... You have some say so in this thing, too.... There are millions of young men who would love to be Mark Bradley, with all the baggage! *So let's not get weary in well doing...if God be for you, who can really be against you!"*

If anybody understood what I might be feeling like right now, it's my father. And he always knew the right thing to say to hold me up. So after building me back up a bit, I said in a more controlled tone, "She didn't say good game—how you feeling—sorry you lost—I'm proud of you—I'm here for you, I love you, none of that.... She just jumped right through me."

"Hang on Mark and keep walking by faith.... Forgiveness must be granted moment-by-moment," He said.

"It's all on her at this point," I said. "I've done all I can do."

"Would you like to invite them to go eat with us?" He asked.

"Nah, I'm good…. she wouldn't do it anyway," I replied.

"You sure? I can always go chase her down and ask her," He replied.

Again, it was this attitude among the many things for which I respected so much about my father. He just found ways to love her despite their resentment of him. However, I withdrew from his suggested offer, knowing that she really wouldn't have accepted the invitation anyway.

As we made our way out of Dolphins Stadium, it became clearer to me than ever that all the positive e-mail's my mom and I exchanged, hadn't brought us closer together, it amazingly seemed to push us further apart. She had come somewhat clean with me, but it appeared that she had not done the same with the rest of the family.

So as this nightmare in Miami comes to an end, despite my father's encouragement, I was ready to run to the end of the earth with no plans of returning—ever!

38

Divine Prediction

After failing to win the BCS Championship for the second straight year, had me completely down in the dumps. Most players have never had the opportunity to play for a conference championship, let alone two National Titles, back-to-back. And what was now evident regarding my mother, caused even more confusion between us. I was hopeful that one day she would turn that corner and be the mother I never had.

But it was obvious that her admission of the truth was to be just smoke and mirrors. And now that it's out there, documentable, it appears as if she regretted ever having shared this truth, which gave me even less hope of us ever having that strong mother/son relationship I desperately wanted. I now understood clearly that my father's innocent involvement in my life didn't strengthen my tie with my mother, it destroyed it.

Nevertheless, classes had resumed and I was just not feeling it—life had become a major drag for me. I was no longer having thoughts of suicide, but I was still struggling with trying to learn to accept living life detached from my mother, as her statement '*nothing is going to go right for you, until you get right with me,'"* began to reestablish its ring in my head.

Everything I thought I had learned from my father, spiritually, now seemed more like a blur—an illusion, almost too good to be true. Not that I doubted if God was God, but all of these trials and tribulations brought into question whether God was really aware of me, and my needs. I didn't know anyone else that had to tangle with these kind of life-changing problems with their mother, nor was I aware of anyone that had the kind of dynamic relationship with their father, as I did with mine.

At this stage, I understood that being raised in a broken home created all kinds of psychological issues, but I never thought that being alienated by my mother would be much more painful than being disconnected and separated from my father, even though he carried the blessing. Furthermore, it was also pretty apparent, that had my Dad been as selfish, irresponsible and vindictive as my mom, he would've never had any chance to get to know much of anything about me, if he had ever known about me at all.

So not knowing what was next in life for me, I became very discouraged and decided I would go home, back to Dallas and try to regroup as I figure out how to live this life without my mother, and perhaps this game of football I've now learned to love so much.

As I lay in bed, depressed, my father entered my bedroom and motioned for me to come. And I rose from my position of anguish and followed him down the stairs and out the front door. He hit the button on the garage opener and suddenly pointed over at this black-on-black 2005 SL55 AMG Mercedes Benz and then tossed the keys to me and said, "Merry Christmas! Happy New Year! Happy Birthday!"

"Happy Birthday…. New Year.... Christmas is over—to who?" I asked confused.

"Why do you always try to act like Willie foo-foo with me, Mark—you know exactly what's going on here—congratulations," he said.

"Noooo! Is that the same SL from the dealership I saw during Christmas?!"

"That would be it?! He replied with a smile.

"But where is your SL? You traded in for this one?" I asked, as I began to approach this beautiful piece of machinery.

"Well, I figured since I couldn't keep you out of mine, you needed one of your own."

My next response I'm sure woke up half the neighbors in this quiet Colleyville cul-de-sac, but I couldn't help myself. I ran out of the garage into the street screaming at the top of my lungs, "Come on man! What you tryin to do to me! I can't drive that!"

"Mark!" He said. "Get your butt back in this garage and out this cold weather!"

"I can't drive that, Pops! That's a hundred and forty thousand dollar car!"

"Get back in here now!" He said, trying to keep from laughing at me.

As I slowly walked back towards the garage, I couldn't help but to wonder why is this man so good to me, and how in the world can my mother still be so cold towards him? But as I fade back, there it was, looking just as sweet as any SL *drop top* Benz I'd ever seen.

Once he got me to calm down, he said, "If you want to continue changing your life, you gotta change your thoughts, Mark…. *As a man thinks in his heart, so is he....* Enjoy, and remember, own the car don't let the car own you—cool?"

"Cool," I said as he started toward the front door to reenter the house.

I stood there, thinking, *"Wow! I recall just a few years ago, of not even being allowed to drive one of my family's cars, which was just sitting collecting dust, when I really needed a car. But this man gives up a hundred and fifty thousand dollar vehicle of his own for me to have a new one, even after having already giving me a new car.*

Now I know that most people don't have a parent that could provide these kinds of gifts, but relatively speaking—the Nissan truck sitting in my grandads driveway would've meant just as much to me as this sacrifice, had he and they been willing to show their love by making such sacrifice. But despite that comparable fact, my father's counsel was incomparable. His constant advice was just as rich as this car. I then began to reflect on the comment he slipped in as he was making the transfer; *if you want to continue changing my life, you gotta change your thoughts.*

Suddenly, I rush in to thank him and to inquire about the statement.

I grab a chair at the kitchen bar as he was making a protein shake before his morning run, "Dad, I appreciate you lifting my spirits with such an overwhelming gift.... My mind has been all over the place since we got back from Miami.... The loss; and all the media comments about that play; the emotional stress; and my mother's behavior was just a lot to deal with at one time.... And now that football appears to be completely over, it's just been tough to focus."

"Mark, all is well, son," he said as he continues making his shake.

"Well, I know it will be at some point but for now, listening to the media constantly beat me up, my mom not returning my calls has just been hard. So I needed to get out of Oklahoma for a while to regroup," I replied.

He then stops what he's doing, looks across the bar counter, and said, "Don't over process all this son.... Many of these things just goes along with the territory.... And by the way, SC may have been the better team.... And last time I checked, Coach Stoops is one of your biggest supporters, Mark Bradley.... And I assure you, that one day soon, your mother will be too.... In the meantime, keep the faith, stay on your knees and keep God's word before your eyes with the same level of commitment you study your playbook, and maybe you won't be so offended when a comment is made about you that you don't quite agree with," he said, as he held up his study Bible.

"I'm tryin but it just doesn't seem like there's enough time to get it in," I replied.

"Well, I suggest you figure it out son, you've read with your own eyes, *man shall not live by bread alone, but by every word that proceeds out of the mouth of God*— Deuteronomy 8:3, and that includes football young-fella."

I paused as I thought about that comment and how real it was, before saying, "Dad, you need to be in somebody's pulpit."

"I am—haven't you noticed," as he gives me that look, *Church is in session now.*

"Pops, I'm serious!" I shot back with a grin. "You've taught me more about the word sports and God than any church or university I've ever attended."

"Well, I can't tell.... So I must need to change my message, deacon," he replied.

"Trust me, the message is gettin through, Bishop," I fired back with a smile.

"Mark, go get packed up and get your butt back to Norman," he said, while grinning..

"I love you man.... I'm elated you're my father," I said with smirk on my face.

"No, Mark—you're elated that Dad just purchased you a hundred-and-forty-thousand dollar-vehicle," he replied, as I began to laugh. "Now get your butt back to Norman and get that *ribbon and piece of paper* the Arts and Science Department gives out in that lil folder on commencement day, known as a degree."

"A ribbon and a piece a paper?! I shouted with laughter.

"Yes! And while you're at it, you might want to workout juust a little—if you still wanna play ball and extend your career," he said, as he gulps down the rest of his shake.

"So you really think I got a shot?" I asked as I suddenly began to get serious.

"Mark, despite how discouraged you may still feel about that game, which no one player contributed to, its time to let it go.... You are a heckuva player, son, and you'll always play like the player you think you are.... So get rid of the Orange Bowl image, you are not that player that made that mistake," he said as he heads for the door to go on his run. "And by the way," he says, "the NFL combine is in a few weeks in February, get yourself ready…. I'm pretty sure you'll be invited."

"But not everybody that gets invited to the combine gets drafted, Pops."

"True—but not everybody that gets drafted received an invitation. So either way, get yourself ready to perform if you still wanna play," he replied.

"Does that really happen?" I asked.

"Mark—where's you faith? You're a 'Top Forty' draft pick, son. Get yourself prepared if you're serious," he says, as he exits the house.

A few months later, as he predicted, I got invited to the NFL Collegiate Combine held in Indianapolis, Indiana. Didn't perform as well as I'd hoped but it was respectable. I was disappointed but Coach Schmidt did a great job preparing me for the workout while my Dad/Agent prepared me for the many interview requests eventually received after my workout.

But, then, it was suddenly April—Draft Day 2005. And despite the positive feed back from the scouts, I hadn't really heard from any teams. So I wasn't too confident that anybody would really take a chance with a guy with my stats. However, my father hasn't been wrong forecasting these events just yet, but this time I think he's definitely out done himself with the whole *Top Forty* thing.

Despite my numbers as compared to other eligible receivers in the draft, he truly believed that I was the best athlete in this draft. And if we added a little, of what he called, divine favor, he felt confident in his *divine prediction.*

So, at his request, I decided to watch the draft with him, in Dallas, instead of hanging out doing something else like—the mall. And finding out that there would be others there, made me even more uncomfortable. They were a few of his business partners whom he worked closely with to observe this embarrassing day.

In attendance were Jackie, Scott West, and David Paulson, all waiting to cheer me on or help me cry. So as we watched the draft coverage on ESPN unfold, I began nervously listening to all his assessments with greater interest. And unlike some of the panel, my Dad has actually been in an NFL front office position with first-hand experience of what really goes on behind the scenes on draft day with these NFL teams. So he knew the kind of conversations and decisions that were perhaps being made around the league. And David was also informative and insightful after having a stellar career at the Air Force Academy and a brief NFL career himself.

"What teams do you think will likely draft him?" Jackie asked.

"Well—Baltimore, Jacksonville, Atlanta, and Chicago are the teams in need of receivers and most likely to select a receiver in the first and second rounds or in the *top forty* players," he says, as he looked over across the room at me and winks.

"So *'top forty'* means what exactly?" She asked.

"For Mark, it means late first or early second. Teams like the Jaguars and Bears who are looking for receivers are positioned in those slots," he replied, "which is about the 21st pick and 39th pick."

"And as you mentioned earlier, Baltimore is another possibility with the 22nd pick," she said, as she was given the assignment to keep track of what receivers went where.

"Correct," he replied, as he looks at me again, and asked, "You good?"

"Yeah—I'm straight," I replied, as the negative tension inside me began to build. I then reclined on one end of his modular sofa, shoes off, pillow under my head. His guests were all sitting on the bay window bench overlooking this really nice pond that flowed throughout his sub-division. And throughout the process, my Dad sat back in his usual cool, calm and collected state of mind-set, while I felt tensed and anxious.

With Jacksonville on the clock, Jackie broke the brief silence and said, "Mark, call Jerry Jones and tell him you want to stay at home and play for the Cowboys."

Everyone giggled with her a bit and agreed that would be the ideal situation.

Then NFL commissioner Paul Tagliabue stepped up to the microphone, as I suddenly thought, *Okay, Dad—here goes strike one.*

"With the 21st pick in the 2005 NFL Draft, the Jacksonville Jaguars select, Matt Jones wide receiver from Arkansas."

Everyone tried not to act too disappointed as Jackie took notes, while Scott and Dave looked on with concern. But my Dad glances over at me again and winks as if to say, *"All is well, son."*

Scott squares his shoulders and said, "They did take a receiver though, Mark—so it sounds like Pops might be on the right track!"

I slightly grinned at his comment, but had no response. Quite frankly I didn't think Scott's comment carried any value, so I just remained status quo, now thinking the even that 99 cents mall will do at this point.

My Dad then says, "If the Ravens don't cooperate, Chicago must be the one—at 39."

"With the 22nd pick of the 2005 NFL Draft, the Baltimore Ravens select, Mark.... Clayton, wide receiver from Oklahoma."

As you could imagine, the name Mark mixed with wide receiver and Oklahoma made us all pause for a split second. There was total silence and then sudden excitement and then a subtle deflation, as we began to register that it was "Mark...Clayton" out of Oklahoma—not wide receiver "Mark...Bradley."

Then there was a big sigh by everybody in the room before my Dad said, "Now that's a really good pick for Baltimore—MC can play," as we all stood and clapped for my teammate and good friend Mark Clayton. And all along, I'm thinking, *There goes strike two, Pops!*

"With the 27th pick of the 2005 NFL Draft, the Atlanta Falcons select, Roddy White, wide receiver Alabama Birmingham."

And BAM, there it is! The umpire calls ***strike three!*** I felt really bad for my Dad who has been so accurate with his predictions over the years with most everything involving me. So I then just closed my eyes, pretending to have fallen asleep as the feelings of embarrassment began to overtake me, too. But my father, surprisingly, didn't seem discouraged at all. After the 37th pick, he knew that Chicago would be on the clock, which would be the true inevitable—***third strike,*** given the fact that the Bears held the 39th pick of his predicted top forty.

So in an effort to soften the blow for both of us, I pretended to wake up and just break my silence, "Man this is crazy—they have taken eight receivers!"

And my Pops just calmly looks over at me again, and said, "Mark—all is well, son."

Twenty-minutes later, the Chicago Bears are now *on the clock.*

Suddenly, it seems like it's gotten extremely hot in here. I get up and go check the thermostat, and it's steadily producing the way it's been designed—pumping ice-cold air. I then go back to my spot while looking at the clock in the corner of the ESPN set, trying to turn it back.

At this point, I didn't want to even hear the selection, knowing that Randy Johnson was about to finalize this deal by throwing a straight fastball right down the middle of the plate—***for strike four!*** And there was nothing I could do to save my Pops.

The clock was now down to three minutes and I began to feel nauseous as my Dad's cell phone rings. He gets up and goes to his office, which set adjacent to the media room where we were huddled up, as the NFL's Director of Football Operations, Gene Washington, now steps to the podium, as my Dad reenters the room:

"With the 39th pick of the 2005 NFL Draft, the Chicago Bears select, **Mark.... Bradley,** wide receiver from Oklahoma."

Jackie screamed while Scott and Dave jumped up and high-fived each other as I looked over at my father in complete shock, and said to myself, *You got to be kiddin me!*

My Dad just winks at me, again, as I suddenly placed my hands on top of my head with eyes of disbelief! The emotions began to over flow as my father walked over and hugged me and said, "*All things are possible to them that believe*—congratulations son," as his cell goes off again, to which he answers and then hands it to me, "Its Jerry Angelo, the GM of the Chicago Bears," as he then points toward the master bedroom.

"Hi Mark—this is Jerry Angelo! Congratulations! We are proud to have you part of our football team! You ready to go to work?!"

"Yes sir," I replied, as I made my way to the bedroom with tears beginning to fall.

"Our staff will be in touch with you later today with your itinerary regarding your trip to Chicago—and congratulations once again. I'm sure your dad is proud of you."

"Thank you, sir." I replied.

My Dad entered the room looking for me just as I was hanging up, after a brief celebration with his associates. I had stepped into the walk-in closet and before I knew it, all the unexpressed emotions of the past twenty-two years just erupted in a way it never had in the past—I began to cry heavily and out of control. When I looked up, seeing my Dad, I immediately embraced him, as he said, "Congratulations, son, you've earned your way into the National Football League as one of the *top forty players* in the country out of Arkansas Pine Bluff—how bout that," he said with what had to be extreme jubilation for him.

And although these were mainly tears of extreme joy, they were also mixed with tears of extreme pain. So much so I couldn't hardly breath, couldn't talk or even walk at this point. I was just so overwhelmed I couldn't get anything out. All I could do was let it all out, everything. So I just cried and cried on my father's shoulder while he celebrated with me while consoling me at the same time. And after about five-minutes of trying to regroup, I said with both joy and pain, "Dad…Thank…You!"

"It's okay, son…. I know it's been a long hard road, but you did it."

I finally gathered my composure a bit to say, "No Daddy—you did it. You did it, Pops.... You took a rebellious scared kid, who had no hope and no confidence and loved him all the way to his dream…there is no way possible I could have done any of this without you.... So thank you so-so-so much for never giving up on me...for always believing in me, Pops.... I just wish my mother loved me the way you do," as the tears rumbled their way out of this broken but yet excited young man.

Now Danny's face is flooded with tears as he looked to his son with adulation, and said, "Its going to be alright, Mark.... In due time, your mother is going to be fine.... And it will be as if the fallout never even happened," he said. "Now, come on let's get cleaned up, we got guests waiting.... And give her call with the update, even though she's probably already heard about it."

I nod in agreement as he began to thank the Lord for this glorious day, asking God to restore and do a quick work in my relationship with my mother. We both then took a moment to splash some cold water on our faces in the double sinks in the master bathroom while he left me behind to make that suggested phone call to my beloved mother, hoping she would be ready to reunite and seriously move forward.

"Hey baby, I heard the good news!" She immediately said once she heard my voice.

"I figured as much," I replied, as I was still trying to completely gain my composure.

"Well, congratulations—we're all excited down here…. the phones have been ringing off the hook…. I'm so proud of you, son!"

"Thanks—its nice to hear you say that. But I was just calling to update you."

"Daddy and everybody is just thrilled!"

"Good, I'll give him a call," I replied.

"Please do.... He and Mama been calling everybody bragging about their grandson."

"Will do," I replied, while I reflected on what this could have been like to have had my mother here, too, to share in the moment. But as much as I wished we could have a more lengthy conversation, I had learned to keep these chats with her fairly short in hopes of maintaining civility. And, for me, this was a moment to be enjoyed—not debated. And just as I thought it—she went there.

"Oh—by the way, have you hired an Agent yet, I still got a guy that wants to rep you."

I paused for a moment, reminded of the time she attempted to push this card back in January, while we were in Miami. I quickly said, "Nah—I'm good, Mom."

She then paused and asked, "So, you signed with one already?"

"Yeah—I did," I soberly replied.

"Who?" She asked.

"I asked my Dad to represent me."

Her response to that said it all.

"Oh—okay.... okay.... well then...." So I decided to cut this before it got out of hand, "Mom—I'm good, all is well.... But I do have to get going. The Bears have already booked my flight to Chicago—so I'll call you later in the week."

She paused again, and said, sounding disappointed, "Okay—well—congratulations."

We hung up, and I took a deep breath and exhaled, relieved knowing that the last time I stepped into my father's master bedroom, I was a downtrodden, unwanted injured collegiate football player. But now, praise God, I'm stepping out of it as an NFL top draft pick. It's just amazing what faith can do even to a troubled young man's life.

The very next day, a limo picked me up at Chicago's O'Hare Airport and took me to Halas Hall, the Chicago Bears practice facility, where I was greeted by Head Coach Lovie Smith and his staff. And for the next couple of months went a whirlwind of mini-camps, orientations and workouts, during which my Agent/Dad negotiated, on my behalf, a five-year deal which would allow me to pay a few bills.

I had been assigned the jersey number fourteen, which wasn't really working for me. So I decided to approach Tony Medlin, the team's long-time equipment manager, about changing to a more traditional number for a wide receiver—one in the eighties. But before I did so, I called my Agent/Dad to get his opinion as to what number he thought might best fit me and my personality, since there is so much these days that goes into the marketing of a player.

As he shared, I suddenly decided to go with jersey number 16; my Dad's high school and college number combined. I wanted to wear a number that had a deep rooted significance, and 16 was definitely it.

By early July, just a few weeks away from my first NFL training camp, I decided to return home to Dallas and enjoy the rest of this vacation. But a phone call would threaten to turn this retreat into another chaotic family warfare. I was upstairs getting ready to shower after waking from a short nap. My cell suddenly rings back-to-back-to-back-to-back. It was an unknown call, but I decided to answer. It's one of my relatives from Arkansas. And I must have sounded groggy because his first response was:

"Get up.... I need to holla at you!"

I then asked concerned, "What's up?"

"I said get up, I need to holla at you?!" He slightly shouted again.

"I am up," I replied, as I then turn off the water of the shower.

"Why you trippin?!" He asked with hostility.

"Trippin? Trippin how?" I asked.

"Trippin with your family!" He shot back.

"You serious?" I asked, knowing where this was now headed.

"You heard me, I didn't stutter!" He fired back angrily.

"Hold on," I said and hit mute, rushed downstairs so my father could hear this conversation. Once I got situated, I pressed speaker and said, "Go ahead, I'm listening."

"You need to stop trippin with ya family!" He repeated with hostility.

"And I asked trippin how?"

"We raised you, Mark! You wouldn't be where you are if it wasn't for us—the Davis family.... Everything you got, you got because of us!" He threw out.

"You serious?" I asked

"I said we raised you when yo daddy was no where to be found, Mark.... I was the one who raced you in the forty-yard dash and held your hand when you got hurt at UAPB.... When you transferred to OU—it was I who had barbecues at my house pullin your stats off the internet passing them out—gettin the word out about you.... so you need to stop trippin and remind yourself who really loves you, negro.... Because it appears that you done forgot where you came from!"

And just as I was about to go completely off, he motioned for me to let him finish.

"And by the way, *we will* be in Chicago," he said. "Make no mistake about that, *we will* be in Chicago, partying and kicking it with you every other weekend partna—you can get ready for that! Hell, we want some bragging rights too. Send us a bunch of tee-shirts and hats too, so we can brag and boast around here in town. So you can get ready, *we will* be at your doorstep ready to kick it with you. So I highly suggest you stop hiding behind yo damn daddy and be yo own damn man!"

At that comment, I was about ready to snap, but my father suggested I let him finish!

"Mark, are you listening to me?! He asked.

"Yeah, I hear you talking," I replied, ready to just let it go, but then he went there.

"Yo daddy ain't the only one who can give good counsel—call me some time and let me shoot some knowledge at ya.... Remember, he didn't even want ya at one point, so stop showin yo tail with yo family, Mark...we expect you to do better and treat us like we *deserve* to be treated—that's all I gotta say about it—congratulations—keep God first and stop hiding behind yo damn daddy.... And *we will* see you in Chi-town."

Then he just hung up.

As you might have imagined, I was past being heated, "What in the hell is wrong with these folks!" I shouted. "What does racing me in a forty and having barbeques at his house got anything to do with anything?! And I know they put him up to doing this."

"Mark, calm down, son."

"Did his barbecues help pay for my tuition! Did it help pay for my room and board! Did it help pay for my transportation—No! Then what the hell is he talking about?!"

"Mark, calm down, son."

"And if I hear of one more family member dogging my father, just because they want to vent, then I'm tellin you right now, we gon have a serious situation, Daddy!"

"Mark, sit down, son."

"What they need to do is focus on their own damn kids and leave me the hell alone!"

Danny paused trying to keep his composure and said again, "Mark, sit down, son."

"I rather stand—I'm to hot too sit down!" I shot back, heated.

"I understand, but I need to talk to you, Mark."

"All of'em, just full of resentment.... And wonder why I won't come back home?! Please! At the rate this thing going, I ain't ever going back around all that mess!"

Danny patiently listened, before pointing at the chair, "Mark," he said calmly.

I, then, took a seat on the sofa next to his as he allowed me to cool off for a few minutes, before saying, "If you don't get what I'm about to say, son, somebody, without a doubt, is going to get seriously hurt, which also means somebody will end up in jail. So, I need you to chill out for a minute and hear me out."

I looked straight ahead, furious, with no response, ready to be the one headed to jail.

"If this relative has any idea of what he really just said, then what you've just heard is perhaps your family's perspective on *Faith, Family* and *Fatherhood;* and where they probably stand with this thing called *love, life* and *relationship,* which has robbed more young men of their dreams than the streets themselves," he said. "Validating that *'a man's enemy is they of his own household.'*"

"But Daddy," I replied, still heated, as I jumped in to share my position...." But he cuts me off and asked me again to just hear him out.

"You must be the bigger man, son, and take the low road and forgive them, so that you can keep your mind focused on your dream, your future, and your relationship with God.... This is how you walk this thing out in love, son.... You feel me?"

"But they best leave me the hell alone," I replied with anger.

"And if they don't," he said, "then what? Are you ready to potentially go to jail, or attend somebody's funeral, because you couldn't control your rage, which is only from the pit of hell?

"I'm just saying," I replied.

"And I'm just saying, son, this out of control anger is usually the first step towards murder; it leads to an explosion; its momentary insanity.... This thing can get way out of hand, quickly, Mark. Many of the deaths being reported across America, took place at the hands of a relative or friend, the law calls them "crimes of passion." So, please understand that this kind of family fallout where envy and jealousy and bitterness seems to be at play, can get someone killed if you give anger a chance to fester, son."

Once again, he talks me out of a multitude of stupid decisions I was about to make against a member of my own family. I was ready to throw down, with years of frustration boiling inside me. I wasn't trying to hear a word from God, I wanted to act on a word from Mark!

"This is a *spiritual warfare, son, not a fleshly one,"* he went on to say. "And the sooner you get that revelation in your head, the better you'll be able to deal with these situations differently.... This is why I keep pushing you towards the word, so that you can use it when these kind of threatening challenges knock at your door."

"But I gotta respond, Dad," I replied, being in between these emotions.

"Not necessarily, but under these circumstances, I think you should," he surprisingly said. "But how you respond is critical, son.... Your response should be geared toward minimizing the anger, not giving it more life," he said. "Especially with threats of just showing up at your door-step. So, a soft answer will turn away the stupidity, but harsh words will only stir up more strife, son."

"Why doesn't any of this ever really bother you?" I asked, agitatedly.

"It does—I just choose to not give it life…. I don't see the flesh and blood warfare anymore, it's spiritual," he replied. "The reason we're having so many problems in this world today, is because of these same issues going on inside our family's today. And at the heart of it is fear, hatred, and envy towards one another. So, I just decided I was going try doing it the Lord's way, not man's way; and believe what God says about me, not what the world says about me... I'd like to have your family's approval, but I don't need their approval in order for me to go on and live a life of happiness, fulfilled."

Pausing, I asked, "So how you suggest I get back at this enemy flapping his gums?"

"You can't, until you calm down and put your love hat on, son."

"Okay," I replied, taking a deep sigh, "so after I calm down, how do I get back?"

"The same way you got your Mom to open up, send him your thoughts by way of e-mail, documenting how you feel, uninterrupted.... But don't make any threats or use any profanity, Mark.... That doesn't mean you can't be frank, but you can't use words and punctuations that will kindle more anger.... Do you understand me?"

"But Daddy—this dude needs to understand, I'm a grown ass man!"

"But what I'm still trying to get you to understand, son, is there are a bunch of grown ass men out there that are *six foot under* or *in the penitentiary* trying to prove just that, Mark. So, let's calm down and understand that all is well; thinking this thing through before you respond, son...its the only way to deal, if we're going to give love a chance."

"I just want him to realize, Dad, that I'm not that lil fearful and clueless kid anymore—and fed up with all these shots they keep taking at my father—that craziness is going to stop, today, now!"

"Well, don't sweat the negative comment about me, son.... I'm a big boy, Mark. I can handle the attacks—just don't let their negativity produce negativity in you, too. The last thing you need is to jeopardize your future behind all of this *unnecessary* strife going on with your family.... The *only person* you should have any real concern for right now, is your mother. The rest of them, stay away until we see a brighter day."

"Time doesn't always change people, Pops," I said, as I began to calm down a bit.

"No, it doesn't, but time will gives us the space to make better decisions, which could help bring about change, son.... So, be patient," he said.

I decided to take his advice, maintain my composure, and send him an e-mail too.

Dear Relative—First of all, life is too short for all this family strife. The Lord has been way too good to all of us to continue on with this nonsense. Secondly, I'm a grown man dog, and I suggest you respect me as a grown man. So don't call talking to me like I'm a kid anymore, especially when you're operating on limited information. Thirdly, I highly suggest you check with me, first, before just showing up on my doorstep. That's what grown men do—respect other grown men's privacy.

And finally, I'm tired of you guys taking shots at my relationship with my Dad, so I suggest you chill with that nonsense too. The man has done nothing but love me despite all the strife he had to endure with my family, which means I couldn't be in any better hands than my father. So trust me, I'm grateful to God I have a father I can hide behind. Isn't that what fathers are supposed to do, protect their cubs from a world of predators?

Furthermore, if you recall, for twenty years, I tried life your way and it simply didn't work for me. But to make sure we're on the same page here, let me make clear, I'm not a Mayberry, or a Davis, or a Terry—I'm a Bradley, and damn proud of it! And all of this craziness about how you guys are 'solely' responsible for these new accomplishments going on in my life—is simply ridiculous.

In closing, I'm not interested in your bragging rights. Boasting in the faces of people less fortunate, is arrogant. One biblical verse that comes to mind says, "be careful of thinking more highly of yourself than you ought." So I'm trying to learn how to be humble after growing up around so much pride. So please forgive me, I'd now rather be grateful and thankful than always proud and cocky—Mark.

The very next day I got a call from my mom. I had forwarded her a copy of my e-mail letter too. From the ambient noise, I knew she was calling from work.

"Mark, I don't know what all was said between you guys, but everybody in the family don't feel the same way, son. And I heard that he was drunk so there's no tellin what he might have said to you."

"Mom, first of all, the man wasn't drunk, especially at 8 a.m. He's not an alcoholic. Second of all, I haven't known my family to feel any other way.... But if you would just sit down with all of them and tell them the truth—the whole truth, Mama—it might stop some of this nonsense."

"I have told them the truth, Mark! And anybody else that asks about you and your Dad.... I told them that he promised to take care of you when you left for Oklahoma, and he did.... He's done that," she said surprisingly with a tone of hope I'd never heard.

But I couldn't let her totally off the hook, "But you see, Mom, that's my point, he's been there for me long before I left for Oklahoma, but for some reason you refuse to acknowledge that.... But I'm done with all this backbiting and definitely with all the negative comments about my father.... I tried to make that clear in my last serious conversation with you, which I thought you understood, too, but I guess not."

"Well—all I got to say son is, we love you, Mark," as she hung up.

But as this crazy unfortunate saga continues, with my Mom anchored right down in the middle of it, what happens next would sadly change everything in this family *forever* and *ever* and *ever.*

39

Collateral Damage

It was now week eight of the regular season and the Bears were in Detroit to play the Lions. Mark had earned his way into the starting line-up while Danny watched the game from home in Texas. After a 5-11 season, the Bears went into the Motor City at 3-3 with a rookie at quarterback, Kyle Orton, filling in for the injured Rex Grossman. And as Mark had hoped for, he was having a great game, despite a slow start to his 2005 season. And by the start of the second quarter, he had five receptions for 88 yards and on his way to a pro-bowl kind of day.

But after catching a crossing route—making one man miss—hurdling another—Mark goes down untouched, clinching his right knee, as the Bears sideline goes silent. Danny stood up from his sofa at home and began to pray—in silence.

"Come on, come on, son—get up baby," he said underneath his breath.

Then one of the announcers made reference to the cart being brought out, which is never a good sign if you know anything about football injuries. As they were getting Mark loaded onto the cart, Danny rushes to his closet to pack his bags while still listening to the announcers report of the situation.

He then exits the house in a rush to catch the next Chicago flight to O'Hare, when he gets a call from the Bears team chaplain, who had become one of Mark's spiritual advisors. He gives him an update on his son's condition and then hands the phone over to the Bears trainer, Tim Bream.

"Danny—it looks like he may have snapped his ACL, which means he'll be out for a while. But let's see what the MRI says tomorrow, that will give us a better snapshot of exactly what we're dealing with here."

Danny thanks him and asked if he could speak to Mark. Tim then handed the cell to Mark, who was laying on a training table with an ice pack on the injured knee.

"Mark—talk to me, big-timer? How we doing?" Danny asked.

"Can you believe this?" Mark dejectedly replied.

"You can handle it champ," Danny shot back. "You're blessed and highly favored—so keep your head up, son, the best is still yet to come.... I should be at the Bears facility by the time you guys return," he said, as we hung up.

I'm thinking, *you can't be serious—why is this happening to me? Another surgery?!*

I then slap the table, knowing from previous experience that this feels just like another ligament injury, which will require surgery. I'm now saying to myself, *most of my life I've had to overcome some kind of devastating circumstance just to be free.... If it wasn't my mother, it was my family; if it wasn't an athletic issue, it was an academic issue; one day I'm a Mayberry—the next day I'm a Bradley being raised by a Davis, and living with a Terry.... Every which way I turned there was something monumental I had to deal with just to survive.... When was it going to end?!*

All the while, I'm still hearing my mother's voice ringing in my head, *nothing is going to go right for you, Mark, until you get right—with me!*

The thought of going through another gruesome rehab program again—was unimaginable. I knew what it took to get healthy, but I didn't know if I had what it took to get healthy one more time.

And maybe she's right, I said to myself. *Maybe I do need to get right with my Mom.... But then again, right how? In what way? What did I do that was so wrong, that needed to be righted?* I asked myself, with doctors now standing over me checking the knee.

Once we made it back to Chicago, my father was indeed waiting to take me home as the meds had me heavily sedated. I wasn't just in a lot of pain physically, but mentally and emotionally as well. While my father helped me get situated in bed, I flipped on tube began listening to the local sportscasters grim report of my future with the Bears, which just sent me over the edge.

My Dad, then, grabs the remote, flips off the television, and said, "Only listen to people who say *you can*, never those who say *you can't,* cool?"

But I was already spent and just started unloading on him, right there on the spot.

"I just don't get it! What am I missing?! Why does this keep happening to me?!"

Danny paused and slowly takes a seat on the edge of the bed, ready to listen.

"What am I doing wrong?! I'm doing everything I know to do! So why does it seem like I'm the only one injured all the time?! Maybe my mom is right, maybe I should get right with her before I can expect anything to go right for me! But I can't figure out what in the world could I have done to my mother that would require a need for me to right with her! Get right how?! Get right about what?! I asked with both frustration and disappointment tugging at my heart. "So why she keeps saying it?! I can't think of one thing I could've done to my mom, not one! So, what am I doing wrong, Dad?!

Danny hesitates to answer, knowing that his confused son might not be finish.

"I've been working my butt off to get to this stage in my life, and every single freakin year I'm having to deal with a doggone knee issue.... Everybody else seems to stay healthy, why can't I?!" I asked again with anger.

There's a long pause as Mark lays his back onto his bed, closes his eyes as tears run down the side of his face. And Danny waited just a little while longer to speak just in case Mark wanted to continue venting, to release more of his pent up thoughts and feelings. So after it appeared that he was done Danny decided to speak by first explaining that he didn't have all the answers but did have a few that he thought would help bring clarity to his situation.

He starts out by saying that he felt that many of my physical issues were due to stress and perhaps circumstantial. And that Football is a contact sport, known as the game of injuries. People get injured from time-to-time, though he didn't believe in coincidence, which meant that my *self image, my imagination,* the things I *thought* about the most, things I *feared* the most could be the very things that were coming to pass in my life. And I agreed with that, I feared injury more than I should've being a pro-ball player. And I talked about it a lot, which made his next point more than valid.

"If you're going to be that strong and fearless believer the bible talks about, son, you gotta stop the *stinking thinking* and having all these pity parties, always feeling sorry for yourself and speaking words of defeat and death.... *Life and death is in the power of your tongue....* You get to decide how this thing in life goes down.... Speak words of life, not destruction; words of hope, not despair; words of health, not injury."

"But I'm reading my bible and praying everyday, Daddy," I replied confused, trying to get a better grip on all these why's and reasons going on in my life.

"Yes, but 2 Timothy 2:15 says study the word, not just merely read it, son. Then you would be able to properly weather these storms.... You're not just merely reading your offensive playbook, are you? No, you're all over it day and night meditating on all your assignments, that you may go out and perform it on any day or night." He said. "Well, the playbook of life requires the same kind of commitment and focus if you want to perform out here in the game of life.... And trust me, one is way more important than the other.... In fact, your spiritual man will make you a better football man, not weaken it...and teach you that life is not all about you, Mark Bradley—its about blessing others."

"All these thoughts of fear came from all that strife I grew up in," I responded.

"Well, where ever you find selfishness, you'll find a boat-load of fear, Mark; and where ever you find love, you'll always find a boat-load of faith," my Dad replied. "So, again, it sounds to me like you need to get your love walk right.... *God has not given you a spirit of fear, but of power, love and a sound mind.... As a man thinks in his heart, so is he."*

"Where do you think I should start?" I asked

"By settling in your heart, once and for all, God's word for your life, *letting God be true and every man a lie,*" he said. "Until then, you'll live life full of anger, bitterness and doubt.... And the Lord said, *let that man expect to receive nothing from me.*"

"I guess I just need to work on building my faith more."

"Perhaps, but it depends on what you mean by building your faith, son. According to this book," he said, as he held it up, "you either have faith or not, and *mustard seed* type faith is all we need to get results, Mark.... And quite frankly, it would help if you stop playing many of these destructive video games laced with fear, death and destruction. Its working counter-productive to everything you're studying in this word."

And that comment struck a nerve with me. I loved my video games.

"But they just video games!" I replied, not quite understanding this spiritual angle.

"Yeah, video games that adversely affect your thoughts and imagination, Mark—canceling out faith.... This book says we must guard our hearts, and we do that by monitoring what we allow through our *eye gate* and *ear gate;* that's if we choose to *let God be true,*" he replied, as I began to see his point of how I might be losing these battles in my mind, which is affecting my words and consequently what I believe. And since selfishness and fear seems to be dominating my way of living, perhaps this spiritual insight might just be my problem.

He then addressed the issue regarding my mothers ridiculous comment about the status of my well-being: "If I recall, you had this same injury at Arkansas Pine Bluff, son, when everything seemed to be *'very right'* between you and your mother, correct?"

"Yeah," I replied in a much more calmer tone.

"Well, let's not connect the two—one has absolutely nothing to do with the other, Mark.... Secondly, Denise is perhaps bothered by their lack of direct access to this new life that you were suppose to be enjoying with them—not me," he said. "And she's not quite ready to come to grips with the fact that she/they eliminated themselves with all that strife, confrontation and division going on inside that household. And the only way to get back at me is to now lash out at you," as tears began to fall heavier from my eyes.

"But this is my mother still trippin with me like this Daddy!"

"I understand, but this whole thing about you *needing to get right with your her, or else,* is simply your mom's way of expressing her dissatisfaction towards you because of her *unjustifiable* anger towards me, son.... However," he said, "Denise is going to be just fine in due time, and you guys won't even be able to remember these differences ever occurred.... I don't know when that day will be, but I do know that one day, your relationship with your mother will be just as good if not better than this relationship you have with your father.... So, just hang on in there, son."

As I lay there pondering his words of wisdom, I thought, *how amazing is it for both my parents to have grown up in the same town, drank the same water, went to the same schools, believe in the same God, but yet saw these same life-changing situations very differently. My Dad tried viewing things from a spiritualistic perspective; my Mom often saw them through a humanistic one. One displayed selfishness, while the other made sacrifices; one operated out of fear, the other out of faith.*

However, despite these multitudes of fears, which I'd been raised in, whatever level of faith I now had was about to be tested to the max. I'd always heard from my father that faith is not faith until its been tested.... *and that the trying of our faith works patience.*

Well, in my mind, this test could not have been any tougher. And by the way, I did finally come to a realization that truthfully, I hadn't *wronged* my mother or *dishonored* her in any way. In fact, after further thought and prayer on the matter, I, too, felt my mother's dissatisfaction towards me was indeed directly connected to her *unjustifiable* anger towards my father, which had always been the case with my mom.

A few months later, as they prepped me for yet another knee surgery, I went in this time feeling relieved of all that unnecessary pressure my family had placed upon me due to this unwarranted competition thing they had going on with my Dad.

Nonetheless, by late August 2006, I was headed to our team hotel the night before a preseason game, after having spent the winter and summer rehabbing my surgically repaired knee. I wasn't quite a hundred percent, so I was only playing sparingly. My cell phone rang, and surprisingly it was my grandma Leola.

"Hey—what's up?" I asked.

"Nothin much," she replied, as she jumped right into her reasons for calling, "Odell and I are in town and he was wondering if you could get him a couple of tickets to the game tomorrow night, he wants to take one of your relatives," she said. "I know it's last minute but we didn't decide to come help him move until the last minute."

"When did y'all get to town?" I asked, trying to get a feel for how last minute this actually really was. They all knew the NFL ticket rules, but for some reason none of them ever seem to want to follow them, which made it harder on me to get them tickets.

"We came in late last night on the bus, or better yet early this morning," she replied with a tone that expressed her tiredness.

"You and granddaddy came up on the bus from Pine Bluff?!" I asked surprisingly.

"Yeah—your grandfather won't fly, so we took the bus all the way from Pine Bluff to Chicago—a long-long ride," she added.

"Grandma, don't you think you're doing a lil too much—you were just in San Francisco a couple of weeks ago at one of our games?" I asked out of concern.

"Well—it's Odell that's really wanting to go. I told them it might be too late for you to provide us any tickets, but they insisted I try to contact you anyway," she replied.

"Tell him I doubt very seriously if I can get tickets the night before the game."

"Well, I've already told them as much and reminded them that the same thing happened to me in San Francisco—when we too decided to come too late and ended up having to buy tickets," grandma Leo said.

"Correct—but I'll see what I can do," I replied disappointed, looking for a way to not have to go track down tickets for my elderly grandparents at the last minute, to which I, then, said, "Grandma, tell them a regular season game would be better, I'm not even playing tonight—plus, it's going to be really hot and muggy out there."

"Well—your grandfather and relative want to come. So call us back and let us know if you can get three tickets," she said.

"Okay," I replied after a deep silent sigh, again thinking of a way to get out of this.

Meanwhile, I could hear my grandpa Odell mumbling in the background, which said to me that, he either believed I didn't want to get tickets, or had tickets and just didn't want to share them with him. And for years, they knew how the ticket request worked but they just *refused* to abide by these league rules, which are etched in stone.

Nevertheless, as I hung up, I didn't like the idea that they let my grandmother, at her age, take a bus ride from Pine Bluff to Chicago to help someone move, after just flying across country from Little Rock to San Francisco. This was just unacceptable. That can be hard on a young person in good health, much less an older person with bad health.

So I pulled into the valet area of the team hotel and told the attendant to hang on before parking my car. I then called my Dad in Dallas, apprising him of the situation.

"Mark, it's going to be tough but let me see what I can do."

"But what really bothers me the most, Dad, is that the primary reason they came to Chicago was to help a relative move back to Pine Bluff—not to attend the game. My question is why couldn't some of the other healthy family members come up and help their relative move, especially in the middle of the summer!" I said with more concern.

"Yeah, at their age, it might be better if you didn't extend tickets to them even if we did find them," my Dad said. "Finding the tickets is one thing—but it's the parking and walking and sitting in all that heat for three-four plus hours would be my real concern, son, which is why I don't let my parents do it anymore. But, I have a parking pass they can use but it's at your house in Vernon Hills."

"Yeah, and unfortunately, I'm already downtown at the team hotel with no time to spare. Our team meeting starts in about thirty minutes and it will take four plus hours to go that far north and back with this traffic," I replied.

"Nah, you don't have the time to make that happen," my Pops replied.

Suddenly, I agreed, this was not a smart thing to do, so I withdrew.

"With grandma Leo's health conditions, she don't need to be out there in that heat like that.... I'll just call them back and tell'em the truth, I don't have any tickets."

"Understood," my Dad replied. "And a smart move, by the way," he said.

We hang up and I called grandma Leola back and informed her I didn't get tickets. And she said, disappointedly, "okay," as she made clear again, that it was *Odell* that was pushing to go, not her. And with that, I got out of my SUV, handed the keys to the valet guy and headed to my room and on to our team meetings.

However, the next day, all entrances to Soldier Field were packed with rushing Bears fans. And among them are Odell, Leola and the family relative, who apparently chose to ignore Mark's advice and came to the game anyway in hopes of purchasing tickets at the gate. And as predicted, it was hot and very muggy that Chicago evening.

So after walking a considerable distance, in that brutal heat, Odell suddenly notices Leola's pace begin to slow and she appears to be having trouble breathing. As he turns to assist her—she collapses. Odell screams her name and kneels down to help her. The relative, who had gone up ahead, rushes back, having heard Odell shout for help!

"What happened?!" The relative hollered.

Odell cradles Leola's head in his arms and shouted, "Call 9-1-1!" The relative frantically dials, as some fans stop and gawk, while others keep moving. The game was more important than a person they didn't know, even if such person was perhaps having a heart attack!

A few minutes later, the ambulance arrived and paramedics worked quickly to assess Leola's condition, loaded her into the ambulance and raced to the hospital, Chicago Medical, as Odell and the relative began to make their way back to the car so they too could get to Chicago Medical in a hurry.

Inside the stadium, Danny and Salena had just arrived after taking an early morning flight from Dallas. And by the middle of the fourth quarter, Mark indeed had barely broken a sweat, when Danny feels his cell vibrating on his hip. He looks at the caller ID and sees that it's his mother, Shelly. He then answers with eyes fixed on the game.

"Danny!" She said with urgency.

"Yeah, what's up?" He responded with concern as he places his free hand over the opposite ear in an effort to hear more clearly.

"I just got a call from Denise, Odell and Leola were on their way to the game in Chicago and it appears that Leola may have had a heart attack outside of the stadium."

Danny drops his head in disappointment, knowing the situation.

Shelly continues, "She said the paramedics rushed her to Chicago Medical downtown—do you know where that is?"

Salena could see by the look on Danny's face that something was seriously wrong, as he then motioned to her to grab their things, pointing toward the exit, "No I don't but I'm sure I will find it," he replied.

Danny hangs up and immediately calls Denise, as he and Salena make their way to the Skyline Suite elevators. Denise picks up on the first ring, and Danny gets straight to it as if this was his mother.

"Dee, shoot straight with me, how serious is it?" He asked.

"I don't know—I'm still waiting to hear back from daddy," Dee softly replied through sobs. "But they do think its a heart attack."

"Where did they take her?" He asks.

"Chicago Medical," Denise replied.

"Okay," he replied. "I'm headed to the locker room to grab Mark, the game is about over. In the meantime, don't overreact, keep the faith, I'll be in touch," he said as he hangs up rushing towards the elevators."

Once on the ground and out the elevator, Salena asked, "What happened?"

"I'll update you in the car," he replied, as they jogged from one end of the stadium to the other to get back to the underground parking for players.

Since Mark didn't play, he was one of the first out of the locker room. Danny had a key so as they were entering his car, Mark then slides into the back seat with both knees on ice, obviously disappointed that he didn't play, and said, "Let's roll—get me back to Vernon Hills.... I need some food, rest and sleep, like now."

"Well—we can get the food, but the rest and sleep may have to wait," Danny replied.

"Why, what's up?" I asked.

"It appears your grandparents didn't take your advice, they came to the game anyway."

"They did?!" I asked.

"Yes, apparently so," he replied, as he started up the SUV and began to negotiate their way out the parking garage.

"What happened?" I asked with concern.

"Well—according to your mom, Leola didn't fare well," my Dad said.

"What happened?" I asked again, knowing that his next statement wouldn't be good.

Danny pauses, knowing likewise the effect of what his next statement might have on an *already* emotionally distressed young man. "The word is Leola collapsed outside the stadium and had to be rushed to Chicago Medical for what appears to be a heart attack."

"Are you serious?!" I asked with great disappointment.

"That's what we've been told," he replied as he turned on the emergency flashers, as I then buried my face in my hands as tears started to bust out.

"I told her not to do this, Dad!" I expressed with anger.

And Salena, now having the 411 says, "For real—it was way too muggy and hot for someone her age to be coming to a football game—I don't care who's playing!"

"Mark—as I told your mother, let's not overreact just yet, son. Let's see what her condition is first. The last thing your grandmother needs right now is for you to show up emotional and unstable—so let's keep our composure—aright? You did your part, son. You tried to discourage this but they unfortunately chose to do it anyway."

Wiping my eyes and face, we could see Chicago Medical in the distance as I began to feel nauseous. My Dad turned into the parking area closest to the Emergency entrance, and then reached back and grabbed my hand and Salena's and began to pray, whatever the issue may be.

After approaching the emergency room receptionist about Leola Davis's whereabouts, we were told to follow the signs to the ICU waiting area, which I immediately knew then, that this was not good. There we found Odell, my rarely seen relative that they came to help move and another family member. And right off the doggone bat, I could tell where my grandfather was going to try to place the blame.

"Mark, all she wanted to do was come see you play—she just wanted to come see you play, son," he said sadly.

I glanced over at my Dad as he slightly glances at me in reference to Odell's comment. I could sense the negative energy all around me as soon as we entered the waiting room. The rarely seen relative, whom I didn't know too well at all, barely looked me in the eye as the other sat composed but confused.

Truth is, as I mentioned earlier, my grandmother had just been to a game of mine in San Francisco two weeks ago, and based on my conversation with her yesterday, she made it clear that it was my granddad *Odell* who was determined to come to this game—not her. And that made sense to me, given the fact that he had not yet been to an NFL game. And I knew how competitive they were with one another.

But after seeing the outcome, he obviously didn't want to shoulder any of the responsibility for this tragic event. So, as I was putting these pieces together, the doctor came in and further verified my suspicions, which went kind of like this:

"It appears that Leola Davis has indeed had a *massive heart attack.* Unfortunately, fluid has set in on her brain and she's been unresponsive to medication since her arrival.... Does she have any medical conditions we should be aware of?" She asked.

Odell replied softly, "Well—yes—she's had some heart problems in the past, but she walked with me a mile or two three times a week," his voice trailing off at *times a week.*

The doctor began to make notes on her clipboard as she asked, "Was she taking any medication for her condition?"

"Yes ma'am, I believe it was nitro... nitro... glycerin," Odell replied, "The one that you place under your tongue."

After jotting down more notes, the doctor said, "May I ask what was she doing at an NFL football game, in this kind of weather, with this kind of heart condition?"

There was a slight pause in the room before my granddad said, "She was just trying to go see her grandson play...we just thought since she walked and exercised at the track with me three times a week, she'd be okay," Odell added.

With a grave look on her face, the doctor managed to make eye contact with all of us, but in particular Odell, and replied, "Well sir, if she had been prescribed *nitroglycerin*, at her age, it probably wasn't wise for you to allow her to attend *any* major outdoor sporting event, especially one in weather that was *unfavorable t*o her kind of condition.".

The well known relative, who was not present at the stadium, jumps in and says to Odell, "She's right daddy, she wasn't in that kind of shape to be in that kind of heat!"

The doctor made another note before saying, "Well, unfortunately, Ms. Davis is currently on life support and it doesn't look good at all...she is in a coma and it is my expert opinion, it's not likely she'll recover.... So if you want to come and see her, now is the time.... But you can only come two at a time."

I, then, looked over at my Dad again, took a deep breath, and suddenly realized that my grandmother Leo is practically—dead!

40

The Aftermath

As the reality of my grandmother being lifeless set in, all of this backbiting, envy, selfishness and pride going on within the walls of my family may have lead to her death, prematurely. This wasn't just about getting to go to a football game—this was about forcing a door open that wasn't even closed, much less locked.

But unfortunately, it was them who was closed, spiritually, not me; evident by their unwillingness to be fair, forgiving and respectful towards one another, making that environment at home that much more unsafe and unhealthy for me to deal with.

So as I motioned for my father to pair up with me, the better-known relative got up the same time I did to be my mate. As we followed the doctor down the hall to my grandmother's room, I was numb—it was a surreal moment. And the closer we got to her room the more claustrophobic I felt.

Once I saw all the monitors and tubes hooked up to her, it was just way too much for me to handle. It was unreal what I felt on the inside. So I walked out just as quickly as I walked in, with tears streaming down my face, saying to myself, *Grandma, I told you not to do this,* as I began asking God to give me the strength to deal with this crazy untimely circumstance.

I wiped my eyes and headed back into the waiting room, nodding to my Dad that all was well. And with that one relative still back, he decided to go back and pray for her, in hopes of a miracle.

When they returned he gathered all of us together by joining hands and led us, also, in a prayer. As he closed, knowing that I was struggling and they were uncomfortable, he then started trying to get a handle on what we could do next. And once he discovered that my mom and the rest of the family would be in later that morning, given that it was now 1:30 a.m., he offered to put everyone up in the Bears team hotel for as long as needed, being that they had already helped pack up the relative for which they'd come in town to help move.

As they openly accepted this much needed arrangement, my Dad and I immediately rushed over to the Hilton along with Salena, to reserve these rooms, accommodating about six family members. And by 3:00 a.m., we are on the road back to Northern Chicago, an hour plus drive, to regroup and digest this unfortunate event. And with no sleep, by 6 a.m., I was back at work getting treatment on my surgical knee when my position coach, Darryl Drake, enters the raining room and makes known that he was aware of the situation with my grandmother, after my Dad had contacted the teams cardiologist early that morning seeking additional info about her state of condition.

He asked, "How is she doing?"

"It doesn't look good—they're not giving her much hope," I replied, somberly. "So, I'm probably going to need a few days off to deal."

After he assured me that I should do just that, I immediately called my Dad to inform him I would be home earlier than once expected and ready to head back to Chicago Medical to be with my family. He offered to drive me since I hadn't had any sleep. And just as I was pulling up to my house, about 7:00 a.m., my cell phone rang. The caller ID said it was the *well-known* relative from the hospital calling. I quickly picked up as I'm entering the house but placed him on hold to carry a piece of equipment the trainers sent home with me for treatment.

Once inside, I resumed the call on speakerphone as I began to change clothes.

"What's the latest?" I asked. "We were just about to head back that way."

"Well—it appears that she's not going to make it, Mark. And if I were you, I wouldn't come back to the hospital right now—it just wouldn't be wise."

I paused, as I looked over at my Dad, who was entering the room after hearing his statement, not knowing which comment I should respond too. The reality of her not making it was tough enough, but the statement that *it just wouldn't be wise to come back,* stunned me.

So I asked, "Why—what's going on?"

"It just wouldn't be wise at this time—let some of this craziness die down before you make your way back this way," he said with concern.

"What craziness—what are you talking about?!" I asked.

"They've already gotten started with the name-calling, Mark. So it would be wise to stay away right now," he strongly implied. "And just so you'll know, they decided *not* to use the rooms you guys paid for last night.... They said they would rather sleep on the floor at the hospital than to use those rooms you and your Dad paid for."

"Come on man—you can't be serious!" I said disappointedly.

"I can't talk freely, but I wouldn't make that trip right now, Mark—they clownin."

"Who is they—I wanna know exactly who they is?" I asked.

"Again, I can't talk right now—just don't come back until further notice," he said, and then hung up, which caused me to shout, "What the hell is wrong with this family?!"

"Don't know, but I think you should stay away until further notice," Danny replied.

"This is crazy! I knew they would try to blame me for her death, Daddy!" I said, severely frustrated. "So yeah, I'm going," I replied, as I continued getting dressed.

"Mark, this has become a hostile situation, son. I told you this a while back that this is the kind of environment that could get somebody seriously hurt."

"Dad, I can't let them unfairly disrespect me and blame this all on me!"

"Son, you are not going back to Chicago Medical until we hear more positivity come out of there," my father calmly said.

"Dad, this is low-down dirty wrong, and you know it," I shot back with disgust.

"It is son, but remember, you gotta be the bigger man, Mark Bradley…. Don't stoop to their level—rise above it…you know the deal here."

"Yeah, I do know the deal, but this junk been going on for twenty-five freakin years?!"

"And it will be twenty-five more if you don't stay the course, son."

"I'm cool, I just wanna go see who they is," I replied.

"You *are not* going back to that hospital at this time, son.... So give me the keys."

"Well—if they think I'm going to take responsibility for their mess, they have lost their mind! What they ought to be asking themselves is why they let their sixty-five year old elderly mother *with a heart condition* get on a Greyhound bus, of all things, and ride for two days just to help a relative move after flying cross country and back?!"

"I think it is the question they're perhaps asking themselves, son. But apparently, they're not quite ready to deal with the obvious answer," my Dad replied.

"Well, if they can all fly up here to see her laid up in the doggone hospital, *in a coma*—they could've brought they butt up to help this relative move!"

Still the voice of reason, my father replied, "Well—I'm sure all that, too, is on their minds. But unfortunately, son, they may not be ready to shoulder that responsibility just yet, either…. So, let's wait and see how the rest of the day plays out...why don't you try to get some sleep—you've been up all night, son."

And just as he made that comment, my cell phone rings again, and the caller ID said this time, it was my Granddad Odell.

"Don't answer that," my Dad quickly and firmly suggested. "Let him leave a message."

And I didn't, despite how much I wanted to defend myself from all these years of abuse, especially under these circumstances. And he indeed leaves a message—an angry one at that. So, I hit speakerphone to hear his message.

"Hey Boy—this your grandfather! I highly suggest you give me a call!"

I looked over at my Dad, "Boy! Nah, I'm not callin him back, I'm going to sleep."

And before he could respond, my cell rang again—this time it was the rarely seen relative. But before my father could stop me from answering this call too, I had already pushed talk, ready to put an end to this silver anniversary get-after-Mark-day mess:

"This Mark, what's up?!"

"You turned your damn back on your family—boy!"

"Come again!" I asked frankly.

"You heard me—I didn't stutter…you turned your back on your family, boy! Your grandmother came to see you play and you don't even have enough respect to be here for her! They won't tell you but I'm gon tell you like it is—you should have kept your butt up here at this hospital with the rest of us all night too!"

"Are you serious?!" I said.

"You heard me!" The relative boldly replied. "The Bears ain't that damn inconsiderate! Who you think you foolin! We raised you, the least you could do is be here for your Grandmother and Grandfather! She died trying to come see you play! She's laying up in this hospital because of you! And you got the nerve to not even be here!"

At that my Dad had heard enough. He whispers to me, "Give me the phone."

"No, Daddy—I got this," I whispered back, waving him off.

"Mark," *he said with his eyes!*

But Mark's mind was made completely up, this had now become his battle—not his Dad's anymore. And he was determined to not only defend his father—but also himself.

"Wait-a-minute, wait-a-minute.... Hold up—hold up partna! Are y'all trying to say that I'm responsible for Grandma Leo's death?!"

"You heard me! She wouldn't even be in this hospital if she hadn't been trying to come see you play! So don't play me, we raised you boy! And you turned your damn back on your family!" He continued to rant.

Mark then looks over at his Dad again, drops his head and then suddenly explodes.

"Shut the hell up damn it! You haven't done a damn thing for me, or anybody else in this family for that matter! So, shut up! Who in the hell did you raise?! Yo thirty-year old daughter is still living with Mama Leo right now; taking care of yo responsibilities partna! So, shut up and get on with all that BS! You are the last some-damn-body in a position to say anything damn thing to me, especially about my whereabouts!"

"Negro, please! We raised you Mark!" The relative shouted back, as he tries to regain control of the conversation, but Mark demands the floor.

"Furthermore—you shouldn't had yo elderly mother on a bus for two days attempting to come to a *freakin* football game in nearly a hundred degree temperature!

Especially after spending the whole day helping *you* move an entire *freakin* apartment! So, take *the plank out yo own eye,* then you might be able to see straight!"

And before the relative could get in another word, Mark clicked him off, as Danny sat with his arms crossed, head back, with that look of a concerned father—witnessing this family now taking their resentment and bitterness toward his son to a whole new level, as he bites the bait.

And Mark continues, as he dials another number: "You know, I once had some hope, but I'm done! I'm lettin my Mom know right now—I AM DONE!"

"Mark—give me the phone, son," Danny said calmly again.

But Mark was in a zone—determined to set the record straight for the last time.

And, by the time she answered, he was passed being heated, he was now a furnace.

"Mama—for the last time, tell your trifling, envious, playa hating family to leave me the hell alone," as tears rushed out his eyes.

"Mark—I don't have anything to do with this, son!"

"I'm tired Mama! This craziness has only been going on for twenty-five freakin years, Mom! And I will not be placed in the middle of this stupid and senseless war anymore!"

"Mark—I'm not involved in this, son," she repeated.

"If not, then why aren't you defending me, Mama?! It took somebody else to warn me not to come back to the hospital, why didn't you call me?!"

"They don't listen to me, Mark!" She said.

"They didn't have a problem listening to you the past twenty years, why not now?!"

"Mark! I'm not in it, son, that's between you and them!" Denise replied.

"Well—neither am I anymore! So, if I get one more call from *anybody* in this family, other than you, they think I've turned my back, I'll forget they even exist!

"Well, that's between you and them, Mark," Denise shot back, again.

"Okay, but here's the deal from this point forward, if you wanna stay in the middle of all that strife with them—that's on you! But I **am not** coming back into all that mess and open myself up again to all this resentment going on inside this family!"

As I hung up the phone, I was an emotional wreck, thinking, *Lord, I have obeyed my mother and the rules of that whole family as you had commanded me to do growing up under their roof, but I also recall, you commanding parents 'not to provoke' their children to wrath, but to bring them up, raise them, in the word and admonition of God.*

It was obvious that my mother's side of the family had simply rejected this often preached sermon. So before there was a chance of any further *provocation*, I apologized to my father, and gave up my cell in an effort to help him protect me—from me.

And after I tossed it, he just simply said, *"This battle is not yours, son, it belongs to the Lord,"* as he gets up and then exits the room.

A whole new level of pain and frustration just literally poured out of me that day with every teardrop. As I sat there in deep thought, I was trying to remember a time—any time, I had a happy moment with my mother. And for the life of me, I couldn't recall—not a one. Twenty-five years of my life, and I could not recall one time I had a glorious moment with my mother.

The next day, as predicted, my Grandmother Leola was taken off life support—she had passed away. And given the *tension* and *rumored threats* made by a few of my family members, I decided not to even attend her funeral. Unfortunately, this situation had just become way to unhealthy to even make an appearance.

Nevertheless, I sent my condolences to help my mother fund portions of the memorial service. But being blamed for her death was about as senseless and disgraceful as it could possibly get. And the one thing I had to come to grips with, in the midst of all of this, was the fact that my mother's love for me came with conditions. And until this day, she, except for on one occasion, has refused to socialize with or come around my father and I, together, even though again, he's the *biggest fan* she has among the whole cast of family members.

Therefore, as a result of all of this, the question I propose is this: Where are we really headed in this country when young men, especially "decent" young men, who want to do the right thing; trying to do the right thing, willing to learn how to do the right thing, are being denied their biological rights of doing the right thing, by an entire family? What level of dysfunctionalism has the family unit risen too, whereby believers, Christians, church going people in this great nation, has begun to operate at such levels of strife, anger and resentment that they would use their own kids as pawns to fight these unnecessary personal battles without even blinking?

Children, teenagers and young people's lives are being destroyed, daily, by the selfishness and bitterness being displayed by our own parents; causing all kinds of discord, while leaving these generational curses in place and unbroken, as we become even more desensitized towards *love, life* and *relationships* from a heavenly perspective, which is a love that is never rude, conceited, or envious; nor is it self-seeking, touchy, or fretful. But rather patient, kind and gentle. And, at the core of it, I've learned that true love takes no account of the wrong done to it. Its always ready to believe the best of every person, not rejoicing at injustice, but rather cheers for that which is right and truth. Simply put, *love never fails*. And I thank my father, in totality, for choosing to allow the Lord to change and impact his life with this kind unconditional love, peace and grace, that positioned him and equipped him with the ability to exemplify portions of this kind of love towards me and my *entire* family.

Having said all that, knowing the reality of the above truth, I'm not sure if I, under these same circumstances, could exemplify this same level of fight to be there for my son or daughter, as my father had been there for me, without either being thrown "in jail" or simply walking away from "the hell" that no parent should have to endure.

Which begs another question, where would **"I"** be, if my beloved father had thought like me? And where would **"he"** be, if he had thought and reacted like them?

Whatever the case, after closely evaluating my answer to these life-changing questions, it became clearly obvious to me that, though I dearly loved my mother, I might be "dead" without my father. And though he obviously loved his son, he might be "incarcerated" without his father—God.

41

1nsepara6le

The following week, in our usual spot underground at Soldier Field, we were holding hands as my father begins our traditional pre-game prayer. But this time, in the wake of recent events, we both struggled to get through this one. I hadn't had a chance to grieve just yet, and he hadn't had a chance to breathe just yet. So with our emotions running extremely high, tears rushed out of us both, as we tried to cope.

As we exited the car, I reached back and grabbed my post-game grip, hit the key fob to lock the doors, and tossed the key to him. He made eye contact with me to ensure I was okay and said that he was proud of the way I keep fighting through these challenges with my family, despite how unfair they had been towards me. And that he still believed that the Lord will work this thing out between me and my mother."

"But the threats, and having to back out of going to the funeral, is just low down trifling, Daddy.... But hey, I understand why they're that way," I replied with sadness.

"Just remember, *love keeps no record of the wrongs, son.* You can't love them, if you won't forgive them," my Dad replied. "As you have witnessed, unforgiveness leads to bitterness; and bitterness will rob you of all the joys of life."

I paused and took a deep sigh in an effort to gather myself, wiped my eyes, and dejectedly shot back, "It's hard trying to stay faithful, Pops, when your own family keeps treating you like this."

"I know its not easy, son, but if you'll just hang on, we'll make it to the other side, with your mother on board," he lovingly replied, "without all the confusion and hostility."

I, then, gave him a half-hug and started toward the team locker-room, as he watched me walk away, heavyhearted. But despite his words of encouragement, I continued to struggle with these on going issues with my mother, still trying to understand all the reasons and whys life had to be this way with the people you love most.

And to compound my frustrations, just a few weeks later, after grabbing a burger and a bottle of water from my kitchen, which I picked up on the way home from work, I was heading to my basement to view a collection of DVD's of T. D. Jakes, my father had given me. I suddenly slipped at the bottom of the stairs, causing me to lose complete balance, which forced me to toss the burger and water to brace myself. But before I knew it, I was face down on the floor with a stinger shouting from both my right knee and right ankle.

And the first thing that crossed my mind was, *Oh, God, not the knee again,* as my Dad rushes down after hearing the thump, to find me on the floor moaning and grimacing with pain.

"What happened?!" He asked, as he immediately began to assess the situation.

I tried to respond but I was in such pain I couldn't quite get it out.

He yelled for Salena, who had also made the trip, to bring bags of ice, as he began helping me to my feet.

"Talk to me Mark, how did you fall, son?"

"Those doggone slides got jammed, lost my balance!"

"Where are you hurting?" He asked, as we make it to the sofa.

"Right knee, right ankle—but mainly the knee!" I replied in great pain.

"Back of the knee or front?" He asked.

"All over—it's hurting all over! It feels like I damaged the ligament again!"

He then took a deep sigh and asked, "What's your trainers phone number?"

"Don't know it by memory, it's in my cell," I replied as I noticed blood streaming from my knee and now left elbow, the carpet had scraped the skin off.

My Dad grabs my phone tosses it to me and told me to call the team trainer, now.

Meanwhile, Salena had arrived with the ice but rushes off again to grab the first aid kit, as my Dad placed his hand on my right knee and said a short prayer, as I paused to join him before dialing the team's trainer—Tim Bream.

"He's probably not at the facility at this hour," I said while still grimacing a bit.

"I understand, but we gotta immediately report all off the field accidents or else you would be in violation of your contract."

Bream didn't answer the first call so I hit him back a second time, as Salena returned with the medical supplies and notices my Dad grimacing a bit, too, while holding his right lower abdomen. He had just had *hernia* surgery a few weeks earlier. She slaps a bag of ice on him as she then begins work on my carpet burns.

Dad, then, gets on one knee and begins to wrap the ankle in ice with an ace bandage from the first aid kit. Tim answered the second call and I told him of the situation and exactly how it happened. He likewise told me to apply ice throughout the night and report to the training room for treatment with the first group—and we'll perhaps have an MRI done to make sure that all is still well.

After we hang up, the questions began formulating in my head again, which I say to myself, *why do so many bad things keep happening to me?!* And my Dad, who was just about finished with wrapping my ankle, looked me dead in the eye, and said, "Mark, *you are snared by the words of your mouth, son,* so stop using these words of doubt and unbelief! You are still blessed and highly favored Mark Bradley, regardless! So, by all means, keep the faith and speak words of hope, not fear."

The next day, after seeing the team doctors, I discovered that my right surgical knee that I was certain to be damaged was actually still in tact, but unfortunately, the right ankle wasn't. I had sustained what they call a high ankle sprain, which would keep me out another *four-to-six-weeks.* And Lord knows I did not need any more mental, emotional or physical setbacks. I had also learned, too, in just a few short years in this league, *you can't continue making the club from the tub.* So, I knew that this high ankle sprain was not good. And it did indeed upset a few power people within the organization who made clear their disappointment.

Subsequently, after talking extensively to my Agent/Dad, the ultimate optimist, I knew my days with the Bears was now numbered. Nevertheless, he encouraged me to play it out with class and take advantage of every opportunity the Bears might give me once healthy, to showcase my ability to still perform at a high-level; there were thirty-one other franchises who could be interested.

Therefore, with a heavy heart still lingering from the sudden death of my grandmother, the abandonment of my own mother, and the threats from my family; I had finally accepted the fact that my beloved family had become totally disinterested in me. And even though our team had managed to make it to Super Bowl XLI, with me contributing a few big plays along the way, the Bears had likewise become disinterested in me.

At this point, I was stable, but, yet, still very unhappy about life. No, I wasn't having thoughts of suicide or blaming God anymore, I understood that the responsibility was now on me, them, and us to make this right. But right before we are to go participate in the biggest event on the planet, I get a call from my beloved Mom requesting two tickets to the game with all accommodations included, I might add.

Reminded by the fact that we hadn't really talked since that tragic weekend five months prior, I'm sure you can understand, under these circumstances, why I might be reluctant in granting this particular request, right? So after we hung up, I thought about her demand for about ten seconds, the answer was, *No—I'm not doing it!*

But once I ran my position by my father, his response was, "Yes, son, you are!"

"Come on, Dad, you know all she's going to do is come to Miami and clown!"

"I understand your feelings, son, but she's your mother. Its the right thing to do."

"I just want to enjoy the week, the festivities. I don't wanna be concerned about my mom's behavior. I don't trust her like that, for nearly a week?! She's just way to resentful toward both of us to be in the mix at an event like this!"

"I get that, but denying her the right to attend an event of this magnitude will only cause her to be *more* resentful and bitter towards us. Plus, in that lil town, she'll have to answer a ton a questions as to why she's not at the Super Bowl in Miami with her beloved son, of all places," he replied.

"Pops—come on man!"

"It's the right thing to do, Mark."

I paused, disappointed that he would command that I meet her demand at this stage in the game. But I knew this man loved my mother perhaps more than I loved her. And as I stated before, he was the biggest representative she had with me.

"Who is the second ticket for?" He asked, as I'm pondering how to get out of this.

"My sister she says," I replied a lil disgruntled.

"Well—Salena will make sure she's plugged into all the family festivities, not player festivities—but family festivities, which will keep her busy and occupied. And while she's here maybe I'll get a chance to chat with her about how you guys can reconnect."

"Dad, I'm tellin you she gon clown, and if she does—it's on you."

"Well—Mark Bradley, if she does, we'll just love her through the clownin—cool?"

I reluctantly relent and allowed him to make arrangements for my mom and sister to fly to Miami for five days and four nights to attend Super Bowl XLI, Bears versus Colts—on me. And as predicted, by day two, she had already crossed the line and the clowning had begun.

The night before the game, I get this phone call from one of my teammates, who had never talked, seen or even met my mother, who said a woman had approached him the previous day, claiming to be my mom, and suddenly begins dogging out my father; saying, how he had brainwashed me and turned me against my family, after having never done much of anything for me my whole life, etc. etc. etc.

And to validate my concerns, the very next day, game day, after attending the very event that she *refused* to allow me to attend eleven years earlier, she and my sister unknowingly stepped onto one of thirty empty shuttle buses, headed back to the family hotel and walks *right past* the man that made it possible for all of us to be there, and once again, didn't even speak or acknowledge him!

When I heard this accidentally come out of Salena's mouth, who, by the way, had been a solid fill in as mom over the years—floored me. So, when I asked my Dad about it, he simply just said, "I've learned to just *pray for those who persecute us, son.*"

And once again, I was taken aback by his response. I guess I'm still learning how this whole love thing works, cause if it had been me I'm going completely off! Only the *power* of God could cause a man to have such *self-control* after having gone through years and years of this kind of insult and mistreatment.

So, the following day, after not getting a chance to even play in the game, I began trying to wrap my mind around everything; her behavior; my situation with the team; the loss to the Colts; the injuries; the abandonment; the withdrawal of the family; the death of my grandmother etc. I decided the hell with it—I'm going to confront her. I first call my father to make known the incident involving her approaching one of my teammates. He definitely needed to know this bit of information at least to protect his business. After all, my father is an NFL Agent, and a good one I might add. But this kind of bad press, coming from his *baby's Mama,* could severely damage his agency.

Thus, after updating him on the matter, as usual, he down played it promising to talk to her about the incident once he returned home. But being already heated, while having this discussion, I dialed her up and connected the three of us before he had a chance to discourage me—and I rushed right into it, "Mom, you got a minute?"

"Yeah, what's up, we're at the airport," she replied.

"Dad, you there?"

"Mark, what's up?" He suspiciously asked.

"Mom, question, did you approach one of my teammates slandering my father's name a couple days ago?"

I could almost see my father's head drop through the phone, as she frankly and sternly answered, after pausing, "No! Why?"

"Mom, I don't have one teammate who has ever met you or has ever had a conversation with you, other than Dante Wesley, who knows absolutely nothin about my personal family business.... So, I'm asking you again, did you approach one of my teammates speaking negatively about my father and sharing our personal business?"

"No, Mark, I didn't." She replied as a matter of fact.

"So, you're saying this guy lying?"

"Who are you gonna believe, Mark, me or your teammate?!" She shot back.

Sensing what my response might be, my Dad jumps in and tried to defuse it but I walked right through his attempt.

"So—you're saying that this guy, whom has never met you or talked to you, who now knows some very pertinent private information about our business—is lying?"

"Yeah—Mark—he is. My question is, are you gonna believe him or your mother?"

"Mom, with our history, you don't really want me to answer that question. But answer this, if my teammate is lying, then is my father also lying when he admits that you and Cassie, stepped right by him on an empty family team shuttle and didn't even speak?"

At that, my Dad had heard enough.

"Mark—I think you've said enough, son."

"Answer the question, mom—is he lying too?"

"Dee," Danny says, "let me chat with Mark. I'll call you later in the week to discuss where we go from here—have a safe trip home," as Mark says, "I didn't think so."

Once we disconnected the three-way, my Dad calls me back and had a few choice words for me, which after hearing him out, I realized that this *was not* the way to handle that sensitive situation. But I couldn't get him to accept the fact that my mother just wasn't going to change. And he was trying to get me to understand that in due time, love changes everything. However, the quote that calmed my spirit was when he said, "She can deny our love, but she can't continue to argue with it."

About three weeks later, early March '07, he invited me to come to Dallas to discuss my future with the Bears. But what I didn't know is, the day before I arrived he had managed somehow to get my mother to fly into town also, to discuss our future as a family. I'm not sure how he did it, given the fact that she *has never* been willing to sit down to have a serious conversation about anything regarding us—but he did.

And to document this unforgettable event, he invited my *personal* spiritual advisor to witness their meeting in an effort to have a character present, other than himself, to represent my voice, which is always good for a fair fight. So, as soon I entered the house, he sat me down and said, "The time has come for you and your mother to have a heart-to-heart. She's upstairs, waiting to talk to you."

I was immediately deflated, thinking, *I'm really not in the mood for this,* but then asked, "I thought this was a get-together about my situation with the Bears?"

"It is," he replied. "This *is* that meeting. I've come to realize that one of the things affecting your situation as a player with the Bears is this *destructive* relationship you have going on with your mother. It's affecting your *focus, your attitude, your behavior;* causing you to not sleep, which has affected your health, causing many of your physical setbacks you're having."

"But you know I didn't start this nonsense with my family, Dad."

"I do.... But you didn't have to start the fight to be guilty of keeping it going, son."

"But I don't believe I've been guilty of keeping this craziness going?" I replied.

"Well, you don't have to believe that either, for it not to be so, Mark."

"What have I done, Daddy?!"

"The mouth often exposes what's going on in your heart, son.... *Out of the issues of the heart the mouth speaks,"* he said. "You now seem to have that vengeful mind-set I've been trying to help you avoid. And we've been given marching orders to love one another, not fight with each other, son. So, it's time you and your mother to make peace."

"It's not me who has refused to make peace!"

"That would be correct, but peace can't be made if you've close the door to peace. And I'm concerned that you have, which can only mean you're still harboring a lil unforgivingness towards your family, Mark."

"Yeah, I'm still a lil hot about her coming to Miami spreading my business among my teammates, and definitely hot about being blamed for the death of my grandmother."

"And I understand that, it's a very difficult thing to process and get over. But, if she's ready to make peace son, then you must be willing to make peace."

"As of yet, she hasn't made peace—all she's done is lie, deny and sigh when I've asked her about it."

"But we've all been given second, third and fourth chances in life to get it right—and in my case a thousand-and-four chances—and counting. There is no reward for those who *only* love those that love them.... I'm suggesting, you open up your heart again, and give her a chance to be that mother you've never had."

At that, I took a deep breath and leaned back in the chair knowing that everything he's sharing was divinely true, but it still just didn't feel right. But if there was anybody that could have quit, threw in the towel and turned his back, it was my father. Apparently, he understood these storms and how to weather them in hopes of a brighter day. So, I relent and decided to give it a chance, I guess.

But Danny notices, pauses, and then said, "Mark, listen to me, son, this is serious business here. Don't let your feelings rob you of an opportunity to make peace with your mother. You know the deal here, *we walk by faith, not by feelings....* So open your heart, think before you talk, and keep your imagination in check. And if I'm right, this will be one of the many breakthroughs you and your mom will experience together, the rest of your life.... Are you with me?" He asked with that look that said, *now is the time.*

I nod in agreement thinking, *I hope your right, Pops—I sure hope you're right!*

The doorbell rings, my spiritual advisor had arrived. My father informed him that we'll try soloing it first, before calling him up. So as we made our way up the stairs and down this hallway that led to the entertainment room, I suddenly begin to feel a little light-headed and nauseous, but fought it off. I knew I had to trust God in a way I never had before—this was a first for all of us.

When we entered, she was sitting in a chair at the head of the room, staring out the window with her back to us, flanked by two love seat sofas with a coffee table in the middle. I take a seat on the sofa to her right while my Dad took the left. My first glance at her said that she had not slept in days, but I had seen this rodeo before and road the pony. So I was ready and prepared to wheel and deal. She didn't look at me right away, and barely spoke, which always meant bad news.

My Dad broke the ice, and said in no specific order this: "Mark, your mother and I had a long-long conversation last night about you, me, us and the rest of the family; discussing where did this ship go so wrong and how we can perhaps turn it around. And before we realized it, it was about five a.m. when we concluded. Your counselor sat in on the session and we were encouraged by what transpired. But I told your mother that in order to do this right, it would be best that she share her thoughts and feelings directly with you. She agreed and asked me if I would sit in, given the fact that she has never took the time to visit with both of us, together, regarding these issues over the years. So, hear her out before you respond or make any remarks, understood?"

I nod in agreement ready to see how she might try to stage this particular come back.

Then he turned to my mom and said, "Denise, we love you, share your heart and speak freely and as openly as you so please. We're all in this together," he said, as he then leans back into his space and gives her the floor.

And then there was this long pause. My head was down so I couldn't see her face, nor could I tell what she might have been doing, but when I looked up, I noticed in my peripheral, that she was now staring at me with tears streaming down her face. And suddenly she spoke these words in general and in no particular order:

"Mark, this is the hardest thing I've ever had to do. There are so many places I could start, and I'm not sure where to even begin. But first off, let me say, I am so sorry for the pain I've caused you over the years, son," as more tears rush out of her. "I never really knew how much my actions were hurting you or your father or how much it was damaging our relationship. Unfortunately, for me, I was selfish, angry, and obviously jealous; jealous of him and the relationship you had with him. And it hurt so bad to know how much my behavior cost the both of you," she said, as her voice rumbled in agony. "And despite all the negative things I've said about your father over the past twenty-five years, Mark, he has been nothing but a good friend to me and obviously a great father to you—and I am so proud of the young man you've become under his guidance. He's done an incredible job with you—better than we could have ever done. And I applaud him for showing all of us that there is a better way to parent—God's way," she amazingly said, as my Dad reached over to grab a wad of tissue for her. "And if it had not been for your father's patience and kindness, I couldn't have arrived at this place with you today, either. He is indeed the biggest fan I have among the family, but honestly I've known that all along.... I came here to set the record straight between us and to come totally clean with you before I did so with the rest of the family, whom I'm sure won't receive what I have to say very well, since after all, I'm the one who started all of this craziness; turning them against your father.... But I've decided I will not continue to take responsibility for their desire to keep this senseless war going—I'm with you, if they want to continue to live in strife, then that's on them—but I'm done with it also.... So, I've asked God to forgive me, your father to forgive me, and now I'm asking you to forgive me, Mark."

Then she turned toward my Dad and said, "And thank you again, Danny, for being a wonderful example to our son—and for not quitting on me, despite how unfair my family and I have been to you."

My Dad wipes his eyes and gently nodded his head as to say, *you're welcome.*

I took a deep breath and chose this moment to speak, as tears well up in my eyes, too.

"You robbed me of twenty plus years of my life with my father, while abandoning me at the same time, Mom—do you realize that?"

"Yes, son, I do.... And I am sincerely sorry. It was wrong—I was flat out wrong. I should've been there for you, instead of forcing you to choose between your parents."

"But you had the whole family trippin with me about this, Mama!"

"I'm sorry, Mark.... I did contaminate them, knowing that your father had *never* done anything to me to warrant my behavior," she painfully replied, with tears flowing heavy.

"For twenty-five years, Mom?!"

"I'm sorry, son, I let my personal interests get in the way—please forgive me? As I told your father, I am ready to move forward and build that relationship with you that we've never had," she said, wiping away more tears.

"But can we really do that at this point, Mom? I'm not so sure anymore."

"Yes, Mark, we can, son.... I know there's a healing process involved—but I'm ready to be that mother you never had, son," she replied, wiping away more tears.

And then suddenly, out of nowhere, it happened—it happened! That thing that I've been waiting and wanting to feel for twenty-five years finally happened! I took another deep breath as I looked over at my Dad, who nods his head in agreement as tears continued to drizzle down his face, too. And all the weight that I didn't even realize I was carrying—was gone! I felt as if the *peace of God* had entered the room, and the tears began to just rush out of me, like a full-fledge dam that just broke.

This was the greatest feeling of joy I'd yet to experience. And yes, Dad, this was indeed *the breakthrough* I needed most in my life. And fittingly, it was *finally* my mother, who hustled over to console me, not my father, as the war between us had come to a complete end; proving, once again, that powerful bible verse my father had taught me along the way: *"With God, all things are possible to them that truly believe."*

The next morning, after having breakfast with my parents for the first time ever, we drop her off at Dallas Love, as she made her way back to Little Rock; and on to DFW for me, as I prepare making my way back to Chicago, this time filled with extreme joy.

As we pull up to the terminal, before exiting, I took this time to express to my father how much I appreciated his enduring love and patience towards me and my family.

And he just simply said, "Son, I learned somewhere along the way, that the greatest gift a father can perhaps give his children, is to love their mother."

"Well, contrary to popular belief, it's not just fathers' who have failed to understanding this thing call *love, life,* and *relationships,* but way too many mothers' are starting to lose their understanding of it, too."

"Perhaps, but let's give her credit, it took a lot of guts and courage for your Mom to take this step.... Let's now focus on helping her forgive herself, and establish that relationship with her son she's never had," my father gently replied.

"I'm definitely with that, but just know, we couldn't have *ever* made it through this craziness without you, Pops," I said sincerely, with deep appreciation.

"Thanks be to God, *who always causes us to triumph,* young-fella."

"You said in due time, He'd bring us through.'

"Did He do it?!"

"Yes He did," I shot back. "But I still can't thank you enough, Pops, for not letting anything or anybody keep you *separated* from me."

And my father just smiled modestly, as he always does, looked away, then back at me, and said these seven memorable words, "Never forget son, true love—is 1nsepara6le."

Acknowledgement

As I thought about the number of people that helped shape me into the person I am today, 'The' most difficult thing I began to encounter was trying to remember them all. And just when I thought I had finalized this inclusive list, I thought of one more person whom I just couldn't leave out. So, to keep from forgetting any of these special people, let me say to each one that impacted my life, during this journey, 'Thank You' for your words of encouragement during some difficult times, even though many of you had no idea what my deepest struggles were at such time. And to every single participating character that consented to the telling of this story, 'Thank You,' and may the good Lord bless your every worthy endeavor for supporting this project.

However, many of you would understand why I must single out a few people, especially my mother, whom I honor, love, and adore, despite our tragic past. The love of God has caused us both to draw near to Him as we work at building that *loving relationship* we never had. And I applaud her for consenting to the telling of this story, so that other young mothers' may not make many of these same *destructive* decisions, which often leaves their children feeling uncovered, unloved and unwanted.

Likewise, I must point out my appreciation for my maternal grandfather, who was my protector and served as *the only* father I really knew in my early-early years. And to my beloved-belated grandmother, who was taken away from us way too soon: I love you and miss you, grandma. Your voice didn't go unheard.

And I would be remiss to not express my deepest gratitude toward the Bradley family, in particular my grandparents, Julius and Shirley, who always made me feel welcomed, forgiven, and accepted. They are truly classy people and I'm proud to be their grandson.

And it's also imperative that I thank Bob Stoops and Merv Johnson for giving me a chance to be a part of that special-special program at the University of Oklahoma, which brought out the best in me as a student-athlete. And Catherine Kelly, my instructor, whose second-chance decision blessed my life—I will forever be grateful to her.

It would also be thoughtless if I didn't thank Jerry Angelo and Lovie Smith for selecting me in the collegiate draft, giving me an opportunity to keep the dream alive. They both are exceptional people and I enjoyed being a part of the Chicago Bears organization. Jim Christman, Darryl Drake, and Cliff Stein—thank you.

And to Mack Brown, who first exposed me to major-college football, I thank him for inspiring me to never under estimate the privilege of having a father that not only understood the business of sports, but one that really cared about parenting. He took the time to personally show us around that great facility of theirs at the University of Texas, and I immediately saw why my father held him in such high regards. His words of encouragement made a life changing difference that terrifying day in Austin. And lastly to Darren Woodson, his words of encouragement are still imbedded in my heart, today—I will never forget you 28. Thanks for helping my father help me.

And speaking of my father, words cannot describe how much this man means to me. I know that there are a lot of terrific Dads throughout this great nation, but I am convinced my father has to be among the best a young man could have. Though his humility would not ever allow him to brag or boast about his affection for his family, especially that of his son, if it had not been for the love, wisdom, and faith of this man—this particular story could not be told. He's the catalyst that made it all possible. His strength through this process was amazingly commendable. And I thank God every day for the man He gave me *as father* in this earth. Life would be very-very different without his *divine* guidance. So big-cheers to my 'Pops' for giving me the assistance needed to share this romantic love story; taking on the unexpected daunting and painful task of helping me put pen to paper. No one could have captured our voices the way he did. And I simply could not have done this without his *unadulterated* support.

Therefore, it is my prayer that his example might encourage and inspire other fathers, who are in need of understanding and direction, *to lead, love* and *lend* of themselves to their children the way my father sacrificed and surrendered his life to be there—for me.

Finally, and most importantly, I take enormous pleasure in thanking MY LORD and SAVIOR—CHRIST, JESUS, who gave His life that I may have life, and life more abundantly. In all I do—I now do unto Him...For He is worthy to be praised!

Scriptural References

Chapter 1: Reflections

3 “Evil company corrupts good habits.” (1 Corinthians 15:33)

“Wisdom is the principle thing; Therefore get wisdom. And in all thy getting get understanding.” (Proverbs 4:7)

Chapter 2: Duplicity

9 “Blessed shall you be coming in, and blessed shall you be going out.” (Deut 28:6)

11 “Jesus Christ is Lord.” (Philippians 28:6)

“we have been sanctified through the offering of the body of Jesus Christ once for all.” (Hebrews 10:10)

“I will praise You, for I am fearfully and wonderfully made; Marvelous are Your works.” (Psalms 139:14)

“Before I formed you in the womb I knew you; Before you were born I sanctified you; I ordained you a prophet to the nations.” (Jeremiah 1:5)

“The thief does not come except to steal, to kill, to destroy, I have come that they may have life, and that they may have it more abundantly.” (John 10:10)

“By that will we have been sanctified through the offering of the body of Jesus Christ once for all.” (Hebrews 10:10)

“If we confess our sins, He is faithful and just to forgive us our sins and cleanse us from all unrighteousness.” (1 John 1:9)

“for all has sinned and fall short of the glory of God.” (Romans 3:23)

“For by grace you have been saved through faith, and that not of yourselves; it is the gift.” (Ephesians 2:8)

“And do not be conformed to this world, but be transformed by the renewing of your mind, that you may prove what is that good and acceptable and perfect will of God.” (Romans 12:2)

Chapter 5: Predicament

38 “I will never leave you or forsake you.” (Hebrews 13:5)

Chapter 7: Explosion

56 “Trust in the Lord, and do good.” (Psalms 37:3)

57 “Watch and pray, that ye enter not into temptation: the spirit indeed is willing, but the flesh is weak.” (Matthew 26:41)

Chapter 8: Repercussions

59 “Death and Life are in the power of the tongue. (Proverbs 18:21)

61 “In the world you will have tribulations; but be of good cheer, for I have overcome the world.” (John 16:33)

69 “Love never fails.” (1 Corinthians 13:8)

“Be doers of the word, and not hearers only, deceiving yourselves.” (James 1:22)

Chapter 11: Responsibility

87 “all have sinned and fall short of God’s glory.” (Romans 3:23)

“But thanks be to God, who gives us the victory through our Lord Jesus Christ.” (1 Corinthians 15:57)

Chapter 14: Entanglement

121 “And if a house be divided against itself, that house cannot stand.” (Mark 3:25)

“I will praise thee; for I am fearfully and wonderfully made: marvellous are thy works; and that my soul knoweth right well. (Psalms 139:14)

“If we confess our sins, he is faithful and just to forgive us our sins, and to cleanse us from all unrighteousness.” (1 John 1:9)

Chapter 15: Jealousy

124 “Do not be deceived, God is not mocked; whatever a man sows, that he shall also reap.” (Galatians 6:7)

Chapter 18: Toleration

154 “For we dare not class ourselves or compare ourselves with those who commend themselves. But they, measuring themselves by themselves, and comparing themselves among themselves, are not wise.” (2 Corinthians 10:12)

“And you, fathers, do not provoke your children to wrath, but bring them up in the training and admonition of the Lord.” (Ephesians 6:4)

“Moreover if your brother sins against you, go and tell him his fault between you and him alone. If he hears you, you have gained your brother.” (Matthew 18:15)

155 “If you can believe, all things are possible to him who believes.” (Mark 9:23)

Chapter 20: Humility

163 "Bless them that curse you, and pray for them which despitefully use you." (Luke 6:28)

Chapter 21: Exposure

175 "Wisdom is the principal thing; Therefore get wisdom. And in all your getting, get understanding." (Proverbs 4:7)

"Preach the word! Be ready in season and out of season. Convince, rebuke, exhort with all long-suffering and teaching." (2 Timothy 2:4)

182 "For God has not given us a spirit of fear, but of power and of love and of a sound mind." (2 Timothy 1:7)

"With men this is impossible, but with God all things are possible." (Matt 19:26)

"I can do all things through Christ who strengthens me. (Phil 4:13)

"For He Himself has said, I will never leave you or forsake you." (Hebrews 13:5)

"For God is not the author of confusion but of peace," ((1 Corinthians 14:33)

"Behold, I am the Lord, the God of all flesh. Is there anything too hard for Me?" (Jeremiah 32:27)

"Resist him, steadfast in the faith, knowing that the same sufferings are experienced by your brotherhood in the world." (1 Peter 5:9)

"Now the parable is this: The seed is the word of God." (Luke 8:11)

Chapter 26: Divine Forgiveness

231 "Do not be deceived, evil company corrupts good habits." (1 Corinthians. 15:33)

"There's a way that seems right to a man, But its end is the way of Death." (Proverbs 16:25)

232 "If we confess our sins, He is faithful and just to forgive us our sins and cleanse us from all unrighteousness." (1 John 1:9)

"For we walk by faith, not by sight" (2 Corinthians 5:7)

Chapter 28: Divine Divinity

241 "evil company corrupts good habits." (1 Corinthians 15:33)

Chapter 29: Divine Intervention

251 “For we wrestle not against flesh and blood, but against principalities, against powers, against the rulers of the darkness of this world, against spiritual wickedness in high places.” (Ephesians 6:12)

252 “For by grace you have been saved through faith, and that not of yourselves; it is the gift.” (Ephesians 2:8)

“But God delivered him out of all his troubles, and gave him favor and wisdom in the presence of Pharaoh.” (Acts 7:10);

“I can do all things through Christ who strengthens me.” (Phil 4:13);

“no weapon formed against you shall prosper.” (Isaiah 54:17);

“by whose stripes you were healed.” (1 Peter 2:24;

“God is not respecter of persons.” (Acts 10:34);

“God shall supply all my needs according to His riches in glory by Christ Jesus.” (Phil 4:19)

Chapter 30: Divine Force

265 “For we walk by faith, not by sight.” (2 Corinthians 5:7)

266 “Owe no man any thing, but to love one another.” (Romans 13:8)

“Honor your father and your mother, that your days may be long upon the land which the Lord your God is giving you.” (Exodus 20:12)

Chapter 31: Divine Confession

270 “but with God all things are possible.” (Matthew 19:26)

Chapter 32: Divine Results

276 “All things are possible to him who believes.” (Mark 9:23)

277 “God has not given us a spirit of fear, but power, love, and a sound mind.” (2 Timothy 1:7)

“With God, all things are possible to him who believes.” (Matthew 19:26)

278 “I can do all things through Christ who strengthens me.” (Philippians 4:13)

“All things are possible to him who believes.” (Mark 9:23)

281 “For if you forgive men their trespasses, your heavenly Father will also forgive you.” (Matthew 6:14)

Chapter 33: Divine Revelation

285 "God is no respecter of persons." (Acts 10:34)

292 "Nothing shall remain the same. Exalt the humble, and humble the exalted. (Ezek 21:26)

"Hatred stirs up strife, but love covers all sins." (Proverbs 10:12)

"Trust in the Lord with all your heart, And lean not on your own understanding; and in all your ways acknowledge Him and He shall direct your path." (Proverbs 3:5)

"Be strong and of good courage, do on fear or be afraid of them; the Lord your God, He is the One who goes with you." (Deuteronomy 31:6)

"For He Himself has said, I will never leave you or forsake you." (Hebrews 13:5)

Chapter 34: Divine Support

295 "But let a man examine himself, and so let him eat of that bread, and drink of that cup. (1 Corinthians 11:28)

"evil company corrupts good habits." (1 Corinthians 15:33)

297 "Wait upon he Lord, And keep His way, And He shall exalt you." (Psalm 37:34)

Chapter 35: Divine Faith

309 "Death and life is in the power of the tongue." (Proverbs 18:21);

"God is no respecter of persons." (Acts 10:34)

"I say to you, whatever things you ask when you pray, believe that you receive them, and you will have them." (Mark 11:24)

"But with God all things are possible." (Matthew 19:26)

Chapter 36: Divine Guidance

320 "For if ye forgive men their trespasses, your heavenly Father will also forgive you." (Matthew 6:14)

Chapter 37: Divine Reaction

329 "All we like sheep have gone astray; We have turned, every one, to his own way; And the Lord has laid on Him the iniquity of us all." (Isaiah 53:6)

"Beloved, let us love one another, for love is of God; and everyone who loves is born of God and knows God." (1 John 4:7)

"If we confess our sins, He is faithful and just to forgive us our sins and to cleanse us from all unrighteousness." (1 John 1:9)

330 "Flee sexual immorality. Every sin that a man does is outside the body, but he who commits sexual immorality sins against his own body." (1 Corinthians 6:18)

331 "Therefore, having been justified by faith, we have peace with God through our Lord Jesus Christ." (Romans 5:1)

"Therefore be imitators of God as dear children." (Ephesians 5:1)

339 "And let us not be weary in well doing: for in due season we shall reap, if we faint not." (Galatians 6:9)

"If God is for you, who can be against us?" (Romans 8:31)

Chapter 38: Divine Prediction

342 "For as he thinks in his heart, so is he." (Proverbs 23:7)

347 "all things are possible to him who believes." (Mark 9:23)

352 "a man's enemies will be those of his own household." (Matt 10:36)

Chapter 39: Collateral Damage

357 "casting down arguments and every high thing that exalts itself against of God, bringing every thought into captivity to the obedience of Christ." (2 Corinthians 10:5)

"Finally, brethren, whatever things are true, whatever things are noble, whatever things are just, whatever things are pure, whatever things are lovely, whatever things are good report, it there is any virtue if there is anything praiseworthy - meditate of these things." (Philippians 4:8)

"Death and Life are in the power of the tongue. (Proverbs 18:21)

"For God has not given us a spirit of fear, but of power and of love and of a sound mind." (2 Timothy 1:7)

"For as he thinks in his heart, so is he." (Proverbs 23:7)

358 "forbid: yea, let God be true, but every man a liar." (Romans 3:4)

"for he who doubts is like a wave of the sea driven and tossed by the wind. For let not that man suppose that he will receive anything from the Lord; he is a double-minded man, unstable in all his ways." (James 1:6)

"if you have faith as a mustard seed, you can say to this mulberry tree, 'Be pulled up by the roots and be planted in the sea,' and it would obey." (Luke 17:6)

"I will set nothing wicked before my eyes." (Psalms 101:3)

359 "knowing that the testing of your faith produces patience." (James 1:3)

Chapter 40: The Aftermath

369 "Hypocrite! First remove the plank from your own eye, and then you will see clearly to remove the speck from your brother's eye." (Matthew 7:5)

"Children, obey your parents in all things, for this is well pleasing to the Lord." (Colossians 3:20)

"And, ye fathers, provoke not your children to wrath: but bring them up in the nurture and admonition of the Lord." (Ephesians 6:4)

370 "Be not afraid nor dismayed by reason of this great multitude; for the battle is not yours, but God's." (2 Chronicles 20:15)

"A false witness who speaks lies, And one who sows discord among brethren." (Proverbs 6:19)

"Love suffers long and is kind; love does not envy; love does not parade itself, is not puffed up; does not behave rudely, does not seek its own, is not provoked, thinks no evil; does not rejoice in iniquity, but rejoices in the truth; bears all things, believes all things, hopes all things, endures all things. Love never fails."

(1 Corinthians 13:4-8)

Chapter 41: 1nsepara6le

375 "You are snared by the words of your mouth; you are taking by the words of your mouth." (Proverbs 6:2)

376 "But I say to you, love your enemies, bless those who curse you, do good to those who hate you, and pray for those who spitefully use you and persecute you, that you may be sons of your Father in Heaven." (Matt 5:44)

379 "Keep your heart with all diligence, for out of it spring the issues of life." (Proverbs 4:23)

"For we walk by faith, not by sight." (2 Corinthians 5:7)

"For if you love those who love you, what reward have you? Do not even the tax collectors do the same?" (Matt 5:46)

382 "Jesus said to him, "If you can believe, all things are possible to him who believes." (Mark 9:23)

"But thanks be to God, which always causes us to triumph in Christ, and maketh manifest the savour of his knowledge by us in every place." (2 Corinthians 2:14)

"For I am persuaded that neither death nor life, nor angels nor principalities nor powers, nor things present nor things to come, nor height nor depth, nor any other created thing, shall be able to separate us from the love of God which is in Christ Jesus our Lord." (Romans 8:38-39)

IMAGES

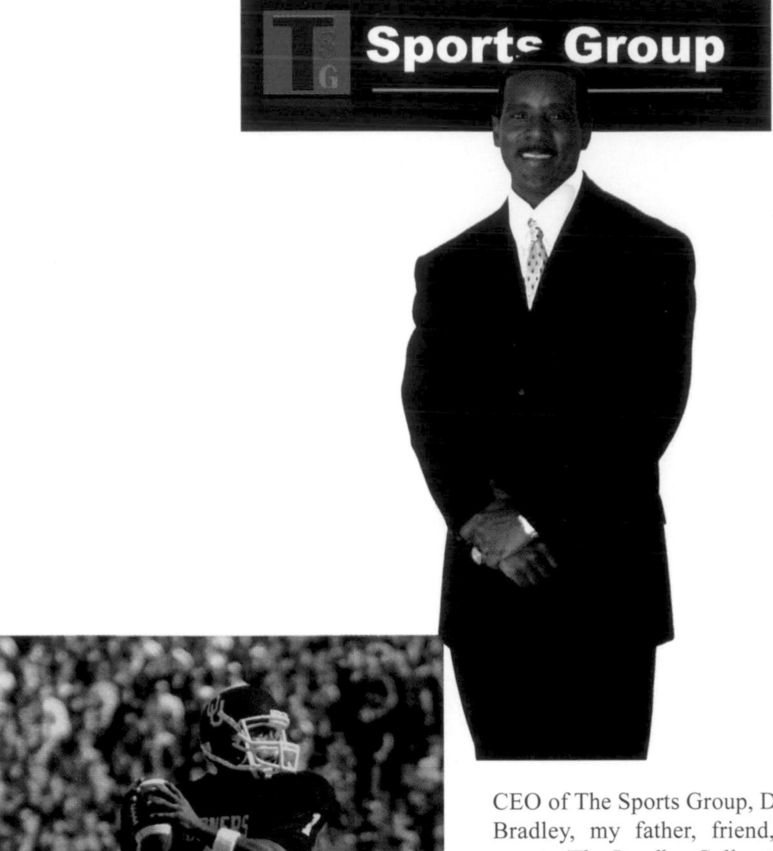

CEO of The Sports Group, Danny Bradley, my father, friend, and agent. *(The Bradley Collection)*

(Courtesy of the University of Oklahoma)

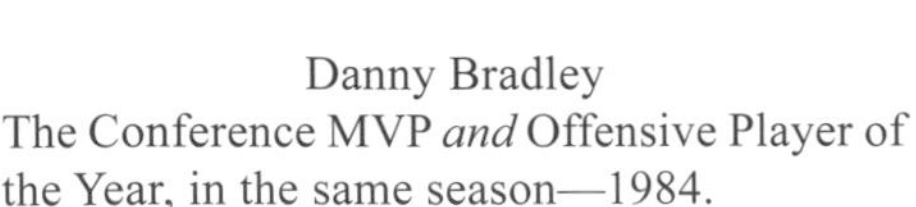

Danny Bradley
The Conference MVP *and* Offensive Player of the Year, in the same season—1984.

Danny Bradley - Detroit Lions
(1987)

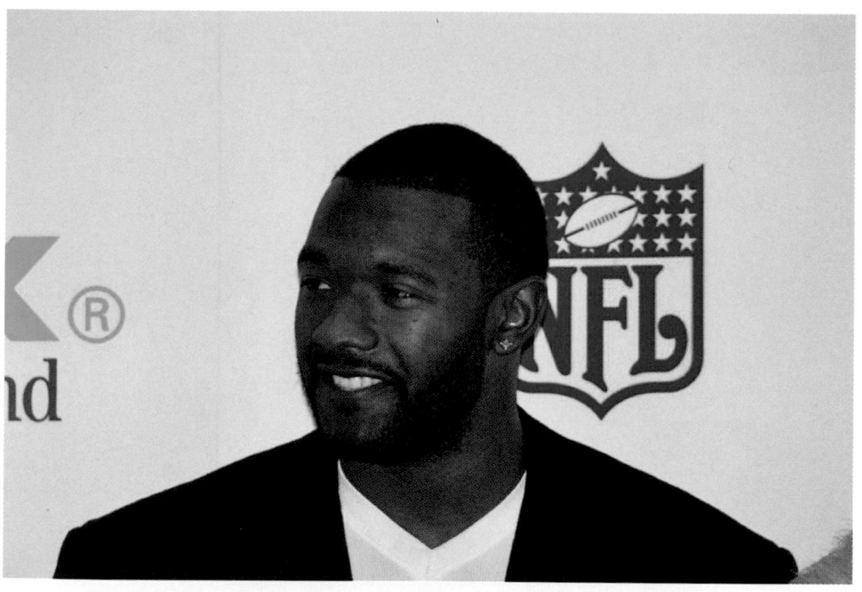

NFL spokesman, Mark Bradley, representing the Chicago Bears in the community.
(Courtesy of the National Football League)

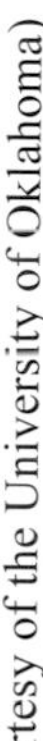
(Courtesy of the University of Oklahoma)

The Sooners 2004 "Best Athlete"
Mark Bradley

Chicago Bears vs. Saints 2007
Mark Bradley

The team that came one win short of a Super Bowl XX, which ironically lost to the Chicago Bears in the NFC Championship Game at Soldier field, that later became the team that would draft me in 2005. The 1985 Los Angeles Rams team photo, Danny Bradley, (front row, #34)

(Courtesy of Los Angeles/St. Louis Rams)

A dream fulfilled! Mark Bradley, number 16, pictured here alongside his 2006 NFC Champion teammates, Chicago Bears.

(Courtesy of Chicago Bears)

Clock-wise, roaming the Cowboys sideline, during a Super Bowl-bound season (1995), receivers coach Hubbard Alexander, special teams coach Joe Avezzano, and my father, Danny Bradley, center..... *(Courtesy of The Bradley Collection)*

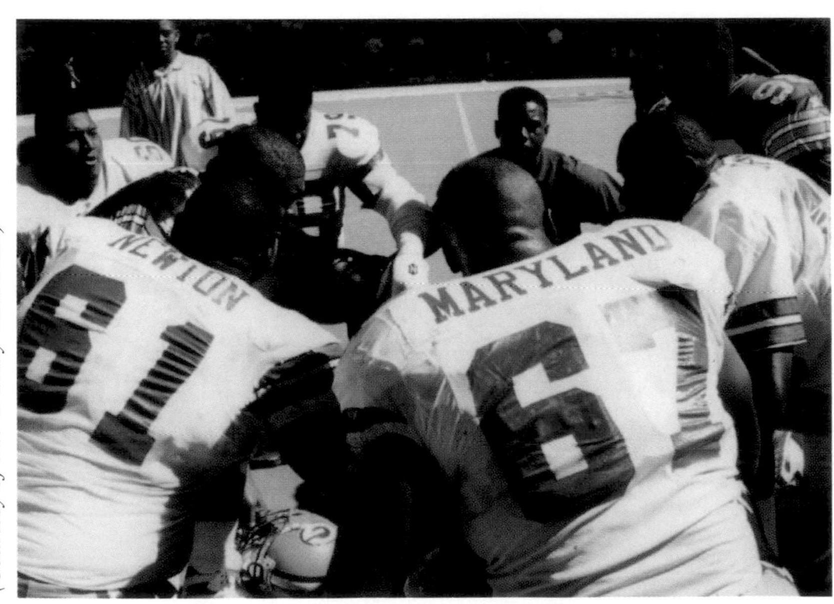

(Courtesy of The Bradley Collection)

Giving God the glory after the 1995 NFC championship game between Dallas and Green Bay: Clockwise--Danny Bradley, Sean Jones, Michael Irvin, Russell Maryland, Nate Newton, Reggie White, Derrick Kennard, and Erik Williams.

Excited and ready to cheer on the Bears despite a rainy Super Bowl day, from-left to right: Byron K. Reed, Sabrina Ernest, my father, Danny B., and Natalie Green.
(Courtesy of The Bradley Collection)

(Courtesy of Associated Press)

Media Day – Super Bowl XLI

Super Bowl XLI
Bears - Colts

A cheerful photo-finish following one of their weekly family bible studies-from left to right: Julius 'JB' Bradley, Danny, Mark, Ataleo Ford, and Scott West.
(Courtesy of The Bradley Collection)

Another photo of us studying "the word" to show themselves approved (at my Dad's home) in Southlake Texas. The subject that night was "The Grace of God."
(Courtesy of The Bradley Collection)

(Courtesy of the Univeristy of Oklahoma)

My father Danny at practice (1984)

(Courtesy of The Oklahoman)

Mark at practice (2004)

"Copyright 2004, The Oklahoma Publishing Company"

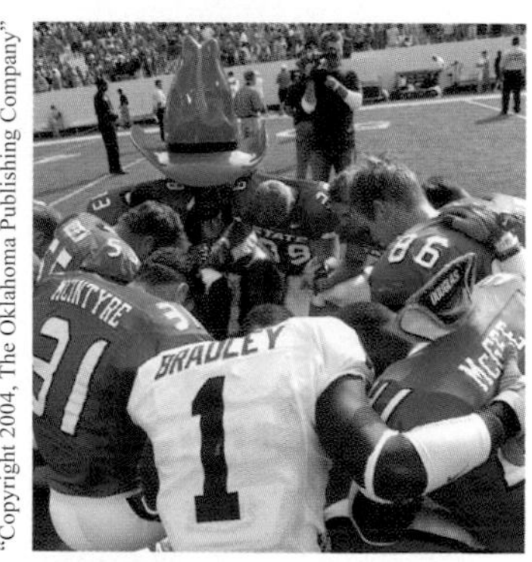

MB prays afterwards with his OSU brothers in the faith 2004.

Sooners Illustrated told the story, in 1984, of how my father first became enamored with OU Football through Switzer's willingness to play black quarterbacks. He gazes at one of his favorites, #6 Thomas Lott.... *(Courtesy of Sooners Illustrated)*

(Courtesy of Pine Bluff High School)

To validate his destiny, my father wore #6 in High School after watching T. Lott lead OU into the 1979 Orange Bowl against, ironically, Lou Hotltz and the Arkansas Razorbacks.

(Courtesy of The Bradley Collection)

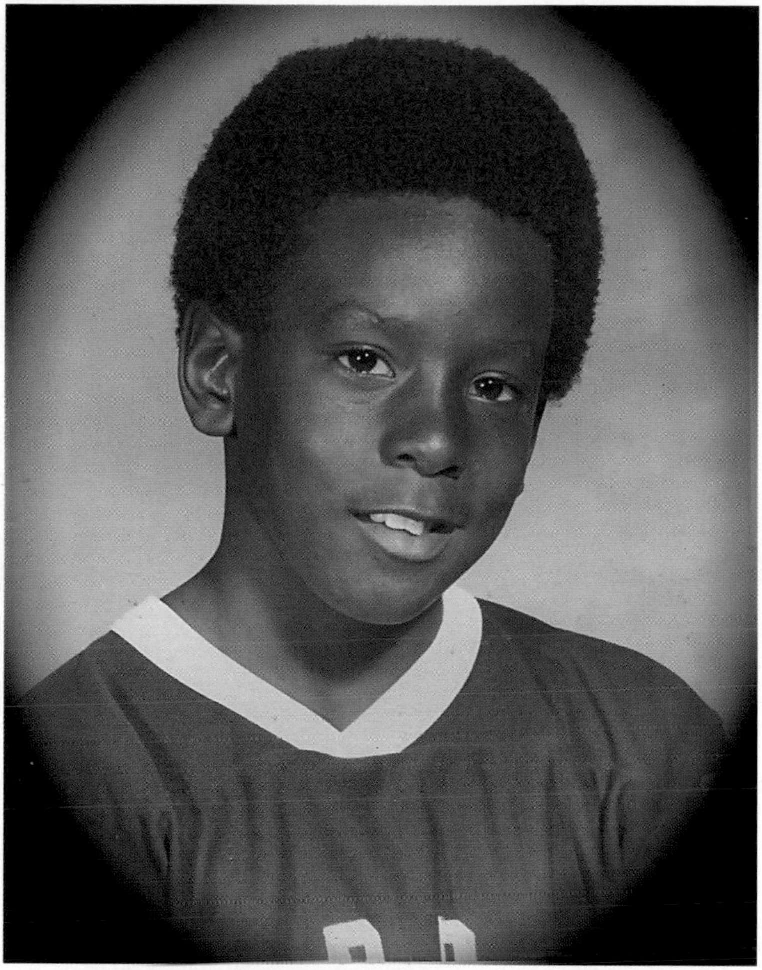

Above: My father, Danny Bradley at age 10—1973

(Courtesy of The Bradley Collection)

Below: The only shot of my Dad and I as a kid—1990

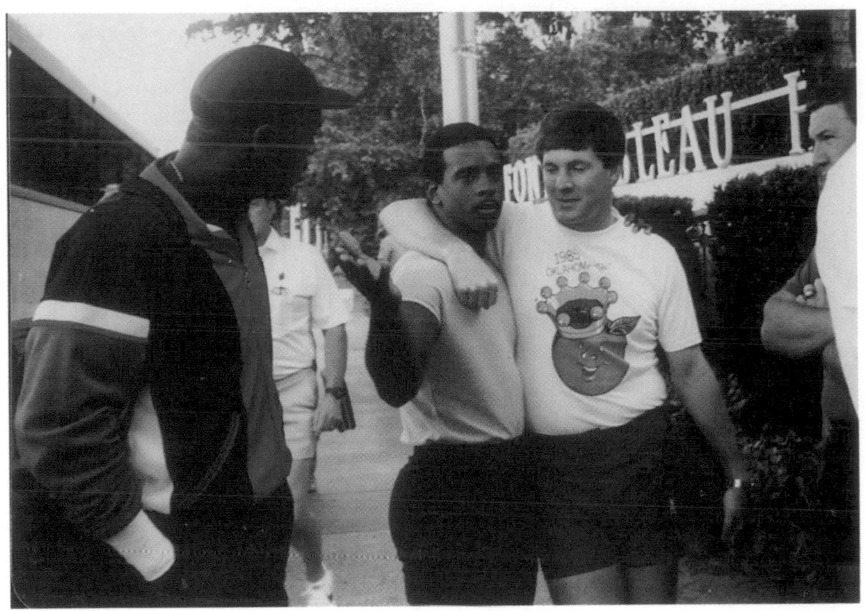

(Courtesy of The Bradley Collection)

Coach Mack Brown, OU's offensive coordinator, then, hugs his MVP quarterback, Danny Bradley, before the Sooners National Championship game; the '85 FedEx Orange Bowl in Miami, as Buster Rhymes and Coach Jim Donnan looks on.

One of my favorite pics of my father in the Red River Shootout; #1 Texas vs. #2 Oklahoma, which ended in a 15-15 tie in '84. But this play help put the Sooners up 15-12, with just 2:04 left in the contest. *(Courtesy of the University of Oklahoma)*

Senior Day at OU; left to right, me, my half-sister, Mom and Dad.
(Courtesy of The Bradley Collection)

Mark Bradley receives his degree from the University of Oklahoma.
(Courtesy of The Bradley Collection)